Fungal, Bacterial, and Certain Nonparasitic Diseases of Fruit and Nut Crops in California

The authors are:

Edward E. Wilson, Professor of Plant Pathology, Emeritus, Department of Plant Pathology, University of California, Davis.

Joseph M. Ogawa, Professor of Plant Pathology, Department of Plant Pathology, University of California, Davis.

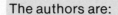

Division of Agricultural Sciences UNIVERSITY OF CALIFORNIA

 PLANT
PESTICIDE USE WARNING — READ THE LABEL

Pesticides are poisonous and must be used with caution. READ the label CAREFULLY BEFORE opening a container. Precautions and directions MUST be followed exactly. Special protective equipment as indicated must be used.

STORAGE: Keep all pesticides in original containers only. Store separately in a locked shed or area. Keep all pesticides out of the reach of children, unauthorized personnel, pets and livestock. DO NOT STORE with foods, feeds or fertilizers. Post warning signs on pesticide storage areas.

USE: The suggestions given in this publication are based upon best current information. Follow directions: measure accurately to avoid residues exceeding tolerances, use exact amounts as indicated on the label or lesser amounts given in this publication. Use a pesticide only on crops, plants or animals shown on the label.

CONTAINER DISPOSAL: Consult your County Agricultural Commissioner for correct procedures for rinsing and disposing of empty containers. Do not transport pesticides in vehicles with foods, feeds, clothing, or other materials, and never in a closed cab with the vehicle driver.

RESPONSIBILITY: The grower is legally responsible for proper use of pesticides including drift to other crops or properties, and for excessive residues. Pesticides should not be applied over streams, rivers, ponds, lakes, run-off irrigation or other aquatic areas except where specific use for that purpose is intended.

BENEFICIAL INSECTS: Many pesticides are highly toxic to honey bees and other beneficial insects. The farmer, the beekeeper and the pest control industry should cooperate closely to keep losses of beneficial species to a minimum.

PROCESSED CROPS: Some processors will not accept a crop treated with certain chemicals. If your crop is going to a processor, be sure to check with the processor before making a pesticide application.

POSTING TREATED FIELDS: When worker safety reentry intervals are established be sure to keep workers out and post the treated areas with signs when required indicating the safe reentry date.

PERMIT REQUIREMENTS: Many pesticides require a permit from the County Agricultural Commissioner before possession or use. Such compounds mentioned in this publication are marked with an asterisk (*).

PLANT INJURY: Certain chemicals may cause injury or give less than optimum pest control if used: at the wrong stage of plant development; in certain soil types; when temperatures are too high or too low; the wrong formulation is used; and excessive rates or incompatible materials are used.

PERSONAL SAFETY: Follow label directions exactly. Avoid splashing, spilling, leaks, spray drift or clothing contamination. Do NOT eat, smoke, drink, or chew while using pesticides. Provide for emergency medical care in advance.

Additional copies of this book may be ordered by writing:
Agricultural Sciences Publications, Division of Agricultural Sciences,
University of California, Berkeley, California 94720.

Price: $18.00

Make checks or money orders payable to: The Regents of the University of California.
California residents must add sales tax. All sales are final. No returns for cash or credit.

Library of Congress Catalog Card Number: 79-63107. ISBN: 0-931876-29-X

Priced Publication 4090

2m–3/79–VL/ME

Preface

The information herein was originally compiled for the use of students in a class dealing with fruit and nut tree diseases and given at the University of California at Davis. Color and black and white photographs showing typical disease symptoms are included to show symptoms and signs which cannot be properly described in the text.

Only those diseases affecting California's fruit and nut trees are described in detail, although diseases occurring in other Pacific Coast states are sometimes mentioned. Included are: bacterial, fungal, and certain non-parasitic diseases of pome and stone fruit, olives, and English walnuts. For figs and minor crops, only bacterial and fungal diseases are described. Viral diseases of stone fruit are ommitted because they are thoroughly covered in the U.S. Department of Agriculture Handbook 437 issued January 1976. Viral diseases of apples and pears are described in Technical Communication No. 30 of the Commonwealth Bureau of Horticulture and Plantation Crops, East Malling, Maidstone, Kent, England and edited by A. F. Posnette. With a few exceptions, such as bitter pit of apple and internal bark necrosis of apple, effects of excesses and deficiencies of soil chemical elements are not described as they are extensively covered in "Temperate to Tropical Fruit Nutrition," Horticultural Publications, Rutgers State University, 888 pages, 1966; Norman F. Childers, Editor.

Chestnut, filbert, macadamia, pecan, persimmon, pistachio, and pomegranate are of less importance in California, but certain diseases of these crops are briefly mentioned in section VII.

The host-disease index which begins on page 187 gives a cross-index of pages and photographs in which the diseases and hosts are discussed or illustrated.

Color photographs begin on page 83.

ACKNOWLEDGMENTS

The authors benefitted greatly in the preparation of this book from research experience gained as staff members of the University of California, Davis; from using portions of this book in teaching graduate students; and from critical information and references obtained from colleagues on the Davis, Berkeley, and Riverside campuses of the University. Those who have generously given advice on the various sections are: E. E. Butler, W. Harley English, John M. Mircetich, and William J. Moller of the Department of Plant Pathology, University of California, Davis, and H. Ronald Cameron, and Iain C. MacSwan of the Department of Plant Pathology and Duane L. Coyier of the U.S. Department of Agriculture at Oregon State University, Corvallis. Others who helped in the preparation are G. A Chastagner, M. L. Chiarappa, S. T. Koike, B. T. Manji, P. L. Sholberg, and M. E. Weir, all of the Department of Plant Pathology, Davis. Final reviews of the manuscript were made by D. E. Munnecke and R. D. Raabe, Department of Plant Pathology, Riverside and Berkeley.

Special thanks are extended to Mrs. Erna S. Thompson, Mrs. Barbara J. Overson, and Mrs. Elizabeth Jeffrey of the Department of Plant Pathology, University of California, Davis for typing and compiling the manuscript, and to Vince Lawton and Marvin Ehrlich, Agricultural Publications Office, Richmond, for editing and valuable layout suggestions.

Edward E. Wilson
Joseph M. Ogawa

CONTENTS

I. POME FRUITS AND THEIR DISEASES

NONPARASITIC DISEASES OF APPLE AND PEAR

POSTHARVEST DISEASES OF APPLE AND PEAR FRUIT

II.   STONE FRUITS AND THEIR DISEASES

BACTERIAL DISEASES OF STONE FRUIT

FUNGAL DISEASES OF STONE FRUIT

NONPARASITIC DISEASES OF STONE FRUIT

POSTHARVEST DISEASES OF STONE FRUIT

III. DISEASE ATTACKING SEVERAL GENERA OF FRUIT AND NUT TREES

BACTERIAL DISEASES OF FRUIT AND NUT TREES

FUNGAL DISEASES OF FRUIT AND NUT TREES

IV. ENGLISH WALNUT AND ITS DISEASES

BACTERIAL DISEASES OF ENGLISH WALNUT

FUNGAL DISEASES OF ENGLISH WALNUT

NONPARASITIC DISEASES OF ENGLISH WALNUT

V.   THE OLIVE AND ITS DISEASES

BACTERIAL DISEASES OF OLIVE

FUNGAL DISEASES OF OLIVE

NONPARASITIC DISEASES OF OLIVE

VI. THE FIG AND ITS DISEASES

VII. MINOR CROPS AND THEIR DISEASES

APPENDIX

I. POME FRUITS AND THEIR DISEASES

THE APPLE (*Malus communis* D.C.)

The cultivated apple probably originated in southwest Asia where forests of wild *Malus* species were known to occur. It apparently derived from *Malus sylvestris* Mill (*Pyrus malus* L., *M. domestica* Barth.) or hybridization between *M. sylvestris* and other wild *Malus* species. Some early apple trees grown in the U.S. probably were hybrids between *M. sylvestris* and wild North American species such as *M. ioensis* Britt. Certain horticultural cultivars probably are derived from *M. baccata* Borkh., the wild Siberian crab (1, 3).*

The apple has been cultivated in Europe and Asia for many hundreds of years, but wild apples were eaten long before man attempted to domesticate them. Reputedly, several horticultural cultivars were grown in Greece as early as 325 B.C. (7). From such early centers of civilization, the apple was taken to other parts of Europe, and gradual selection by nature and man resulted in types adapted to the climatic conditions of that continent.

Vegetative propagation was practiced in Europe long before America was colonized. Nevertheless, the first domestic apple trees of the New World grew from seeds. Consequently most if not all early American cultivars were developed on this continent. Some Russian cultivars, later to become popular in the U.S., were introduced in the nineteenth century (2).

Commercial apple orchards as known today were practically nonexistent in North America until the beginning of the twentieth century. Western New York and Virginia were the first places in which apple growing became a successful business. The extensive apple orchards of the Pacific Northwest came into existence during the early years of this century. The Hood River Valley of Oregon had developed apple culture by 1910, the Wenatchee and Yakima valleys of Washington shortly thereafter.

Important apple production areas in the U.S. and Canada are: 1) New York, New England, Nova Scotia; 2) New Jersey, Delaware, Maryland, West Virginia, Virginia and the Carolinas (commercial apple-growing is not successful south of northern Georgia); 3) The Ohio River Valley, northern Ohio, Michigan, Wisconsin, and southwestern Missouri, northwestern Arkansas, and eastern Oaklahoma; 4) California, Washington, Oregon, and British Columbia.

Because of diverse climatic conditions, cultivars grown in one of these areas may not be grown in another. Delicious (and its red mutants), Winesap, Rome beauty, and Golden Delicious, are grown in most of the areas with different degrees of success. Jonathan and Grimes Golden are grown extensively in the mid-Atlantic states, mid-western states, and to some extent in the Pacific Northwest, but are of little importance in California and the New York-New England-Nova Scotia area. Other important cultivars in one area or another are or have been McIntosh, Gravenstein, Yellow, Newtown, Spitzenburg, Stayman Winesap, Golden Russett, Fameuse, Wealthy, Courtland, Baldwin, and Northern Spy.

California's 19,000 acres of apple orchards, which constitute about 8 percent of the nation's total, are planted primarily with Gravenstein, Yellow Newtown, Golden Delicious, and Red Delicious. Of these the Gravenstein, a German cultivar is mentioned in the American literature of 1824 and could have been first planted at Fort Ross in 1820. Apples were growing in 1792 at Mission Santa Clara and mission San Buena Ventura, brought here by

---

*Numbers in parentheses identify "References" which follow each subsection.

J. F. Eschscholtz (who also gave the botanical name to our California poppy in 1824). Professor E. O. Essig of the University of California described an old Russian Gravenstein orchard at Bodega and included a photo of an old Gravenstein apple tree. Named cultivars such as Rhode Island Greening and Winesap were planted in Napa Valley near Calistoga in 1850, and in 1851 sample fruit brought to Sacramento from Oregon sold for 1 dollar each. The nursery catalog of Warren and Son in Sacramento had 37 apple cultivars listed. Smith's catalog of 1856 listed 56 cultivars, and by 1858 apples were selling for 25 to 50 cents a pound. Santa Clara County was then the leading county in apple production, thanks to Captain Joseph Aram who later started a nursery close to the old Southern Pacific Railroad depot in San Jose.

In 1925 the leading apple-producing counties were Santa Cruz, Sonoma, and Kern. The first report of tree decline, possibly due to oak root fungus was in 1858 in San Jose. The University of California established a test orchard in 1874, and in 1894 listed 200 cultivars under investigation. Later, the California Standard Apple Act insured consumers of a pack free of defective and diseased fruit. Control of codling moth without use of lead was one of the priority programs (2).

Many of the oldest orchards in California were planted on so-called French roots (4), which were nothing more than roots of trees produced from seed imported from France and Austria. In recent years, however, nurserymen have employed roots of seedlings of the common American cultivars. The East Malling Experiment Station of England has developed the so-called Malling rootstocks. These are selections from European types which can be readily propagated from root cuttings; they are being used more extensively in the U.S. (4).

THE PEAR (*Pyrus communis* L.)

The ancient Greeks knew this fruit and had distinct cultivars of it, and the Chinese developed edible cultivars many hundreds of years ago.

The pear has been grown in California since the establishment of the first Spanish mission in San Diego in 1769. Mission Monterey (established in 1770) was also one of the centers of distribution. Only 220 non-Indians were known to be living in California in 1790 and when California was ceded to the U.S. in 1847 there were about 15,000. During the 1848 gold rush a young man settled 2½ miles above Sacramento on 50 acres of land and established the first important nursery in California. In 1858 pears were selling for 25 to 50 cents a pound, and

overproduction undoubtly resulted. In 1859 California had about 212,650 pear trees; in 1930, Sacramento County alone had over 728,000 bearing trees. Estimates for 1974 show 22,384 acres (4 million trees) which produced about 50 percent of the nation's crop.

Modern domestic pear cultivars were derived from at least two species, *Pyrus communis* L. and *P. serotina* Rahd. (*P. pyrifolia* Nakai). *Pyrus communis* is a native of southern Europe and southern Asia. French and Belgian orchardists and nurserymen of the eighteenth and nineteenth centuries played leading roles in the developing of improved cultivars from this species (5). Many of these were introduced into the U.S. and retained, in part at least, their French names. As early as 1830 a nursery in eastern U.S. was offering 30 or 40 cultivars for sale. *Pyrus serotina*, the sand pear of horticulturists, is a native of China and also grows wild in Japan—the Orient's domesticated pears have largely been developed from this species. A few of the cultivars (Kieffer and Clapp's Favorite) grown in America were developed from this species, but cultivars of this type have not become generally popular in occidental countries.

Although the pear is almost as widely grown as the apple, commercial production is much more restricted and in the U.S. is largely confined to the western states, particularly Washington, Oregon, and California. Pears are important as food in western Asia, South Africa, and Europe.

The most widely grown cultivar in America is Bartlett, which is known as Williams or Williams Bon Cretien outside of America. More than 88 percent of the 24,384 acres of pears in California are Bartletts. Other cultivars of importance in California are Beurre Hardy, Winter Nelis, Comice, Beurre Bosc, and d'Anjou. Those grown to some extent in different parts of the United States are Clapp's Favorite, Conference, Flemish Beauty, Lawson, Kieffer, and Seckel. Most of the cultivars just mentioned are diploid (34 chromosomes); mutants with a triploid number of chromosomes are Beurre Diel and Vicar of Winkfield, the latter an English variety. A tetraploid mutant of Bartlett, the Max-Red Barlett, discovered in Washington State some years ago, is gaining favor in the Pacific Northwest.

Research at the agricultural experiment stations of Oregon and California has provided much information on rootstocks for pear. In his search for fire-blight-resistant understocks, Reimer (6) in Oregon assembled and tested most known wild species of *Pyrus* and all available horticultural cultivars of domestic pear from Europe, Africa, and

Asia. Day (4) and others have studied the performance of the more widely used understock under California conditions.

The following understocks have been used:

Seedlings of the oriental species, *Pyrus betulaefolia* Bge., *P. calleryana* Decne., *P. pyrfolia* (Burm.) Nakai and *P. ussuriensis* Maxim; seedlings of domestic cultivars grown in America, seedlings from seed imported from France (these are predominantly *P. communis* but possibly are also other European species such as *P. nivalis* Jacq.), and vegetatively propagated plants of quince (*Cydonia oblonga* Mill.)

Fruit blackens on the scion cultivars when Oriental species (except *P. calleryana*) are used as rootstocks. For this reason they have been all but abandoned in recent years. Furthermore, importation of seeds from France was not resumed after World War II. Seedlings of Bartlett and Winter Nelis are extensively used in California. Occasionally, *P. calleryana* seedlings are budded or grafted onto Old Home stock. In a few localities the quince is in demand as a rootstock. Because several pear cultivars do not do well when grafted on quince, the Beurre Hardy, which makes a good union with quince, is used as an intermediate stock when quince rootstock is desired.

THE QUINCE (*Cydonia oblonga* Mill.)

The domestic quince, *Cydonia oblonga* Mill., also has a long history. It is used only for preserves, jams, jellies, so is of slight commercial importance in most fruit-growing countries. Cultivars grown in the U.S. are Smyrna, Pineapple, Champion, and Orange. Trees are propagated by grafting onto quince rootstocks that have been produced by layering or from cuttings.

Quince has been grown in California since the founding of the first mission in San Diego in 1769. In 1848, four cultivars were named in the nurseryman's catalog in Sacramento, and by 1859 there were 45,821 quince trees in the state. The Smyrna was imported by George Roeding of the Fancher Creek Nurseries of Fresno in 1899. The 1930 census showed a reduced trend in quince production, with only 32,633 bearing trees and 10,988 nonbearing trees (2). In 1974, production of quince was insignificant in the U.S.

References

1. Beach, S. A. 1905. Apples of New York. Report of the Agricultural Experiment Station for the year 1903. New York Dept. Agr. Vol. I, 409 pp, Vol. II, 360 pp.

2. Butterfield, H. M. 1937-38. History of deciduous fruits in California. The Blue Anchor Vols. 14 and 15. 38 pp.
3. Chandler, W. H. 1951. Deciduous orchards. Lea & Febiger, Philadelphia, Pa. 436 pp.
4. Day, L. H. 1947. Apple, quince, and pear rootstocks in California. Univ. California Agr. Exp. Sta. Bul. 700. 44 pp.
5. Hedrick, U. P. 1921. The pears of New York. New York Dept. Agr. Twenty-Ninth Ann. Rept. Vol. 2, Part II. 636 pp.
6. Reimer, F. C. 1925. Blight resistance in pears and characteristics of pear species and stocks. Oregon State Coll. Agr. Exp. Sta. Bul. No. 214, 99 pp.
7. Smock, R. M., and A. M. Neubert. 1950. Apples and apple products. Interscience Publishers Inc., New York. 486 pp.
8. Taylor, H. V. 1948. The apples of England. 3rd ed. Crosby Lockwood & Son, Ltd., London. 214 pp.

BACTERIAL DISEASES OF APPLE AND PEAR

Bacterial Blossom Blast of Pear
Pseudomonas syringae van Hall

Blossom blast of flowers is an occasional problem in California pear orchards. Three common causes are: Boron deficiency, lack of winter chilling, and bacterial infection caused by *Pseudomonas syringae* van Hall.

Bacterial blast (fig. 1A) is the most damaging and can make the crop unprofitable to harvest. Brown to black necrotic areas develop on petals and other flower parts and on stems and fruit cluster bases. If the fruit-buds are infected in the green tip or tight cluster stage, they stop growing and drop prematurely. The diseased area usually advances no further than the base of the fruiting cluster, but sometimes it may move down the spur. Killing of flowering spurs can lead to shortage of fruiting sites the coming year. Bacterial blossom blast usually develops most abundantly on the lower limbs. Shortly after blossom symptoms develop, the periderm layer of affected spurs or shoots separates from the underlying tissue, and on drying the separated tissue develops a papery appearance (fig. 1B). This is an important diagnostic feature.

Infected areas on fruit (fig. 1C) appear as black depressed spots, which sometimes cover the entire fruit. On leaves, a red ring frequently surrounds the infected area. Later, this area becomes dry and falls away leaving a small hole.

Cold, wet weather favors disease development, while warm, dry conditions stop its progress. Freezing of tissue may favor blossom infection as an increase in bacterial population on the frozen parts has been observed. Infection has not been observed on frosty nights during bloom when overhead sprinklers are in operation to prevent freezing.

Control of this disease is difficult because favorable conditions for infection are periodic and unpredictable. Once symptoms develop, control is not possible. However, recent tests with fixed copper fungicides and streptomycin (1) indicated that copper sprays applied at green-tip stage of blossom development significantly reduce blossom blast. Copper spray at the green-tip stage followed by a streptomycin spray during early bloom also reduced the disease significantly.

References

1. Bethell, R. S., J. M. Ogawa, W. H. English, R. R. Hansen, B. T. Manji, and F. J. Schick. Copper-streptomycin sprays control pear blossom blast. Calif. Agric. 31 (6):7-9.

Crown Gall of Apple, Pear, and Quince
Agrobacterium tumefaciens (Smith & Townsend) Conn.

Crown gall caused by *Agrobacterium tumefaciens* (Smith and Townsend) Conn. may cause losses of nursery trees. The disease has rarely been observed on mature apple trees; on mature pear trees it is common, but not as common as on stone fruit trees.

Control measures in the nursery have involved seed treatment with sodium hypochorite and soil treatment with methyl bromide.* Direct seeding in nursery rows has become a common practice to avoid injury to roots during transplanting. More details on biological control of crown gall by using a nonpathogenic strain of crown gall bacteria are provided in section III.

Fireblight of Apple, Pear, and Quince
Erwinia amylovora (Burrill) Winslow *et al.*

"Fireblight" is the name most often applied to this disease. In California, however, it is best known on the pear and is called "pear blight." On apple it is a minor problem in California, while on quince it can be severe. Other names formerly used were "spur blight," "fruit blight," "twig blight," and "blossom blight."

---

*Permission from County Agricultural Commissioner required for purchase, possession, or use.

Fireblight is believed to be of American origin—it was known in this country many years before it was discovered abroad. In 1794, William Denning (25) wrote that he had known the disease on apple, pear, and quince in the Hudson Valley for some years. Before the middle of the next century it became established in orchards of the midwestern states. On the Pacific Coast the disease was apparently first identified in 1887 near Chico, California. By 1900, severe epidemics had destroyed one-third of the pear crops in Fresno, Kern, and Tulare counties, and the pear industry has never regained its importance in them. Pear growing was next established in the Sacramento Valley. Fireblight occurred there in the 1920's and 1930's and periodically thereafter, the most recent outbreak being in 1970 (9).

Fireblight apparently now occurs wherever pears or apples are grown. It has been identified in New Zealand, Japan, more recently in England (1957), the Netherlands (1966), Poland (1966), France (1972), and Belgium (1972), (85). In Spain it is known only on hawthorn.

Symptoms. Leaves, green shoots, fruit, mature branches, and roots are attacked (fig. 2A). Symptoms first appear on the blossoms, which wither and die. Under humid conditions the affected blossoms exude creamy yellow drops of ooze (fig. 2B). From the blighted blossom the bacteria move into the spur and hence into the branch, where it may kill the bark down to the cambium. During the period of activity, affected bark becomes water-soaked in appearance and reddish. After canker extension ceases, the diseased bark becomes brown and dry as it shrinks, a fissure commonly develops along the margins. This is followed by the formation of callus which may entirely surround the canker. Girdled branches die in summer, and these "flags," together with blighted blossom clusters, are the most noticeable symptoms of the disease.

Twig blight, produced by infection of the succulent leafy shoots, often develops major outbreaks of fireblight. In pears, blighted twigs and leaves turn black; in apple they tend to be brown. After sucker infection, the bacteria sometimes extend into the roots. Similarly, infection of suckers which develop on the body of the tree may lead to invasion of the trunk and death of the tree.

Fruit infection sometimes occurs. Infected green fruit quickly develops a dark-green, water-soaked appearance, and under some conditions is covered by droplets of ooze or tendrils of bacteria. Sometimes pear fruit is infected after it is harvested and packed for shipment; on such mature fruit infection results in circular, black, sunken lesions which seldom are more than an inch in diameter or more than one-fourth inch deep.

In early stages of shoot infection the bacteria occur intercellularly, forming what Nixon (63) described as "zoogloeal" masses which migrate through the tissue by means of pseudopod-like extension. The host cells adjacent to the bacterial masses collapse and separate, producing schizogenous cavities. The bacteria then enters the cells which undergo dissolution. The resulting lysigenous cavities gradually enlarge. As bacterial activity wanes, the bacterial masses go into a cyst stage. Haber (38) described a similar situation in invaded apple leaves. Miller (58), however, found no evidence of zoogloea; he said that the bacteria, in early stages of infection at least, are free-swimming and migrate individually from one cell to another through apertures. The cells first exhibited plasmolytic effects and later separated along the middle lamella, presumably as a result of enzymatic activity. Miller failed to demonstrate the formation of pectinase by the bacteria, however.

Cause. In 1878, Burrill published the first results of studies which proved that fireblight is caused by a bacterial organism (13) and established the concept that bacteria were able to produce plant diseases. Burrill (16) later described the bacterium under the name *Micrococcus amylovorus,* but this was changed to *Bacillus amylovorus* by Trevisan. Under the system of nomenclature later adapted by the Society of American Bacteriologists in 1920, the accepted name is *Erwinia amylovora* (Burrill) Winslow *et al.*

Erwinia amylovora is a short, gram-negative, capsulated, nonspore-forming rod 0.7 to 1.0 μm wide and 0.9 to 1.5 μm long; it is motile by peritrichous flagella, and occurs singly, in pairs, or sometimes in short chains. On agar media, colonies are circular, grayish-white, moist and glistening with irregular margins. The bacteria produce acid without gas from the common sugars. Minimum temperature for growth is between 3° and 8°C, the maximum 35 to 37°C, and the optimum about 23.3°C. Strains differ in growth rates with generation time of 45 to 100 min at 30°C. Growth occurs between pH 4.0 and 8.8, the optimum being pH 6.8.

Strains vary in virulence, morphology, serology (76) and phage typing. The bacteria are unstable when cultured continuously, and single-celled isolates are more stable than are single-colony isolates (41). Of the many tests used to identify populations of virulent strains of *E. amylovora,* the differential medium developed by Miller and Schroth (59) has enabled positive identification and enumeration

within 60 hours. For even more rapid identification, but not for population counts, the use of antiserum in agglutination tests have been suggested (73). Biological tests for pathogenicity are still used to confirm resistance of rootstocks (21, 22, 81). Pathogenicity tests have involved inoculations of green pear fruits (11), shoots of pear and apple (64), pyracantha (70) and apple seedlings (67).

Most recently, Pugashetti and Starr (68) used conjugation to transfer plant virulence in *E. amylovora* from virulent donor strains to avirulent recipient strains in a 3-hour mating period.

Initially, ammonia was suspected as being the necrotoxin produced by *E. amylovora* (35, 53, 54). The principle was shown by Hildebrand (44) to be thermostable and causing cell plasmolysis. It was later shown by Eden-Green (27) to be a high molecular weight heteropolysaccharide with galactose, glucose, mannose, and glucuronic acid residues. Goodman and Huang (34) isolated a polysaccharide from diseased apple tissue infected with *E. amylovora* and named it amylovorin, which is a polymer of galactose (98 percent) with 0.375 percent protein and traces of undertermined substances.

Hosts. Inoculation tests have shown that *Erwinia amylovora* will invade the succulent parts of a large number of plants, and in some it produces typical fireblight symptoms. Virtually all of the plants which exhibit demonstrable susceptibility to the causal bacterium belong to the family Rosaceae. Moreover, only certain genera of the sub-family Pomoideae exhibit susceptibility comparable to that of *Pyrus* and *Cydonia.* For example, species of *Spiraea, Aruncus, Kageneckie* and *Holodiscus* of the sub-family Spiraeoides develop mild symptoms on inoculation, but none of these species is seriously blighted and none is known to develop the disease under natural conditions. Among genera of the sub-family Pomoideae, however, certain species of *Cotoneaster, Crataegus, Aronia, Eriobotrya, Chaenomeles, Docynia, Pyracantha* are readily infected by inoculation, and species in five of the genera are probably reservoirs of the pathogen under California conditions. These are *Cotoneaster pannosa, Crataegus oxyacantha* (English hawthorn), *Eriobotrya japonica* (loquat), *Heteromeles arbutifolia* (toyon) and the fire-thorns: *Pyracantha angustifolia, P. crenulata, P. formosiana* (= *P. koidzumii*) and *P. gibbsii yunnanensis* (78).

Susceptibility of the host and host parts have been related to arbutinhydroquinone complex (39, 40, 65). Beta-glucosidase activity was found to be low in tissues most susceptible to fireblight, tissues such as the nectary and inner parts of blossoms, the midrib, and petioles of leaves and bark of stems. Arbutin was found in greater amounts in fireblight resistant pear cultivars such as Old Home, Keiffer, and *P. serotina* than in the susceptible Bartlett and Forelle (40). The relationship of ammonia production to symptoms has been suggested (54).

Disease development. The fireblight pathogen overwinters in the infected bark tissues of the apple and pear hosts. Other hosts such as loquat, toyon, and some species of fire-thorn also are reservoirs of the pathogen. Twigs as small as 6 mm in diameter, as well as large branches, are "holdover" sites. Keil and van der Zwet (51) were able to isolate highly virulent *E. amylovora* from internal tissues of symptomless side shoots on artificially inoculated apple and pear. Isolations from apparently healthy suckers in blighted Bartlett trees showed *E. amylovora* to occur on 60 percent of the shoots. Whether they overwintered in healthy tissue, as suggested, is questionable, as no field data are presented (76). The primary source of inoculum in spring appears to be both extending and non-extending cankers plus latent infections (76). The pathogen will survive for weeks in detached infected branches and remain alive in soil for a month or more, but probably does not overwinter there. For a time, beehives were suspected of harboring the bacteria, but it was shown that the pathogen remains alive only a short time in honey (4, 13, 30, 36, 58, 88). Morrill (62) isolated virulent bacteria from pear buds in early spring in Utah, but similar isolations from pear buds in California yielded negative results (76).

When humidity is high in spring, the bacteria ooze to the surface of holdover cankers. Though it is agreed that the ooze is the principal source of inoculum for primary infection, considerable disagreement exists as to the manner in which the bacteria are transmitted from the cankers to the blossoms, the first parts to become infected in the spring. Some (7, 36, 44) have cited the development of cone-shaped areas of infected blossoms beneath holdover twigs as evidence that rain water performs this function. Another view is that, though rain water undoubtedly transmits the bacteria downward in the tree, it is not the principal agent responsible for the extensive lateral transmission that has been noticed (32). Moreover, primary infection occurs during rainless weather in the arid regions of the western U.S. Thus it is contended that insects are the major agents of transmission from canker to blossom and from blossom to blossom. Waite (86) and many others have shown that the honeybee is capable of transmitting the pathogen from blossom

to blossom, but this insect is not known to visit the cankers. Ants, beetles, and flies, however, are known to feed on the bacterial exudate. As these insects also visit blossoms in search of nectar, it is believed they are the principal agents in transmission of the bacterium from holdover cankers to the blossom (32).

Once a small percentage of blossoms are infected, honeybees, other insects and rain disseminate the bacteria from blossom to blossom (10, 76). Honeybees are attracted to infected blossoms in the early stages of infection, then transmit the bacteria to healthy blossoms (52). According to Miller (59), bacteria enter the flowers through the stomata on the outside of the receptacle cup; however, Hildebrand noted that invasion is primarily through nectaries, stigmas being next in importance (43). The stomata and hydathodes (84) provide avenues for infection of leaves, stomata on green shoots, and young fruit, and fresh wounds provide the avenues for branch infection (19).

Many investigators have noted that extensive blossom infection by the fireblight organism occurs during rainy or humid weather, and investigation of this revealed that fireblight infection is favored by the lower amounts of sugars (dextrose, levulose, and sucrose) in the nectar of blossoms and hindered by a high amount. Sugar concentration of nectar varies greatly; in humid weather it may be as low as 2 percent and as high as 30 to 40 percent in dry weather. Earlier work indicated that the bacteria grow well at concentrations of 3 to 4 percent but little if any at 30 percent, so it was proposed that the increase in volume of nectar and the corresponding decrease in sugar concentration during periods of high humidity are important factors in the initiation of blossom infection (41, 47, 52, 79). It was also supposed that a decrease in the volume of nectar and the resulting increase in sugar concentration inhibits growth of the bacteria in the nectaries. Recent studies indicate, however, that the bacteria can grow in 30 percent glucose, 35 percent artificial nectar or 58 percent sucrose, and that blossom infections can readily occur at the sugar concentration at which nectar is secreted (44, 46, 76).

Temperature plays an important role in the rates at which the bacteria move through the host tissue. At 15.5°C or below, the progress of the bacteria through succulent host tissue is relatively slow, while at 24°C to 27°C it is rapid. Temperature is possibly one factor responsible for increased canker activity in spring and early summer, and for waning of canker activity in the hot months. Canker increase may occur again with the advent of lower temperatures in early autumn, although it should be pointed out that an increase in atmospheric humidity—a condition which would favor progress of blight in the tissue—also occurs as temperature decreases in autumn.

In some regions, winter temperature affects blight development indirectly by influencing the length of the blossoming period the following spring. Following abnormally warm winters in California, the pear comes into bloom slowly and the blooming period is unusually prolonged. This extends the period during which blossoms may be inoculated. Thomas and Ark (78) cited a season in which the blossoming period of Bartlett was 23 days, as compared to 13, 13, and 12 in the three succeeding years.

Cultural practices influence blight development by increasing or decreasing tree growth. Vigorously growing shoots are more severely damaged by this disease than are shoots of low vigor. Therefore, abundant soil moisture and high soil fertility increase the susceptibility of trees by favoring the development of vigorous shoots.

Control. Though none of the common types of good-quality apples and pears is highly resistant to fireblight, some are so susceptible that they are excluded from commercial plantings in regions where the blight is a serious problem. Among the most susceptible cultivars of apples are Willow Twig, Jonathan, Rome Beauty, and Yellow Transparent (1, 3); among highly susceptible cultivars of pears are Bartlett, Forelle, Beurre Hardy, and Beurre Bosc. Use of a resistant understock for pear has met with some success. Seedlings of Old Home variety, a pear of relatively low quality, are often used as a framework on which commercial cultivars are grafted. Oriental species such as *Pyrus calleryana, P. betulaefolia,* and *P. ussuriensis* have been planted to some extent in the western U.S. but the tendency is to avoid these species owing to unfortunate experience with *P. serotina.* Although these species are much more resistent than the French rootstock *(P. communis),* considerable variations occur among its seedlings (17). In addition, trees on *P. serotina* rootstock are less vigorous than those on *P. communis* rootstock, and the fruit often is abnormal in shape. Most serious, however, is the development known as "hard end" or "black end" when commercial cultivars are grown on these rootstocks.

Surgical treatment, such as the excision of blighted branches and the scarification of cankers on limbs and trunks, is practiced only where the returns for the crop are high. In the pear orchards of California, for example, growers may employ a crew of "blight cutters" whose duty is to patrol the orchard in summer and remove blighted twigs before the bacteria became established in the branches.

Two kinds of chemical treatments were used in conjunction with surgical treatment in the early 1900s. One was the scarification of established cankers and subsequent treatment with a solution containing mercuric chloride and mercuric cyanide, each at one part of chemical to 500 parts of water. To increase the wetting properties of the solution and to retard its drying, 10 percent glycerine was added. The second type involved brushing the diseased branches with a solution containing zinc chloride, hydrochloric acid, denatured alcohol and hot water (23, 24). For several years after its introduction in 1928, the zinc chloride treatment was used extensively in certain pear orchards of California. When applied by experienced persons it proved valuable for arresting the extension of established cankers and for reducing the survival level of bacteria in the orchard. It has been employed much less frequently in recent years, however, mainly because when improperly treated it often led to excessive branch injury.

In 1929, McCowen (57) of Purdue University reported the successful control of fireblight in apple blossoms with weak Bordeaux mixture. A preparation containing 2 pounds of copper sulfate, 6 pounds of lime in 100 gallons of water was sprayed on the open blossoms. Later, two treatments of weak Bordeaux were used with some success in commercial orchards. This led to the introduction of copper lime dust which has been employed successfully in some California pear orchards.

Because copper materials induce damage to lenticels in certain cultivars, streptomycin applied as a spray or as a dust was quickly accepted. Recommendations for control of the disease were as follows: Bordeaux mixture 0.5-0.5-100, proprietary copper sprays as manufacturer directs, or copper lime dust (10-90 or 20-80 at 13 to 25 pounds per acre)—applied at 5-day intervals starting when 10 percent of the blossoms are open and continuing until all late blossoms have shed their petals; or wettable streptomycin spray at 60 ppm or streptomycin dust at 1,000 ppm and 40 pounds per acre may be applied according to the above schedule. Recent studies in orchards where streptomycin has been ineffective have resulted in isolation of bacteria that are tolerant to that chemical.

Early formulations of streptomycin contained 1.5 percent oxytetracycline (Terramycin), and in 1954 English and Van Halsema (29) reported rapid development of streptomycin-tolerant *Erwinia* amylovora. However, the combination of streptomycin and oxytetracycline delayed the emergence of resistant strains in culture. Studies by Ark (6), Goodman (32), Leupschen (55) and others showed that effective control can be obtained without damaging fruit by using low dosages of streptomycin applied at 3 to 5 day intervals. Commercial applications of streptomycin have been made since 1968 (8). In 1972 Schroth, *et al*. (75) reported severe blight development in streptomycin-sprayed orchards; the predominant strains of *Erwinia* isolated were resistant to streptomycin levels over 300 ppm. Schroth, Moller, Thomson, and Hildebrand (76) later reported that varied resistance indicated that resistance was not caused by mutation from a single strain. In those orchards, growers have returned to use of copper sprays (61, 69).

Using the principle established by Brooks (12), Mills (60), and Powell (66, 67), Miller and Schroth (59) developed a monitoring system for the bacterial population on the blossoms and correlated this information with the climatological data. The relation of weather to populations of the bacteria on healthy pear blossoms and subsequent disease development is reported by Thomson, Schroth, Moller and Reil (82). Data accumulated thus far indicate a close correlation between infection, with temperatures over 16.5 °C, and bacterial population on the blossoms. Accurate disease forecasting would enable growers to apply the chemicals only when required, and treatments could be timed for greatest efficacy.

Other methods of disease control such as the use of phage (29), antagonistic bacteria (69), and non-virulent *Erwinia* (89) isolates are being tested.

In California, timing of the first spray during bloom is most critical. When blooming commences, applications begin when daily mean temperatures during March approach 16.7 °C; during April, 15.5 °C; and May, 14.4 °C. Alternate rows are sprayed preferably at night or early morning every 5 days until at least 30 days after full bloom. If rain or hail should occur, orchards are resprayed immediately. If humid weather occurs in June, treatment of ''rat-tail'' bloom is needed. Chemicals used were copper hydroxide, COCS, Streptomycin 17 and streptomycin dust. In orchards known to contain streptomycin-resistant fireblight organisms, the use of copper sprays or dusts was advised.

References

1. Aldwinckle, H. S. 1974. Field susceptibility of 46 apple cultivars to fire blight. Plant Dis. Rep. 58:819-21.

2. Aldwinckle, H.S., and S. V. Beer. 1976. Nutrient status of apple blossoms and their susceptibility to fire blight. Ann. Appl. Biol. 82:159-63.

3. Aldwinckle, H. S., and J. L. Preczewski. 1976. Reaction of terminal shoots of apple cultivars to invasion by *Erwinia amylovora*. Phytopathology 66:1439-44.

4. Ark, P. A. 1932. The behavior of *Bacillus amylovorus* in the soil. Phytopathology 22:657-60.

5. _____ 1937. Variability in the fire-blight organism, *Erwinia amylovora*. Phytopathology 27:1-28.

6. _____ 1953. Use of streptomycin dust to control fire blight. Plant Dis. Rep. 37:404-06.

7. Arthur, J. C. 1885. Proof that the disease of trees known as pear-blight is directly due to bacteria. New York (Geneva) Agr. Exp. Sta. Bul. 2:1-4.

8. Bailey, J. B., and G. W. Morehead. 1970. Streptomycin control of pear fireblight in California. California Agriculture 24(9):14-15.

9. Baker, K. F. 1971. Fire blight of pome fruits: The genesis of the concept that bacteria can be pathogenic to plants. Hilgardia 40(18:603-33.

10. Bauske, R. J. 1971. Wind dissemination of waterborne *Erwinia amylovora* from *Pyrus* to *Pyrancantha* and *Cotoneaster*. Phytopathology 61:741-742.

11. Billing E., J. E. Crosse, and C. M. E. Garrett. 1960. Laboratory diagnosis of fire blight and bacterial blossom blight of pear. Plant Pathol. 9:19-25.

12. Brooks, F. N. 1926. Studies of the epidemiology and control of fire blight of apple. Phytopathology 16:665-96.

13. Burrill, T. J. 1878. Pear blight. Trans. Ill. St. Hort. Soc. 11:114-16.

14. _____ 1879. Fireblight. Trans. Ill. St. Hort. Soc. 12:77-80.

15. _____ 1881. Anthrax of fruit trees. Proc. Amer. Assoc. Adv. Sci. 29:583-97.

16. _____ 1883. New species of *micrococcus* (bacteria). Am. Naturalist 17:319.

17. Cameron, H. R., M. N. Westwood, and P. B. Lombard. 1969. Resistance of Pyrus species and cultivars to *Erwinia amylovora*. Phytopathology 59:1813-15.

18. Carpenter, T. R., and J. R. Shay. 1953. The differentiation of fireblight resistant seedlings within progenies of interspecific crosses of pear. Phytopathology 43:156-62.

19. Crosse, J. E., R. N. Goodman, and W. H. Shaffer. 1972. Leaf damage as a predisposing factor in the infection of apple shoots by *Erwinia amylovora*. Phytopathology 62:39-42.

20. Covey, R. P., and W. R. Fischer. 1973. Short-term population dynamics of *Erwinia amylovora*

in succulent pear tissue. Phytopathology 63:844-846.

21. Coyier, D. L. 1969. Inoculation of apple and pear roots with *Erwinia amylovora*. Workshop Fire Blight Res. Proc. 1st. 57-58.

22. Cummins, J. N., and H. S. Aldwinckle. 1973. Fire blight susceptibility of fruiting trees of some apple rootstock clones. HortScience 8:176-78.

23. Day, Leonard, H. 1928. Pear blight control in California. Calif. Agr. Exp. Sta. Circ. 20:1-50 (out of print).

24. _____ 1930. Zinc chloride treatment of pear blight cankers. Calif. Agr. Exp. Sta. Circ. 45:1-13 (out of print).

25. Denning, W. M. 1974. On decay of apple trees. Proc. Soc. Promotion Agr. Sci. 1:219-22.

26. Dunegan, J. C., H. H. Moon, and R. A. Wilson. 1953. Further results of testing susceptibility of pear seedlings to *Erwinia amylovora*. Phytopathology 43:405. (Abstr.)

27. Eden-Green, S. J. 1972. Studies in fire blight disease of apple, pear and hawthorn (*Erwinia amylovora* [Burrill]) Winslow *et al*. Ph.D. thesis. Univ. London. 202 pp.

28. Eden-Green, S. J., and E. Billing. 1972. Fireblight: occurrence of bacterial strands on various hosts under glasshouse conditions. Plant Pathol. 21:121-23.

29. English, A. R., and G. Van Halsema. 1954. A note on the delay in the emergence of resistant *Xanthomonas* and *Erwinia* strains by the use of Streptomycin plus Terramycin combinations. Plant Dis. Rep. 38:429-31.

30. Erskine, J. M. 1973. Characteristics of *Erwinia amylovora* bacteriophage and its possible role in the epidemiology of fire blight. Can. J. Microbiol. 19:847-45.

31. Fulton, H. R. 1911. The persistence of *Bacillus amylovorus* in pruned apple twigs. Phytopathology 1:68. (Abstr.)

32. Goodman, R. N. 1954. Development of methods for use of antibiotics to control fireblight (*Erwinia amylovora*). Mo. Agr. Exp. Sta. Res. Bul. 540:1-16.

33. Goodman, R. N. and A. Burkowicz. 1970. Ultrastructural changes in apple leaves inoculated with virulent or an avirulent strain of *Erwinia amylovora*. Phytopathol. Z. 68:258-68.

34. Goodman, R. N., and J. S. Huang. 1974. Host specific phytotoxic polysaccharide from apple tissue infected by *Erwinia amylovora*. Science 183:1081-82.

35. Goodman, R. N., S. B. Plurad, and L. Lovrekovich. 1970. Similarity of ultrastructural modifications in tobacco leaf tissue canker either by pathogenic bacteria or exogenous ammonia. Phytopathology 60:1293.

36. Gossard, H. A., and R. C. Walton. 1922. Dissemination of fire blight. Ohio Agr. Exp. Sta. Bul. 357:81-126.

37. Gowda, S. S., and R. N. Goodman. 1970. Movement and persistence of *Erwinia amylovora* in shoot, stem and root of apple. Plant Dis. Rep. 54:576-80.

38. Haber, Julia. 1928. The relation between Bacillus amylovorus and leaf tissues of the apple. Penn. Agr. Exp. Sta. Bul. 228:3-13.

39. Hildebrand, D. C. 1970. Fire blight resistance in *Pryus:* hydroquinone formation as related to antibiotic activity. Can J. Bot. 48:177-81.

40. Hildebrand, D. C., C. C. Powell, and M. N. Schroth. 1969. Fire blight resistance in *Pyrus:* Location of arbutin and beta-glucosidase. Phytopathology 59:1534-39.

41. Hildebrand, E. M. 1973*a*. The blossom-blight phase of fire blight, and methods of control. N. Y. (Cornell) Agr. Exp. Sta. Mem. 207:1-40.

42. _____ 1937*b*. Infectivity of the fire-blight organism. Phytopathology 27:850-52.

43. _____ 1937*c*. The blossom blight phase of fire blight and methods of control Cornell Agr. Exp. Sta. Mem. 207:1-40.

44. _____ 1939. Studies on fire blight ooze. Phytopathology 29:142-56.

45. _____ 1954. Relative stability of fire blight bacteria. Phytopathology 44:192-97.

46. Hildebrand, E. M., and E. F. Phillips. 1936. The honeybee and the beehive in relation to fire blight. J. Agr. Research 52:789-810.

47. Ivanoff, S. S., and G. W. Keitt. 1941. Relation of nectar concentration to growth of *Erwinia amylovora* and fire blight infection of apple and pear blossoms. J. Agr. Research 62:733-43.

48. Jones, D. H. 1909. Bacterial blight of apple, pear and quince. Ontario Agr. Coll. Bul. 176:1-63.

49. Keil, H. L., and T. van der Zwet. 1972*a*. Recovery of *Erwinia amylovora* from symptomless stems and shoots of Jonathan apple and Bartlett pear trees. Phytopathology 62:39-42.

50. _____ 1972*b*. Aerial strands of *Erwinia amylovora;* structure and enhanced production by pesticide oil. Phytopathology 62:355-61.

51. _____ 1972*c*. Recovery of *Erwinia amylovora* from symptomless stems and shoots of Jonathan apple and Bartlett pear trees. Phytopathology 62:39-40.

52. Keitt, G. W., and S. S. Ivanoff. 1941. Transmission of fire blight by bees and its relation to nectar concentration of apple and pear. J. Agr. Research 62:745-753.

53. Lovrekovich, L., H. Lovrekovich, and R. N. Goodman. 1970*a*. Ammonia as a necrotoxin in the hypersensitive reaction caused by bacteria in tobacco leaves. Can. J. Bot. 48:167-71.

54. _____ 1970b. The relationship of ammonia to symptom expression in apple shoots inoculated with *Erwinia amylovora*. Can. J. Bot. 48:999-1000.

55. Leupschen, N. S. 1960. Fire blight control with streptomycin, as influenced by temperature and other environmental factors and by spray adjuvants added to sprays. N. Y. Agr. Exp. Sta. Mem. 375:1-39.

56. McClintock, J. A., and H. L. Facker. 1931. Canker treatment for fire blight control. Tenn. Agr. Exp. Sta. Circ. 36.

57. McCown, Monroe. 1929. Bordeaux spray in the control of fire blight apple. Phytopathology 19:285-293.

58. Miller, P. W. 1929. Studies of fire blight of apple in Wisconsin. J. Agr. Research 39:579-621.

59. Miller, T. D., and M. N. Schroth. 1972. Monitoring the epiphytic population of *Erwinia amylovora* on pear with selective medium. Phytopathology 62:1175-82.

60. Mills, W. D. 1955. Fire blight development on apple in western New York. Plant Dis. Rep. 39:206-07.

61. Moller, W. J., J. A. Beutel, W. O. Reil, F. J. Perry, and M. N. Schroth. 1973. Streptomycin-resistant control studies, 1972. Calif. Agr. 27(6):4-5.

62. Morrill, G. D. 1969. Overwintering of *Erwinia amylovora* inside living host tissue in Cache Valley, Utah. M.S. thesis. Utah State Univ., Logan.

63. Nixon, E. L. 1927. The migration of *Bacillus amylovorus* in apple tissue and its effects on the host cell. Penn. Agr. Exp. Sta. Tech. Bul. 212:3-16.

64. Parker, K. G., N. S. Luepschen, and A. L. Jones. 1974. Inoculation trials with *Erwinia amylovora* to apple rootstocks. Plant Dis. Rep. 58:243-47.

65. Powell, C. C., Jr., and D. C. Hildebrand. 1970. Fireblight resistance in *Pyrus:* involvement of arbutin oxidation. Phytopathology 60:337-40.

66. Powell, D. 1963. Prebloom freezing as a factor in the occurrence of the blossom blight phase of fire blight of apples. Trans. Ill. State. Hort. Soc. 97:144-48.

67. _____ 1965. Factors influencing the severity of fire blight infections on apple and pear. Mich. State Hort. Soc. Ann. Meet. 94:1-7.

68. Pugashetti, B. K., and M. P. Starr. 1972. Conjugational transfer of genes determining plant virulence in Erwinia amylovora. J. Bacteriol. 122:485-91.

69. Reil, W. O., S. V. Thomson, M. N. Schroth, W. H. Griggs, and W. J. Moller. 1974. Pear fire blight control tests, 1973. Calif. Agr. 28(4):4-6.

70. Ritchie, D. F., and E. J. Klos. 1974. A laboratory method of testing pathogenicity of suspected *Erwinia amylovora* isolates. Plant Dis. Rep. 58:181-83.

71. Rosen, H. R. 1929. The life history of the fire blight pathogen, *Bacillus amylovorus,* as related to the means of overwintering and dissemination. Ark. Agr. Exp. Sta. Bul. 244:1-96.

72. _____ 1933. Further studies on the overwintering and dissemination of the fire blight pathogen. Ark. Agr. Exp. Sta. Bul. 283:1-102.

73. _____ 1935. The mode of penetration of pear and apple blossoms by the fire blight pathogen. Science 81:26.

74. Shaffer, W. H., and R. N. Goodman. 1970. Control of twig blight (fireblight) on "Jonathan" apple trees with a combination spray of streptomycin, sulfur and glyodin. Plant Dis. Rep. 54:203-05.

75. Schroth, M. N., J. A. Beutel, W. J. Moller, and W. O. Reil. 1972. Fire blight of pears in California, current status and research progress. I Streptomycin resistance. Calif. Plant Pathology 7. 10 pp.

76. Schroth, M. N., W. J. Moller, S. V. Thomson, and D. C. Hildebrand. 1974. Epidemiology and control of fire blight. Ann. Rev. Phytopathol. 12:389-412.

77. Smith, Clayton O. 1931. Pathogenicity of *Bacillus amylovorus* on species of Juglans. Phytopathology 21:219-23.

78. Thomas, H. Earl, and P. A. Ark. 1934a. Fire blight of pears and related plants, Calif. Agr. Calif. Agr. Exp. Sta. Bul. 586:1-43 (out of print).

79. _____ 1934b. Nectar and rain in relation to fire blight. Phytopathology 24:682-85.

80. Thomas, W. D., Jr., and W. J. Henderson. 1952. Spray experiments for the control of fire blight on apples and pears. 1947-1950. Plant Dis. Rep. 36:273-75.

81. Thompson, J. M. 1971. Effect of rootstock on fireblight in several apple cultivars. Hort. Science 6:167.

82. Thomson, S. V., M. N. Schroth, W. J. Moller, and W. O. Reil. 1975. Relation of weather and epiphytic populations of *Erwinia amylovora* to the occurrence of fire blight. Phytopathology 65:353-58.

83. Thornberry, H. H. 1966. Thomas Jonathan Burrill's contribution to the history of microbiology and plant pathology. Trans. Ill. St. Hort. Soc. Vol. 100. 42 pp.

84. Tullis, E. C. 1929. Studies on the overwintering and modes of infection of the fire blight organism. Mich. Agr. Exp. Sta. Tech. Bul. 97:1-32.

85. Veldeman, I. R. 1972. Discovery of *Erwinia amylovora* (Burrill) Winslow *et al.* in Belgium. Rev. Agr. (Brussels) 25:1487-1594.

10

86. Waite, W. B. 1898*a*. Pear blight and its treatment. East N.Y. Hort Soc. Proc. 2:779-790.

87. _____ 1898*b*. The life history and characteristics of the pear blight germ. Proc. Amer. Assoc. Adv. Sci. 47:427-28. (Abstr.)

88. Whetzel, H. H. 1906. The blight canker of apple trees. New York (Cornell) Agr. Exp. Sta. Bul. 236:103-38.

89. Wrather, H. A., J. Kuc, and E. B. Williams. 1973. Protection of apple and pear fruit tissue against fireblight with nonpathogenic bacteria. Phytopathology 63:1075-76.

90. Zwet, T. van der. 1968*a*. Recent spread and present distribution of fire blight in the world. Plant Dis. Rep. 52:698-702.

91. _____ 1968*b*. Review of fire blight control measures in the United States. Trans. Ill. St. Hort. Soc. 101:63-71.

92. Zwet, T. van der., and H. L. Keil. 1972. Incidence of fire blight in trunks of "Magness" pear trees. Plant Dis. Rep. 56:844-47.

93. Zwet, T. van der., and W. A. Oitto. 1972. Further evaluation of the reaction of "resistant" pear cultivars to fire blight. HortScience 7:395-97.

Hairy Root of Apple
Agrobacterium rhizogenes (Riker *et al.*) Conn.

Early in the studies of crown-gall disease, investigators had noted the development of excessive numbers of fibrous roots from an area at the base of the plant. Hedgecock (3) reported in 1910 that this "hairy root" condition had some definite relations to the malformation known as crown-gall because variations exist, from formation of super-abundant fibrous roots to definite enlargements of the crown-gall type. In 1911, Smith, Brown, and Townsend (13) called attention to the different symptoms produced and the cultural characteristics of various isolates. They questioned whether they were dealing with variations in a species or with different species.

Brown (2), Muncie and Suit (8), and Siegler (12) later studied the hairy-root disease and concluded that it was a manifestation of crown gall. In 1930, however, Riker, Banfield, Wright, Keitt, and Sagen (10) and Wright, Hendrickson, and Riker (15) reported that the hairy-root disease differed fundamentally from crown gall, and gave the pathogen a name other than that of crown gall.

Although hairy-root disease of apple is widespread in the eastern U.S. (14), it is relatively uncommon on that host in California. However, it has been reported on roses in California (1, 9).

Symptoms. Hairy-root disease occurs most commonly on 1- to 3-year-old grafted apple trees (fig. 3). At the union between scion and root piece, an enlargement somewhat resembling a newly-formed crown gall appears. From this arise numerous roots fleshy or fibrous in texture, with many of them containing numerous branches. In addition to the enlargements with excessive rootlet development, there may be other malformations of similar nature but with few or no rootlets. The surface of these enlargements bears numerous convolutions with fissures extending deep into the interior of the enlargements.

The causal organism. Because of differences in bacteriological characters, and host responses, Riker, Banfield, Wright, Keitt, and Sagen (10) and Wright, Hendrickson, and Riker (15) consider the hairy-root organism to be a new species and named it *Phytomonas rhizogenes* in accordance with the generic classification of plant-pathogenic bacteria then in use. According to the classification now in use, the name should be *Agrobacterium rhizogenes* (Riker) Conn. See the later studies of Huisingh and Durbin (6).

The pathogen is a nonspore-forming gram-negative rod, 0.55 to 2.54 μm in length, by 0.15 to 0.75 μm in width, motile by one polar flagellum, and containing capsules. *Agrobacterium tumefaciens* produces some nitrite from nitrates, but *A. rhizogenes* does not. Acid but no gas is formed from arabinose, xylose, rhamnose, glucose, galactose, mannose, maltose, lactose, salacin, and erythritol. No acid or gas is produced from fructose, sucrose, raffinose, melezitose, dextrin, inulin, aesculin, dulcitol, or mannitol. Starch is not hydrolyzed.

In 1970, Keane, Kerr, and New (7) claimed that when isolates from crown-gall and hairy-root malformations were compared biochemically, serologically, and pathogenically, two types could be distinguished. One containing isolates which induced tumors, root-proliferations, and nonpathogenic forms, the other containing only pathogenic forms. They suggested that only one name, *A. radiobacter,* be used to designate the organism; pathogenicity being indicated by a varietal epithet and the biotype specified.

Disease development. Riker, Banfield, Wright, Keitt, and Sagen (10) reported that in inoculation tests the hairy-root organism produced symptoms on rose, honeysuckle, bean, Paris daisy, and apple. A large number of other hosts of the organism have since been reported (1, 9).

The pathogen grows best between 20° and 28°C, and at such temperatures symptoms in the form of enlargements at the inoculation point develop in a matter of 2 or 3 weeks; this is followed within a month by development of numerous roots on the enlargements.

The pathogen apparently is capable of living free of the host in soil for a considerable length of time (5). It occurs in large numbers in the tissues of the basal enlargements and readily escapes to the soil, where it is doubtless spread about by water. Other important agencies of dissemination are by insects, such as white grubs, which not only feed upon the basal enlargements, thereby picking up the pathogen, but in subsequent feeding on roots of uninfected plants and inoculate them (5). The bacterium enters the plant only through relatively fresh wounds (5).

Control. In apple, infection by the hairy root pathogen occurs most commonly during or following the grafting process. A root piece from a seedling is fitted onto a scion and the two are secured by wrapping with a suitable material. Formerly, a waxed string was used, but this left spaces through which bacteria in soil water could enter the cut surfaces of scion and root piece. By using a special adhesive tape which better protects cut surfaces, and by dipping roots and scion in a disinfectant, infection is greatly reduced at this stage. Grafts then should be planted in soil known to be free of the pathogen.

When the trees are dug from the nursery row and planted in the orchard, care should be taken to avoid wounding them. Trees should not be planted in soils where the disease has already occurred.

Control of soil-inhabiting insects which feed upon the plant roots, has been suggested as a means of avoiding infection of susceptible trees (9).

References

1. Anonymous. 1954. Thirty-fourth annual report for the period ending December 31, 1953. California Dept. Agr. Bul. 42:234-72.
2. Brown, Nellie A. 1929. The tendency of the crown-gall organism to produce roots in conjunction with tumors. J. Agr. Research 39:747-66.
3. Hedgecock, G. G. 1910. Field studies in the crown-gall and hairy-root of the apple tree. USDA Plant Indus. Bul. 186:1-108.
4. Hildebrand, E. M. 1934. Life history of the hairy-root organism in relation to its pathogenicity on apple trees. J. Agr. Research. 48:857-85.
5. Hildebrand, E. M., and A. J. Riker. 1932. Meeting agriculture's old and new problems with the aid of science. Wisconsin Agr. Exp. Sta. Ann. Rept. for 1931. 152 pp.
6. Huisingh, D., and R. D. Durbin. 1967. Physical and physiological differentiation among *Agrobacterium rhizogenes, A. tumefaciens,* and *A. radiobacter.* Phytopathology 57:922-3.
7. Keane, P. J., A. Kerr, and P. B. New. 1970. Crown gall of stone fruit. II. Identification and nomenclature of *Agrobacterium* isolates. Australian J. Biol. Sci. 23:585-95.
8. Muncie, J. H., and R. F. Suit. 1930. Studies on crown gall, overgrowths, and hairy root of apple nursery stock. Iowa State Coll. J. Sci. 4:263-300.
9. Munnecke, D. E., P. A. Chandler, and M. P. Starr. 1963. Hairy root *(Agrobacterium rhizogenes)* of field roses. Phytopathology 53:788-99.
10. Riker, A. J., W. M. Banfield, W. H. Wright, G. W. Keitt, and H. E. Sagen. 1930. Studies on the infectious hairy root of nursery apple trees. J. Agr. Research 41:507-40.
11. Riker, A. J., and E. M. Hildebrand. 1934. Seasonal development of hairy root, crown gall, and wound overgrowth in apple trees in the nursery. J. Agr. Research. 48:887-912.
12. Siegler, E. A. 1929. The wooly knot type of crown gall. J. Agr. Research. 39:427-50.
13. Smith, E. F., N. A. Brown, and C. O. Townsend. 1911. Crown-gall of plants: its cause and remedy. USDA Bur. Plant Indus. Bul. 312:1-215.
14. Suit, F. R. 1933. *Pseudomonas rhizogenes* R.B. W.K. & S: its host relations and characteristics. Iowa State Coll. J. Sci. 8:131-73.
15. Wright, W. H., A. A. Hendrickson, and A. J. Riker. 1929. Studies on the progeny of single-cell isolations from hairy-root and crown-gall organisms. J. Agr. Research. 41:541-47.

FUNGAL DISEASES OF APPLE AND PEAR

Anthracnose of Apple,
Pezicula malicorticis (Jacks.) Nannf.
Perennial Canker of Apple,
Neofabraea perennans (Zeller and Childs) Kienholz

Apple-tree anthracnose, or "Northwestern anthracnose," has been known in the Pacific Northwest since about 1890 but did not receive critical attention until the early 1900's (10, 11, 12). The disease usually is manifested as a cankerous condition of the branches, but under some conditions it occurs on fruit before harvest or after fruit is picked and stored (10, 11, 12, 30). As a result of his pathogenicity studies, Cordley (12) gave the first comprehensive description of symptoms in the 1900's as well as a description of the conidial stage of the causal fungus, which he named *Gleosporium malicorticis*. Between 1911 and 1913, Jackson (24, 25, 26) contributed further information on the life history of the fungus and described the ascigerous stage, which he named *Neofabraea malicorticis* (Cord.) Jack. and later changed to *Pezicula malicorticis* (Jacks.) Nannf.

In 1925, Zeller and Childs (47, 48) reported another anthracnose disease that was widely distributed in Oregon, Washington, and British Columbia. This disease, originally known to growers as "false anthracnose", was named "perennial canker" by Zeller and Childs. The fungus attacks the bark of the host and produces a ripe-fruit rot. The conidial stage of the causal fungus was named *Gleosporium perennans* Zeller and Childs, and the ascigerous stage *Neofabraea perennans* (Zeller and Childs) Kienholz.

In the Pacific Northwest, these diseases tend to be confined to different climatic zones. On the whole, anthracnose is most prevalent west of the Cascade Mountains, a region characterized by high annual rainfall and moderate winter temperatures. Both diseases occur in the apple districts of the White Salmon-Hood River Valley where the Columbia river breaks through the Cascade Mountains, and where climatic conditions are intermediate between those to the east and west of these mountains.

Anthracnose is sometimes found in other parts of the west, including Idaho and California (4). It has been reported from Nebraska (21, 22), Massachusetts (5), Illinois (1), and Maine (23). It occurs in Denmark (20), Holland (37), New Zealand (3, 6, 14, 15), England (43, 44).

Symptoms: anthracnose. Elliptical sunken necrotic cankers develop in the bark of the host (fig. 4A). Smaller branches are most commonly infected, but at times the scaffold limbs on the trunk may also be involved. The cankers enlarge and then become separated from surrounding healthy tissue by a crack which may extend completely around the affected area. The periderm over the necrotic area cracks and becomes separated into numerous small pieces which curl up at the edges exposing the acervuli beneath the fungus. At first, they appear as small, cream-colored pustules projecting through the periderm. Later, however, they turn dark. On old cankers, the bark, except for the bast fibers, break away. The remnants of the bast fibers running lengthwise of the canker have been referred to as "fiddle strings."

Under certain conditions, fruit become infected by anthracnose either just before or just after harvest.

The lesions are brown, sunken, circular spots in the center of which are the grayish or cream-colored acervuli, frequently in concentric circles. In the early stages the lesions may exhibit what is known as "bull's-eye" or "frog-eye" appearance; a green center surrounded by a brown zone. Though fruit lesions may develop into relatively large sunken spots, anthracnose rarely involves the entire fruit. However, secondary rot fungi commonly enter the anthracnose lesions and complete the destruction of the fruit.

Symptoms: perennial canker. Elliptical roughened cankers (fig. 4B) develop on large or small branches, commonly occuring at places where lateral branches have been removed in pruning operations. Their distinguishing characteristic is a series of concentric callus ridges which form each year after the canker has ceased to expand. An old canker may have numerous ridges, usually one for each year, and so its age may be approximately reckoned. Because of pressure exerted by the developing ridges, the periderm breaks and falls away from the face of the canker. The recurrent annual extension of the cankered area suggested the name "perennial canker."

Another type of canker sometimes forms. This is a circular necrotic area, often surrounding a lenticel, usually shallow in depth, and rarely active for more than one season. Such necrotic spots eventually slough away.

Infection of fruit results in the development of circular, slightly sunken spots, deep brown at the margins and light brown in the center. Such spots are frequently most numerous at the stem end. They increase slowly in diameter and depth, producing a fairly firm spongy rot. The name "bull's eye" rot has been applied to this phase of the disease (16, 17, 18).

The causal organism. The imperfect stage of the anthracnose fungus was incorrectly described as *Macrophoma curvispora* by Peck (36). Later Cordley (12) gave it the name *Gleospora malicorticis* and later the name was changed to *Cryptosporiopsis curvispora* (Pk.) Gremmen. Jackson (24, 25, 26) having discovered the ascigerous stage in 1913 named it *Neofabraea malicorticis* (Cord.) Jack., erecting a new genus. The acervulus stage of the perennial canker pathogen was named *Gleosporium perennans* by Zeller and Childs in 1925 (47, 48). According to Kienholz (28) the ascigerous stage of this fungus was discovered in 1928 by Cooley, who noted its similarity to *N. malicorticis* but preferred to retain the specific name *perennans*. Accordingly, in 1939 Kienholz (28) formally described and named it *N. perennans* (Zeller and Childs) Kienholz. In doing so, he rejected Nannfeldt's (34) transfer of these fungi to *Pezicula,* a genus erected by the Tulasnes in 1865. Nannfeldt based this transfer on a study of *Neofabraea corticola* (Edg.) Jorg. Thompson (41) also objected to the extinction of *Neofabraea,* which he maintained is related to *Pezicula* but is not identical with it. Wollenweber (45), however, recommended the transfer.

Pezicula malicorticis and *Neofabraea perennans* are so similar as to be indistinguishable. The chief differences are found in the shape of the conidia and in the size of asci and ascospores. The former produces curved or hooked conidia, the latter straight or slightly curved conidia. The former produces slightly larger asci and ascospores than the latter (28, 47, 48). Differences in physiological characters are somewhat greater conversion of starch into dextrin and maltose, and greater sensitivity to certain chemicals (tannic acid and malachite green) on the part of *N. malicorticis* (28, 33).

With both the morphological and physiological characters, however, greater variations may exist between different isolates of either species than between the species themselves (28, 33). Moreover, in districts such as the White Salmon-Hood River Valley, where the climate is intermediate between the coastal and interior regions, the fungi themselves tend to be intermediate in type. To quote Kienholz (28, p.662), "A separation of these forms as species based wholly on morphological or physiological grounds appears unwarranted." He also said "Because of the practical aspects of disease control, however, it seems desirable to consider them as distinct species, for the diseases caused by them must be handled as distinct diseases in the orchard."

Irrespective of the view which one might take regarding the separation of species in the basis of parasitic differences, there remains the question of whether symptomatic dissimilarities between anthracnose and perennial canker are due to the parasite itself or to the environment. In the Pacific Northwest perennial canker symptoms are more prevalent in regions of light rainfall and relatively cold winters. Low temperature plays an important part in infection by the perennial canker fungus, but whether or not temperature has a similar effect on infection by anthracnose fungus has not been fully explored. Kienholz (28) remarked on the tendency for symptoms induced by the anthracnose fungus in the Hood River Valley to resemble those of perennial canker, but he was unable to obtain conclusive experimental evidence on this point.

Though Kienholz (28) did not feel justified in combining the two species, he pointed out the inter-

gradations in morphological characters displayed by various isolates of the two species. He and others (18, 19) noted, for example, that certain isolates of the perennial canker fungus produced conidia indistinguishable from the anthracnose fungus. Kienholz (28) observed that saltation was common with both fungi, arising either in colonies from conidia or colonies from ascospores. The saltant from the colony of one species often produced conidia similar to those produced by the other species, so suggested that *P. malicorticis* and *N. perennans* might be strains arising from mutation of a common parent.

The acervuli of both fungi are uniformly distributed over the surface of the canker. They are at first subperidermal then erumpent. The acervulus stroma is a closely packed structure from the surface of which arises numerous simple or branched conidiophores. Conidia of *P. malicorticis* usually are curved, 4 to 6 μm broad and 15 to 24 μm long; those of *N. perennans* typically are straight 4 to 6 μm broad and 12 to 20 μm long. The shape and size of the conidia, however, are greatly influenced by environment and vary greatly among different isolates (22, 28, 35).

The ascigerous stages of the fungi are comparatively rare in nature. The apothecia develop within stromata of old acervuli. Those of *P. malicorticis* are 0.5 to 1 mm in diameter; those of *N. perennans* are slightly smaller. Conditions of moisture and temperature, however, influence the size of these structures. Apothecia of both fungi are sessile, waxy in texture, and gray to flesh-colored. In wet weather they often persist for a considerable time, but quickly disintegrate in dry periods. Asci are indehiscent, clavate in shape, and slightly pedicellate. Those of *P. malicorticis* average 14 μm broad and 103 μm long; those of *N. perennans* 13 μm wide and 98 μm long. Ascospores are one- or two-seriate in the ascus, unicellular until germination when they may develop one to four septa, and are ellipsoidal in shape sometimes flattened on one side. The contents are coarsely granular or finely guttular, and colorless or slightly amber in old spores. On the whole, the acospores of *P. malicorticis* are slightly shorter than those of *N. perennans,* being about 6 μm wide and 19 μm long (22, 28, 35).

Microconidia are produced by both fungi in culture. Their development in positions near hyphal coils, which appear to be the beginnings of the apothecia, suggested to Kienholz (28) that they perform the same function that microconidia perform in other discomycetes.

Host relations and cultivar susceptibility. The fungi attack similar hosts. The following have proved susceptible: Commercial apple, Siberian Crab, Oregon Crab, pear, quince, peach, serviceberry, apricot, cherry, flowering quince, hawthorn and mountain ash. Only on *Pyrus* species, however, do the fungi produce cankers similar to those on cultivated apple in nature. It is thought the Oregon Crab, a widely distributed native species in the Pacific Northwest, may be a natural host of the fungi. Pear and quince are naturally affected by both diseases but have not proved as susceptible as the apple.

Few data are available on the comparative susceptibility of apple cultivars to anthracnose. Baldwin is especially susceptible, but Northern Spy and Ben Davis are rarely affected. Susceptibility is believed to be conditioned by susceptibility of the trees to injury from freezing, and to the attack of the woolly apple aphid. Such cultivars as Esopus Spitzenberg, Yellow Newtown, Rome Beauty, and Jonathan are severely affected by perennial canker in the northwest, whereas Gravenstein, McIntosh, Winter Banana, Delicious, Arkansas Black, Winesap, and Wealthy are much less affected (7, 28). In England, Worcester Pearmain, Bramley's Seedling, Allington Pippin, Laxton's Superb, and Cox's Orange Pippin are said to be most often affected by perennial canker (43, 44).

The disease cycle. Owing to the infrequent development of apothecia by the two fungi, ascospores play only a minor role in disease development. The fungi survive from one season to the next in branch cankers. The perennial canker fungus may exist in a saprophytic state on dead bark for several years, producing conidia most of the time. The conidia are disseminated by rains and infect the branches of the host in autumn and early winter. The apple tree is relatively immune to infection by the perennial canker fungus during the growing season. It becomes susceptible in late September or early October and remains so until December or January (9, 39). Cankers produced by this fungus expand in late winter and early spring but cease activity when the trees begin to grow in spring. Whether or not the tree undergoes periods of susceptibility and resistance to infection by the anthracnose fungus remains to be shown.

The expansion of the diseased area followed by the production of a ridge of callus around the margin of the diseased area, which occurs with perennial cankers each season, was earlier thought to be caused by the annual extension of the fungus mycelium into healthy tissue about the periphery of the canker. This is now said to be caused by infection of tissue by spores produced on the canker itself. Thus, perennial canker and anthracnose exhibit marked dissimilarities. For example, anthracnose disease does not become perennial in the sense that perennial canker does. The cankers of anthracnose appear in spring, grow

rapidly during early summer, and reach their full size by midsummer. They may then become surrounded by a deep crack along which a ridge of callus forms. Unlike perennial canker, however, they exhibit no tendency to continue expansion the following season, though the fungus remains alive on the dead bark and sporulates for a year or so more. Sloughing of the dead bark eventually removes most of the fungus from such cankers.

The anthracnose fungus is capable of infecting the unbroken surface of the twigs; but the perennial canker fungus can enter the host only through some type of wound. Consequently, cankers produced by the former are located any place on the twig, whereas those produced by the latter are usually located only around wounds. Pruning cuts and injuries produced by sunburning are the more common infection sites. Injuries from toxic wound dressings have become infected (38). After infection is established in the branch, the year-to-year expansion of the canker at that particular site is possible only if open infection courts are present in the uninfected tissue around the margins of the cankers. If such courts are present, they are infected by spores from the older parts of the original canker. The agencies which produce these wounds are the woolly apple aphid, *Eriosoma lanigerum* (Haus.) and freezing temperatures (7). The insect is attracted to the succulent tissue produced by healing of bark around the margin of the original canker. In feeding upon this tissue it produces galls, which are more prone to injury by low temperature than is normal bark tissue (13). If temperatures of − 17.8 °C or lower prevail in winter, the galls rupture and provide open avenues for entry of the fungus. When temperatures are extremely low even the normal callus at the canker margins is ruptured, so after a cold winter the fungus may infect the roll of callus formed around the margins of pruning wounds. This, however, is rare compared with the infection of aphid-infested callus tissue. According to Childs (7), Northern Spy, which is almost immune to woolly aphid attack, is rarely infected by perennial canker.

Fruit becomes infected when prolonged rains occur in early fall before harvest. The lesions may appear while the fruit is on the tree or after it is picked and stored.

Control of anthracnose. Control consists of removing cankers to reduce inoculum in the tree, and spraying with a protective fungicide to prevent new infection.

In removing cankers, it may be necessary to prune heavily, cutting away large branches when these are so heavily infected as to involve too much time and effort to remove each canker. Where cankers occur on large branches, as anthracnose cankers occasionally do, excision of the cankered area is practical if enough bark is left to support the branch; the cuts made in such branches should be covered with a protective paint—coal tar has been recommended for this because it waterproofs the wound and prevents entry of wood-rotting fungi (22). This work should be done in summer or early autumn before the acervuli mature. Because the fungus continues to live and grow on dead wood, all severed branches and excised bark should be collected and burned.

Because the fungus infects branches in autumn, summer sprays such as are applied for apple scab are of little benefit in controlling anthracnose. To prevent it, spraying should begin before the earliest time at which infection is liable to occur. In the Pacific Northwest, infection occurs with the first fall rains. These rains may occur in early fall so it is often necessary to spray certain cultivars before harvest. Therefore, one preharvest spray is applied on these cultivars and this protects fruit and branches. A second treatment is given immediately after harvest, and a third 3 weeks later. The last two treatments protect branches until danger of infection has past.

In earlier tests, copper fungicides proved more effective than did sulfur fungicides against the disease. Of the various organic fungicides tested none seems entirely satisfactory, and Bordeaux mixture has remained the standard fungicide material. Bordeaux, however, is objectionable for preharvest application because it leaves a residue on fruit and may injure fruit and leaves. Various attempts to overcome these difficulties have been tried. Heald (22) recommended Burgundy mixture for preharvest application, but pathologists in New Zealand (14, 40, 47) claim that a weak Bordeaux solution (1-3-100 or 2-6-100) gives adequate protection with no appreciable fruit and leaf injury. To increase spreading of Bordeaux over fruit, lime casein (or other type of spreader) is added at the rate of 0.25 pounds per 100 gallons of spray. For postharvest treatment, Bordeaux 8-8-100 has been recommended (22, 42).

Perennial canker. Control measures for perennial canker are aimed largely at removal of the inoculum sources and prevention of infestation by the woolly apple aphid. Such measures are much more likely to produce beneficial results if started before the orchard becomes severely infected, but in badly-infected orchards they are likely to prove expensive and ineffectual. In extreme cases removal of old trees may be the only solution. In replanting the orchard, one should give attention to cultivars most resistant to the disease—for example, Delicious has been recommended for Oregon (7).

Complete removal of affected smaller branches where feasible, and excision of cankers occurring on larger limbs and on trunks, should be done in July or August (7). Surgical work consists of scraping dead bark from the surface of the canker and cutting out the remaining dead tissue with a sharp knife. The cuts should be made in the non-infected tissue no further from the margin of the canker than is necessary to excise all diseased bark. The edge of the excised area should be smooth, because ragged cuts leave places under which the aphids establish themselves.

This operation should be followed in 2 to 3 weeks by an application of a dressing to protect the wound against infection by the fungus and infestation by woolly aphid. Cooley (8) recommended 8 parts of rosin and 3 parts of sardine oil.

Unlike anthracnose, perennial canker cannot be controlled by fall applications of copper fungicides.

To keep woolly aphid infestation at a minimum, trees should receive an annual and thorough application of a contact insecticide (7). Research indicates that the insect is controllable by certain organic insecticides, such as parathion.

References

1. Anderson, H. W. 1940. Apple tree anthracnose in Illinois. Plant Dis. Rep. 24:475.
2. Anonymous. 1931. Late Oregon spray recommendations. Better Fruits 25:5-6.
3. _____ 1939. Thirteenth Annual Report of Department of Scientific and Industrial Research. New Zealand 1938-1939:1-134.
4. Barnett, H. L. 1944. Anthracnose and other diseases in California apple-growing regions. Plant Dis. Rep. 28:717-18.
5. Boyd, O. C. 1939. Northwestern anthracnose of apple reported from Massachusetts. Plant Dis. Rep. 28:125-26.
6. Brien, R. M. 1932. "Delicious spot" on apples due to Gleosporium perennans. J. New Zealand Dept. Agr. 45:215-18.
7. Childs, Leroy. 1929. The relation of woolly apple aphid to perennial canker infection with other notes on the disease. Oregon Agr. Exp. Sta. Bul. 243:1-31.
8. Cooley, J. S. 1942. Wound dressings on apple trees. U.S. Dept. Agr. Circ. 656:1-18.
9. Cooley, J. S., and E. V. Shear. 1931. Relation of perennial canker to its environment. Phytopathology 21:1000. (Abstr.)

10. Cordley, A. B. 1900. Apple-tree anthracnose. Oregon State Bd. Hort. Bien. Rept. 6:405-09.

11. _____ 1900. Some observations on apple-tree anthracnose. Botan. Gaz. 30:48-58.

12. _____ 1900. Apple-tree anthracnose: A new fungus disease. Oregon Agr. Exp. Sta. Bul. 60:1-8.

13. Crenshaw, J. H., and J. S. Cooley. 1931. Experimental freezing of apple trees. Phytopathology 21:997-98. (Abstr.)

14. Cunningham, G. H. 1942. Research work on ripe-spot of apples. Orchardist, New Zealand 15:2.

15. Curtis, K. M. 1953. Cankers in apple and pear trees caused by the ripe-spot fungus, *Neofabraea malicorticis*. Orchardist, New Zealand 26:2.

16. Fisher, D. F. 1925. A new apple-rot disease ("Bull's eye rot"—caused by *Gleosporium* Zeller and Childs). Proc. Wash. State Hort. Assoc. 21:44-48.

17. _____ 1927. Storage rots and their control. Oregon State Hort. Soc. Ann. Rept. 19:87-98.

18. Fisher, D. F., and E. L. Reeves. 1928. Perennial canker. Proc. Wash. State Hort. Assoc. 24:55-61.

19. _____ 1929. Recent studies on perennial canker. Proc. Wash. State Hort. Assoc. 25:155-66.

20. Gram, E., A. Weber, and J. L. Schnicker. 1932. Platesygdomme in Denmark. 1931. Oversigt samlet ved statens plantpatologiske forsog. Tidsskr. Plantev.. 38:349-390.

21. Heald, F. D. 1920. Apple anthracnose or black-spot canker. Wash. Agr. Exp. Sta. Ser. Bul. 64:1-4.

22. _____ 1926. Apple-tree anthracnose. Manual of plant pathology. First Ed. pp. 500-11. McGraw Hill Book Co., New York.

23. Hilborn, M. J. 1938. Northwestern apple tree anthracnose found in Maine. Plant. Dis. Rep. 22:354.

24. Jackson, H. S. 1911. Apple-tree anthracnose. Oregon Agr. Exp. Sta. Circ. 17:1-4.

25. _____ 1912. The development of *Gleosporium malicorticis* Cordley. Phytopathology 2:95. (Abstr.)

26. _____ 1913. Apple-tree anthracnose. A preliminary report. Oregon Agr. Exp. Sta. Bien. Crop Pest and Hort. Rept. 1911-12:178-97.

27. Kienholz, J. R. 1932. Perennial canker and anthracnose fungi: host relations and cultural difference. Phytopathology 22:995-96. (Abstr.)

28. _____ 1939. Comparative study of the apple anthracnose and perennial canker fungi. J. Agr. Research 59:635-65.

29. _____ 1951. The Bull's-eye-rot (*Neofabraea*) problem of apples and pears. Oregon State Hort. Soc. Proc. 66:75-77.

30. Lawrence, W. H. 1904. Black-spot canker. Wash. Agr. Exp. Sta. Bul. 66:1-35.

31. McLarty, H. R. 1933. Perennial canker of apple trees. Can.J. Agr. 8:492-507.

32. McLarty, H. R., and J. C. Roger. 1931. Perennial canker survey in the Okanogan Valley. Can. Dept. Agr. Rept. 1930:108-11.

33. Miller, Erston V. 1932. Some physiological studies of *Gleosporium perennans* and *Neofabraea malicorticis*. J. Agr. Research 45:65-77.

34. Nannfeldt, J. A. 1932. Studien uber die Morphologie und Systematik der Nichtlichenisierten. Inoperculaten Discomyceten. Nova Acta Reg. Soc. Sci. Upsala Sec. 48(2):1-386.

35. Owen, C. E. 1928. Apple-tree anthracnose. Principles of plant pathology. New York: John Wiley and Sons, P. 288.

36. Peck, C. H. 1900. New species of fungi. Bul. Torrey Botan. Club 27:14-21.

37. Poetersen, N. van. 1934-35. Verslag over de werkzaamheden van den Plantenziektenkundigen dienst in het Jaar 1933, 1934. Wageningen Plantenziktenkund. Dienst, Verslag in Meded 76 and 80.

38. Reeves, E. L., M. A. Yothers and C. W. Murray. 1939. Unusual development of apple perennial canker following application of toxic wound dressings. Phytopathology 29:739-42.

39. Shear, E. V., and J. S. Cooley. 1933. Relation of growth cycle and nutrition to perennial apple-canker infection. Phytopathology 23:33. (Abstr.)

40. Taylor, G. C. 1946. Spraying experiments for the control of ripe-spot (*Neofabraea malicorticis*) in the Sturmer apple variety. New Zealand J. Sci. Technol. A. 27:457-69.

41. Thompson, G. E. 1939. A canker disease of poplars caused by a new species of *Neofabraea*. Mycologia 31:455-64.

42. White, E. W. 1922. Apple anthracnose of black-spot control. Sci. Agr. 2:186-91.

43. Wilkinson, E. H. 1943. Perennial canker of apple trees in England. Gardners' Chronical Sec. 3114:159.

44. _____ 1945. Perennial canker of apple in England. J. Pomol. 21:180-85.

45. Wollenweber, H. W. 1939. Diskomyzetenstudien (Pezicula Tul. und Occlaria Tul.). Arb. Biol. Anst. (Reichsanst) Berlin 22:521-70.

46. Woodhead, C. E., and H. Jacks. 1952. Nature and control of ripe-spot of apples. New Zealand J. Agr. 84:239-40.

47. Zeller, S. M., and Leroy Childs. 1925. Another apple-tree anthracnose in the Pacific Northwest and a comparison with the well-known apple-tree anthracnose. Phytopathology 15:728. (Abstr.)

48. _____ 1925. Perennial canker of apple trees. A preliminary report. Oregon Agr. Exp. Sta. Bul. 217:1-17.

Armillaria Root Rot of Apple and Pear
Armillaria mellea (Vahl.) Quel.

Armillaria root rot is not considered an important disease on apples or pears in California. Apple rootstocks are moderately resistant to the disease. Pear rootstocks developed from Barlett and Winter Nelis (both of French origin) seeds are quite resistant, but Oriental pear rootstocks are as a group more susceptible than the French types. Pear roots weakened by the *Prionus* beetle were found to be infected with Armillaria root rot but this was an exception. Thus, pears and apples could be possible replacement crops in soils infested with *Armillaria*.

Details of Armillaria root rot disease are discussed in section III.

Dematophora Root Rot of Apple and Pear
Dematophora necatrix Hartig

The disease. Dematophora root rot (white root rot) affects a wide range of hosts including 170 species and varieties in 63 genera and 30 families (6). Among tree fruits are apples, apricot, avocado, citrus, peach, walnut, almond, pears, and cherries. Other plants affected are the boysenberry, loganberry, and grapes.

The disease occurs in England, Europe, and California. It was reported in the eastern U.S. more than 50 years ago but its occurrence there has not been confirmed in recent years. A similar disease occurs in New Zealand (13) but is said to differ as regards the species of fungus involved (2).

Dematophora is of great importance in Italy (16) and France (12), but somewhat less so in England (8). In California the disease has been confined to apples and pears in the Watsonville and San Jose areas, but it is becoming more important there.

Symptoms. Trees and vines show symptoms of the disease first by yellowing of the foliage and poor growth of the branches. One or all limbs may show this effect. Below ground, the fibrous roots are rotted away, and a white wefty mycelium (fig. 5) may remain in the soil around the rotted roots. Under the cortex of affected roots is found a whitish wefty to floccose layer of mycelium—this is distinct from the more or less leathery, slightly yellow mycelial fans produced by *Armillaria mellea*. Another difference between *Dematophora* and *Armillaria* root rots is in the occurence of rhizomorphs. Though some writers mention *Dematophora* as producing rhizomorphs, Thomas, Hansen, and Thomas (11) state that well-defined rhizomorphs are absent on roots affected by this fungus. Nattrass (8)

mentions a structure which he says is a whitish wefty strand or ribbon bearing no resemblance to the dense rhizomorphs of *A. mellea*. The most definite diagnostic feature of *Dematophora* is the production of the coremia on diseased roots which have been kept in a moist chamber for several days.

The causal organism. Root rots of this type in England, Europe, and California are produced by the same fungus. Hartig (5) first named the conidial stage *Rhizomorpha (Dematophora) necatrix,* and suggested its relationship to *Rosellinia*, an ascomycete. Viala (12) and Prilleaux (10) described a *Rosellinia* associated with the imperfect stage, but did not produce evidence of the genetic connection. Hansen, Thomas, and Thomas (4) provided such evidence. Hence, the fungus should be called *Rosellinia necatrix* (Hart.) Berl. Berlese's name appears as one of the authorities for the following reasons. Hartig had assigned *Rosellinia* to the order Tuberales because he believed the perithecia possessed no ostiole, was tuber-like and subterranean. Berlese (1) later transferred *Rosellinia* to the order *Sphaeriales*. Hansen, Thomas, and Thomas (4), however, report *R. necatrix* as possessing a definite ostiole. The identity of the fungus causing the disease in New Zealand is in doubt. Massee (7) described and named a new specis, *Rosellinia radiciperda,* from material sent from New Zealand in 1895. Earlier, however, he had found the conidial stage of *Dematophora necatrix* in similar material. See Cunningham (2).

Coremia arising from sclerotia produce small, single-celled, colorless conidia on multiple-branched conidiophores. Perithecia are sphaeroidal, erumpent, and situated on a mycelial crust. Asci are cylindrical, and ascospores are one-celled, with a hyaline episore. Characteristic swellings (geniculations) occur at the septa of the vegetative mycelium.

Disease development. Mycelium of the fungus in affected roots remain viable for several years even under the most unfavorable conditions. Ascospores are produced so rarely as to be of little importance in development of the disease. Conidia produced under some conditions are of low viability (4). Infection is believed to occur almost entirely by penetration of the mycelia into susceptible roots. The fungus is spread by growth of the mycelia throughout the soil. Spread of the fungus over long distances occurs through the transportation of affected nursery stock.

Young roots are penetrated directly by the mycelium. Nattrass (8) believed that old roots were not subject to direct invasion but became infected as the fungus grew into them from attached infected young roots.

18

Although the incubation period of the disease is unknown, Hansen, Thomas, and Thomas (4) found that young apple trees were killed within 6 weeks after inoculation.

The fungus develops most rapidly in comparatively cool moist soils.

Susceptibility among varieties and species of economic plants: *Apple:* Golden Delicious, McIntosh, and most clones of the East Malling rootstocks are susceptible. Some resistance is shown by seedlings of *Malus floribunda* sp. and *M. toringoides. Cherry:* Mahaleb, mazzard and sour cherry *(Prunus cerasus)* rootstocks are all susceptible. *Pear:* Most species of pear *(Pyrus)* are susceptible, though certain seedlings of *P. communis* appear to be tolerant of the fungus. Plum: Marianna and myroblan are probably most resistant of the stone fruits used for rootstocks. *Walnut:* Persian (English) walnut *(Juglans regia),* the northern California black walnut *(J. hindsii)* are susceptible, as are the butternut *(J. cinerea)* and the eastern black walnut *(J. nigra). Brambles:* The Himalaya and young blackberries show fairly high degrees of resistance, while the loganberry and the boysenberry are highly susceptible. *Citrus:* rough lemon, sweet and sour orange, trifoliate orange, and Windsor grapefruit are susceptible (6).

Control. No satisfactory control methods have been devised. Godfrey (3) reported tests in which a soilborne *Dematophora* sp. was killed with chloropicrin, but Kahn (6) found that neither cholorpicrin, carbon disulfide, ethylene bromide, allyl bromide, or formaldehyde were very effective against the fungus.

References

1. Berlese, A. N. 1892. Rev. Pat. Veg. 1:5 and 45.
2. Cunningham, G. H. 1925. Fungus diseases of fruit-trees in New Zealand. Brett Printing Co. Auckland, N. Z. 382 pp.
3. Godfrey, G. H. 1934. Control of soil fungi by fumigation with chloropicrin. Phytopathology 24:1145. (Abstr.)
4. Hansen, H. M., Harold E. Thomas, and H. Earl Thomas. 1937. The connection between *Dematophora necatrix* and *Rosellinia necatrix.* Hilgarida 10:561-64.
5. Hartig, Robert. 1883. *Rhizomorpha (Dematophora) necatrix* n. sp. Untersuch. Forstbotan. Inst. Munchen 3:95:153.
6. Kahn, Abdul Hamid. 1955. Dematophora root rot. California Dept. Agr. Bul. 44(4):167-70.
7. Massee, George. 1896. Rot diseases caused by fungi. Kew Bul. 109:1-5.
8. Nattrass, R. M. 1926. The white rot of fruit trees caused by Rosellinia necatrix (Hart) Berl.
   Long Ashton Agr. and Hort. Res. Sta. Ann. Rept. 1926:66-72.
9. Pierce, Newton B. 1892. The California vine disease. U.S.D.A. Div. Veg. Path. and Phys. Bul. 2:1-222.
10. Prilleaux, E. 1902. Les peritheces de *Rosellinia necatrix* Compt. Rend. Acad. Sci. (Paris) 135:275-78.
11. Thomas, Harold E., H. N. Hansen, and H. Earl Thomas. 1934. Dematophora root rot. Phytopathology 24:1145. (Abstr.).
12. Viala, P. 1891. Monographie du pourridie. 95 pp. Georges Masson.
13. Wight, R. A. 1890. Root fungi of New Zealand. J. Mycol. 5:199.

Diplodia Disease of Apple
Physalospora mutila (Fr.) Stev.

A disease with fruit, leaf, and bark symptoms very similar to those of the apple black rot of eastern U.S. was found in California in 1915 (1) and in Oregon in 1920 (4). The pycnidial stage of the causal organism is said to resemble black rot fungus in its ability to infect the host and in many of its morphological features, but differs from it in pycnospore characteristics. In 1933, Stevens (2) reported that he had studied a fungus from these states, possibly receiving at least some of his Oregon materials from Zeller (5) who studied the disease a few years earlier. Stevens (2) concluded that the Oregon fungus was not the imperfect stage of *Physalospora obtusa* but probably was *Diplodia mutila* (Fr.) Mont. Later in England he found and described the perithecial stage *D. mutila* (3), which he tentatively named *Physalospora mutila* (Fr.) Stev.

References

1. Hahn, G. G. 1915. Studies on a California apple canker fungus resembling *Sphaeropsis malorum* Berk. and *Diplodia natalensis* Evans. Unpublished Master of Science Thesis, University of California Library.
2. Stevens, N. E. 1933. Two apple black rot fungi in the United States. Mycologia 25:536-48.
3. _____ 1936. Two species of *Physalospora* in England. Mycologia 28:330-36.
4. Stillinger, C. R. 1920. Apple black rot *(Sphaeropsis malorum* Berk.) in Oregon. Phytopathology 10:453-58.
5. Zeller, S. M. 1924. *Sphaeropsis malorum* and *Myxosporium corticola* on apple and pear in Oregon. Phytopathology 14:329-33.

European Canker Of Apple and Pear
Nectria galligena Bres.

European canker, also known as "apple canker" and "nectria canker," affects apple and pear trees. The disease occurs in the British Isles, northern Europe, Australia, New Zealand, Chile, Canada, and the U.S.

European canker is one of the major apple diseases in England, where it has received more attention than in any other country (4, 5, 6, 15, 16, 24, 25). Severe outbreaks of the disease have occurred in the northwestern U.S. (27, 28).

The disease was reported from California by Smith (19) in 1909 and by Fawcett (12) in 1912. It is found chiefly in apple-growing areas north of San Francisco Bay (23). In most instances earlier outbreaks were relatively unimportant, but since 1955 the disease has caused serious damage in Sonoma County orchards, sometimes killing young trees and the branches of older trees.

Symptoms. Though occasionally fruit and rarely leaves are affected, the most destructive phase is twig and branch infection (fig. 6A).

New cankers, that commonly develop at the nodes of twigs, are elliptical, sunken, dead areas of bark over which the periderm loosens and breaks away. As the causal agent spreads, it encircles and kills the twigs. In other cankers it may spread more slowly. In England, the annual peripheral expansion of the diseased area produces an elongated canker with series of roughly concentric ridges. In western Oregon, where winters are comparatively mild, expansion is said (28) to be a more or less continuous process, resulting in a very long nonzonate necrotic area.

In cool, moist autumn weather, white to cream-colored, waxy conidial fructifications (sporodochia) develop over the cankers. In winter, clusters of small red perithecia appear on cankers one or more years old (fig. 6B).

In moist regions the fruit is sometimes infected. This infection, called "eye-rot," results in the rotting and collapse of the fruit tissue around the calyces (13) (fig. 6C). Lenticel infection is also known to occur (9).

The causal organism. Although Petch (18) suggested that the fungus be transferred to the genus *Dialonectria*, this has not been done by mycologists. The presently accepted name for the perithecial stage is *Nectria galligena* Bres. Earlier workers had called it *N. coccinea* Fries or *N. ditissimia* Tul. Zeller (27) and others, however, showed it to be distinct from these species. The conidial stage, according to Wollenweber (26), is *Cylindrocarpon mali* (Allesch.) Wollenw., though some have called it *Fursarium willkomii.*

The macroconidia of *N. galligena* are produced in white-to-cream-colored masses (sporodochia) scattered over the surface of the canker. Macroconidia are hyaline, cylindrical, straight or slightly curved, 3- to 7-septate structures with rounded ends. They vary greatly in size but average about 52 to 62 μm long and 4.5 to 5.5 μm broad. Microconidia may be produced in abundance by abstriction from hyphal branches. They measure 4 to 7 μm long × 1 to 2 μm broad and are hyaline and one-celled (27).

The bright red perithecia of *N. galligena* (23) are produced in clusters or scattered over the surface of the older cankers, seldom on newly developed cankers. At times the cluster of perithecia surround sporodochia. Mature perithecia are generally ovoid-pyriform, 300 to 400 μm in diameter and about 300 to 450 μm in height. A stroma may or may not be present. The ostiole is raised (16). The asci are stalked, cylindrical to clavate in shape, and bear eight ascospores. These are hyaline, two-celled, 14 to 20 μm long by 5 to 7 μm broad and elliptical in shape.

Susceptibility of apple and pear cultivars. In California, Delicious and its red mutants are the most susceptible cultivars. Gravenstein, Jonathan, McIntosh, and Rome Beauty are infected to some extent but Golden Delicious is rarely attacked. Zeller (28) reported that Bismark, Delicious, Winter Bellflower, Spitzenburg, and Newtown apples, D'Anjou, Howell, and Beurre Bosc pears are susceptible in Oregon. In Europe, the Cox's Orange Pippin, McIntosh, White Transparent, and Winter Gold Pearmain apple cultivars are said to be highly susceptible.

Disease development. The fungus survives from one infection season to the next as mycelia in twig and branch cankers, where they produce conidia and ascospores.

Where rain occurs throughout the year, conidia are present at all times (2), but are most abundant in September and October and least abundant in summer (16). In the drier climate of California, however, they are produced largely during the rainy fall and winter months (9), and are disseminated by spattering rain.

Perithecia are initiated in autumn and mature in winter and spring. In rainy periods, the ascospores may be either forcibly ejected from the perithecia and disseminated by air currents or extruded in a sticky mass and rain disseminated (9). Bulit (2) in France, Munson (16) in England, and Zeller and Owens (29) in Oregon recorded the discharge of ascospores in all months of the year, the heaviest discharges occurring in winter. In California, heavy discharge also occurs in spring (9).

Infection commonly occurs through leaf scars, the major period for infection being in the autumn during the leaf-fall period (6, 24). According to Crowdy (5) the leaf scar is highly susceptible to infection during the first hour after the leaf falls, and becomes much less susceptible in the next hour or so. Tests in California (8, 21) indicated that some leaf scars remained susceptible to infection for 10 to 28 days after leaf fall. According to Wiltshire (24) another period when leaf scars become susceptible to infection occurs in spring, at which time the fungus can enter through small cracks which form in the leaf scar as the result of growth of the twig. Zeller and Owens (29) found that in Oregon the greater part of infection occurs in fall. Evidence in California (9) also indicated essentially no spring infection. Temperature within the range generally occurring in California winters does not limit infection. In the winter of 1958-59, for example, if leaf scars were wounded by cutting with a knife they became infected at various times in winter and early spring. The periods at which no or little infection occurred were those during which little rain fell. Experiments under controlled moisture conditions showed that at temperatures of 14 to 15.5 °C the trees had to be wet for at least 6 hours before appreciable infection of leaf scars occurred. The percentage infection of leaf scars increased rapidly with increases in the length of the moisture period (7, 9).

The incubation period of the fungus in the twig may range from a few days in early fall to several weeks or possibly months during the coldest part of winter (28). In years of early autumn rains in California, twig lesions may become visible in late fall, but in most years they appear in late winter and early spring.

Isolates of the pathogen from birch and aspen did not infect apple trees when inoculated at leaf scars, but apple isolates were pathogenic to pear (9).

The fruit rot phase (eye-rot) is rare in California in the harvest season, but rains thereafter make conditions suitable for infection of fruit left on the tree. In 1965, both calyx-end infections and lenticel infections were found on fruit left on the tree but not before (Personal communication from W. H. English). The symptoms are a brown necrotic, slightly depressed dry decay. No evidence of the fungus is present at first, but after about half of the fruit has decayed white mycelial masses develop at the calyx-end. At lentical infections, the center of the brown circular necrotic lesions are pale-brown.

Control. The principal control measure followed in England (13, 15) consisted in spraying the trees with a fungicide, usually Bordeaux mixture, in autumn soon after leaf fall. Such a method has proved inadequate in California, because the leaves fall gradually over a long period in autumn, and if spraying is delayed until most of them have fallen the rainy season will have begun and infection of the early-formed leaf scars will have occurred. Good control of infection was obtained by spraying the trees with Bordeaux mixture (10-10-100) or basic copper sulfate (5-100) plus 1 gal/100 gal of a good spray oil at the start of leaf fall and at mid- or late-leaf fall (11).

Cankers allowed to remain in the tree not only may kill branches but are sources of inoculum, so they should be removed where possible.

Fruit infections are best controlled by reducing the fungus inoculum in the field with fall field sprays (7).

References

1. Brook, P. J., and F. L. Bailey. 1965. Control of European canker. Orchard. New Zealand 38: 117-18.
2. Bulit, J. 1957. Contribution a l'Etude Biologique du *Nectria galligena* Bres. agent due chancre du Pommier. Am epiphyt. (Inst. Nat. recherche Agron.) 1:67-89.
3. Byrde, R. J. W., S. H. Crowdy, and F. A. Roach. 1952. Observations on apple canker. V. Eradicant spraying and canker control Ann. Appl. Biol. 39:581-87.
4. Cayley, D. M. 1921. Some observations on the life history of *Nectria galligena* Bres. Ann. Bot. London 35:79.
5. Crowdy, S. H. 1949. Observations on apple canker. III. The anatomy of the stem canker. Ann. Appl. Biol. 36:483.
6. _____ 1952. Observations on apple canker. IV. The infection of leaf scars. Ann. Appl. Biol. 39:569-80.
7. Dubin, H. J., and Harley English. 1974. Factors affecting control of European apple canker by difolatan and basic copper sulfate. Phytopathology 64:300-06.
8. _____ 1974. Factors affecting apple leaf scar infection by *Nectria galligena* conidia. Phytopathology 64:1201-1203.
9. _____ 1975. Epidemiology of European apple canker in California. Phytopathology 65:542-50.
10. _____ 1975. Effects of temperature, relative humidity, and desiccation on germination of *Nectria galligena* conidia. Mycologia 47:83-88.
11. English, H., H. J. Dubin, F. J. Schick, and K. O. Roberts. 1971. Chemical control of leaf scar infection by *Nectria galligena* in apple. Phytopathology 61:1320-21. (Abstr.)

12. Fawcett, H. S. 1912. Two apple cankers due to the fungi *Nectria ditissima* and *Nectria cinnabarina*. California State Com. Hort. Monthly Bul. No. 1:247-49.

13. Grubb, N. H. 1921. Tests of fungicides on apple trees. J. Pomology 2:93.

14. McCartney, W. O. 1967. An unusual occurrence of eye rot of apple in California due to *Nectaria galligena*. Plant Dis. Rep. 51:279-81.

15. Marsh, R. W. 1939. Observations on apple canker. I. Experiments on the incidence and control of shoot infection. Ann. Appl. Biol. 26:458-69.

16. Munson, R. G. 1939. Observations on apple canker. I. The discharge and germination of spores of *Nectria galligena* Bres. Ann. Appl. Biol. 26:440-69.

17. Nichols, C. W., and E. E. Wilson. 1956. An outbreak of European canker in California. Plant Dis. Rep. 40:952-53.

18. Petch, J. 1938. British Hypocreales. Trans. Brit. Mycol. Soc. 21: 243-301 (see page 265).

19. Smith, R. E. 1909. Report of the plant pathologist. California Univ. Agr. Exp. Sta. Bul. No. 203:56 (out of print).

20. Swinburne, J. R. 1971. The seasonal release of spores of *Nectria galligena* from apple cankers in Northern Ireland. Ann. Appl. Biol 69:97-104.

21. Wilson, E. E. 1966. Development of European canker in a California apple district. Plant. Dis. Rep. 50:182-86.

22. _____ 1968. Control of European canker of apple by eradicative and protective fungicides. Plant Dis. Rep. 52:227-31.

23. Wilson, E. E., and C. W. Nichols. 1964. European canker of apple. California Dept. Agr. Bul. 53:151-55.

24. Wiltshire, S. P. 1921. Studies on the apple canker fungus. I. Leaf scar infection. Ann. Appl. Biol. 8:182-92.

25. _____ 1922. Studies on the apple canker fungus. II. Canker infection of apple trees through scab wounds. Ann. Appl Biol. 9:275-81.

26. Wollenweber, H. W. 1913. *Ramularia, Mycosphaerella, Nectria, Calonectria*-Eine morphologisch-pathologische Studie zur Abgrenzung von Pilzgruppen mit cylindrischen und sichelformigen Konidienformen. Phytopathology 3:197-242.

27. Zagaja, S. W., W. F. Millikan, W. Kaminski, and J. Myszka. 1971. Field resistance to Nectria canker in apple. Plant Dis. Rep. 55:445-47.

28. Zeller, S. M. 1926. European canker of pomaceous fruit trees. Oregon State College Agr. Exp. Sta. Bul. No. 222. 52 pp.

29. Zeller, S. M., and C. E. Owens. 1921. European canker on the Pacific slope. Phytopathology 11: 464-68.

Miscellaneous Diseases of Apple and Pear Fruits

Diseases mentioned here occur in the Pacific Northwest, where many of the apples sold in California originate. Some of the diseases on the fruit have been reported as occurring in California but are generally of rare occurrence there.

Black rot. This is prevalent in the Atlantic Coastal states (3, 7, 11) but occurs rarely in the far west and California (7, 9, 10, 12). The causal fungus is *Physalospora obtusa* (Schw.) Cke. which attacks leaves, wood, and fruit of apples. The disease on the fruit is primarily of ripe fruit rot, although immature fruit are also susceptible. Infection occurs at insect injuries and wound sites. The open calyx tubes are also susceptible to invasion by this fungus. Typical fruit symptoms are firm brown or concentric zones of different shades of brown. In advanced stages, the infected area is dark brown to black covered with pycnidia (7). Control is obtained by chemical sprays in the orchard to reduce infection of the leaves and wood. Temperatures below 4.4 °C greatly reduce the amount of fruit decay in storage.

Brown rot. Fruit in storage occasionally develop a dark-colored rot with little or no sporulation of the causal fungi *Monilinia fructicola* (Wint.) Honey and *M. laxa* (Aderh. & Ruhl.) Honey. The few large sporodochia that do develop resemble morphologically those of *M. fructigena* and are light brown or gray (9). *M. fructigena* has not been found on pome or stone fruit in California.

Cladosporium-Hormodendrum rots. The fungi *Cladosporium herbarum* Lk. and *Hormodendrum cladosporioides* Sacc. and *Alternaria* sp. are found frequently in moldy core or core rot types of apple fruit rots, and commonly invade apple tissues affected by soft scald. Mechanical injuries provide the most common avenues of entry for these fungi; lenticel invasion apparently does not occur. This type of rot is usually found after fruit has been in cold storage several months (7, 9).

Side rot. This disease, known earlier as "Sporotrichum rot," occurs in many apple-growing regions. In northcentral Washington it is said (1) to be the third most common rot of apples. While the rot does not ordinarily affect a high percentage of the stored fruit, it occurs quite commonly on Delicious and Winesap.

The causal fungus, *Phialophora malorum* (Kidd and Beaumont), McColloch (6), was originally named *Sporotrichum malorum* Kidd and Beaumont and was also called *S. carpogenum* Newton. It produces roughly circular, slightly sunken, light brown spots with distinct margins. The fungus enters the fruit most commonly through punctures and lenticels (2, 4, 8) but also may infect through calyces, worm injuries, or open calyx canals.

Stemphylium and Pleospora rots. *Stemphylium congestum* Newton and *Pleospora fructicola* (Newt.) Ruehle, sometimes produce lesions centered at skin punctures, lenticels, and calyces of stored apples. The imperfect stage of *P. fructicola* is of the *Stemphylium* type (1). In England, *Pleospora pomorum* Horne, which also has a *Stemphylium* for imperfect stage, is said (4) to produce shallow discolored spots on apples. These spots later turn almost black, with submerged perithecia of the fungus developing in their centers.

References

1. English, H. 1944. Notes on apple rots in Washington. Plant Dis. Rep. 28:610-22.
2. Gardner, Max. 1929. Sporotrichum fruit spot and surface rot of apples. Phytopathology 19: 443-52.
3. Hesler, L. R. 1916. Black rot, leaf spot, and canker of pomaceous fruits. N. Y. (Cornell) Agr. Exp. Stn. Bul. 379.
4. Kidd, M. N., and A. Beaumont. 1924. Apple rot fungi in storage. Trans. British Mycol. Soc. 10:98-118.
5. McColloch, L. P. 1942. An apple rot fungus morphologically related to a human pathogen. Phytopathology 32:1094-95.
6. _____ 1944. A study of the apple rot fungus *Phialophora malorum*. Mycologia 36:576-90.
7. Pierson, C. F., M. J. Ceponis, and L. P. McColloch. 1971. USDA, ARS, Agr. Handbook No. 376. 112 pp. 17 color plates.
8. Ruehle, G. D. 1931. New apple-rot fungi from Washington. Phytopathology 21:1141-52.
9. Smith, R. E. 1941. Diseases of fruits and nuts. Calif. Agr. Ext. Cir. 120. 168 pp (out of print).
10. Stillinger, C. R. 1920. Apple black rot (*Sphaeropsis malorum* Berk.) in Oregon. Phytopathology 10:453-58.
11. Taylor, J. 1955. Apple black rot in Georgia and its control. Phytopathology 45:392-98.
12. Zeller, S. M. 1924. *Sphaeropsis malorum* and *Myxosporium corticola* on apple and pear in Oregon. Phytopathology 14:329-33.

Phytophthora Crown and Root Rot of Apple and Pear

Phytophthora cambivora (Petri) Buisman
Phytophthora megasperma Dreschler
Phytophthora dreschleri Tucker
Phytophthora spp.

This disease, which is particularly severe in apple orchards located in British Columbia, has also been reported from Europe and New Zealand. In California, Mircetich (9) and Mircetich, Matheron, and Tyler (10) reported that the disease is as serious on apples as it is on stone-fruit but on pears the occurrence is sporadic. The disease may occur at any age of the tree, but rootstocks are most susceptible during the first years of their bearing life.

Symptoms. Although the feeding rootlets of affected pear and apple trees are sometimes black and dead the most common symptom is an extensive discoloration of the bark tissues at the crown of the tree (5, 8). The newly-affected bark shows various shades of light and dark brown and has a marbled appearance. There is usually a well-defined margin between the diseased and healthy bark. Diseased trees occur at random throughout the planting, evidence that the causal organism is not transmitted from one affected tree to another.

When young vigorously-growing trees become infected their leaves develop a purplish cast in autumn. Infected mature trees, however, have poorly developed chlorotic foliage, produce little or no new growth, and bear small highly-colored fruit.

The causal organism. *Phytophthora cactorum* (Leb. & Cohn) Schroet. is generally regarded (1, 4, 6) as the usual causal organism associated with crown rot of apple. McIntosh (6) found it to be widely distributed in the irrigated soils of the apple-growing areas of British Columbia. It was not found in virgin soils nor in non-irrigated cultivated soils.

Phytophthora cactorum, along with *P. cryptogea* Pethybridge & Lafferty and *P. cambivora* (Petri) Buisman, was found to infect the rootlets of pear, cherry, apricot and peach (5, 6, 7). In California, Mircetich *et. al.* (9, 10) found in their isolations from apples that the most common *Phytophthora* species was not *P. cactorum* but *P. cambivora, P. megasperma* Dreschler, and *P. dreschleri* Tucker, as well as six different isolates of unidentified *Phythphthora* species. Planting 1-year-old apple seedlings in soil infested by *Phytophthora* species showed *P. cambivora* to be highly pathogenic (fig. 7).

All rootstocks tested (MM106, MM104, MM111, MVIIa, MM109) were susceptible to *P. cambivora*, with MM111 being least susceptible.

Both *P. cactorum* and *P. cinnamomi* Rands attack pear in Oregon (2); species attacking pear in California are *P. cambivora* and *P. megasperma*. In experiments in Oregon (2) Bartlett and Winter Nelis pears proved susceptible, whereas Old Home, Old Home X Farmingdale and *Pyrus calleryana* were not seriously damaged.

Control. Rootstocks least susceptible under local conditions should be considered in planning an orchard. Once the disease is established, however, about the only way to suppress it is to remove the soil from around the base of the infected tree, cut away the discolored bark, and allow the exposed tissue to dry.

Details of Phytophthora crown and root rots are discussed in section III.

References

1. Braun, H., and F. Nienhaus. 1959. Fortgefuert Untersuchungen uber die Krangenfaule des Apfels *(Phytophthora cactorum)* Phytopath. Z. 36:169-208.

2. Cameron, H. R. 1962. Susceptibility of pear roots to *Phytophthora.* Phytopathology 52: 1295-97.

3. Fitzpatrick, R. E., F. C. Mellor, and M. F. Welsh. 1944. Crown rot of apple trees in British Columbia —Rootstock and scion resistance trials. Sci. Agr. 24:533-41.

4. Houten, J. G. ten. 1958. Resistance trials against collar rot of apples caused by *Phytophthora cactorum.* Tijdschr. Pantenziekten 65:422-31.

5. McIntosh, D. L. 1960. The infection of pear rootlets by *Phytophthora cactorum.* Plant Dis. Rept. 44:262-64.

6. _____ 1964. *Phytophthora* spp. in soils of the Okanagan and Similkameen Valleys of British Columbia. Canadian J. Bot. 42:1411-15.

7. McIntosh, D. L., and H. J. O'Reilly. 1963. Inducing infection of pear rootlets by *Phytophthora cactorum.* Phytopathology 53:1447.

8. McIntosh, D. L., and F. C. Mellor. 1953. Crown rot of apple trees in British Columbia. II. Rootstock and scion resistance trials of apple, pear and stone fruits. Canadian J. Agric. Sci. 33:615-19.

9. Mircetich, J. M. 1975. Phytophthora root and crown rot of orchard trees. California Plant Pathology No. 24. Pp. 1-2.

10. Mircetich, S. M., M. E. Matheron, and R. H. Tyler. 1976. Apple root rot and crown rot caused by *Phytophthora cambivora* and *Phytophthora* sp. Proc. Am Phytopathology 3:229.

11. Sewell, G. W. F., and J. F. Wilson. 1959. Resistance trials of some apple rootstock varieties to *Phytophthora cactorum* (L. & C.) Schroet. J. Hort. Sci. 34:51-58.

12. Smith, H. C. 1955. Collar-rot and crown rot of apple trees. Orchardist. New Zealand 28:16.

13. Waterhouse, G. M. 1963. Key to species of *Phytophthora* de Bary, Commonwealth Mycol. Inst. Mycol. Papers No. 92.

Powdery Mildew of Apple
Podosphaera leucotricha (E. & E.) Salmon

While powdery mildew of apple occurs to a greater or lesser extent wherever apples are grown, it is a major disease of orchard trees in semi-arid regions. In California it is serious on Jonathan and Gravenstein, and it is destructive in central Washington where summers are rainless. It is quite serious on nursery trees in California as in the more humid eastern states. The disease was first reported in the U.S. about 1877, and the fungus was named in 1888.

Pear and quince are also attacked by the mildew. Considerable difference in susceptibility exists among apple cultivars; Jonathan, Rome Beauty, and Gravenstein being among the most susceptible. Delicious and its red mutants, Golden Delicious and Stayman Winesap, are less affected but may suffer damage when interplanted with a highly susceptible variety.

Symptoms. Leaves, flowers, green shoots, and fruit are attacked. On leaves, lesions first appear as whitish felt-like patches along the margins, commonly on the undersides. The fungus later spreads over the entire leaf blade, down the leaf petiole and over the shoot. Infected leaves are narrower than normal, folded longitudinally, or curled, crinkled, and stiff. When infection is severe, many leaves fall during the summer. With resistant cultivars such as Delicious and Winesap, where infection occurs after leaves emerge, the lesions are at first ill-defined pale spots with reddish or lavender-colored borders (fig. 8A).

On infected blossoms the white mycelial mat may cover the petals, sepals, receptacles and peduncles. Blossom infection is less common than infection of leaves and green shoots, but is important because infected blossoms fail to set fruit (fig. 8B). The fruit is often attacked when young but seldom after it has attained some size. Infected fruit is stunted and its surface becomes severely russeted.

Terminal or leafy shoots are stunted by the fungus and often killed outright. Those that survive the summer may be killed by the low temperatures of winter. Infected shoots that survive the winter and infected buds act as a source of inoculum for the coming season.

The causal organism. The most common powdery mildew fungus on apple is *Podosphaera leucotricha* (E. & E.) Salm. *P. oxycanthae* also occurs occasionally on apple. *P. leucotricha* was described in 1888 by Ellis and Everhart (15) as *Sphaerotheca leucotricha.* It had previsouly been named *Podoshaera kunzei* and later *S. mali,* but in 1900, Salmon (21) gave it its present name.

Like other powdery mildew fungi, *P. leucotricha* produces a white, wefty, loose layer of mycelium on the surface of the host. The fungus obtains nutriments by means of haustoria, which are sent into the host cells. Conidiophores arising from the mycelium produce chains of ellipsoid-to-barrel-shaped conidia 28-30 μm long and 12 μm broad.

According to Coyier (13), conidia are very sensitive to temperatures even at 97 percent relative humidity. They failed to germinate in 6 hours at 4.3 or 10 °C but germinated well in 24 hours. Exposure to a temperature of 32.2 °C for 6 hours produced limited germination, in 24 hours only 10 percent germination. At a temperature of 21 °C, 70 percent germination occurs in 6 hours and 88 percent in 24 hours. Mycelial growth is also best at 21 °C and still high at 15.6 and 26.7 °C.

Cleistothecia produced on twigs are gregarious, 75 to 96 μm in diameter, subglobose. Appendages are of two kinds: 3 to 11 apical appendages, erected with undivided ends or sometimes dicotomously branched 1 to 2 times; basal appendages which are short, tortuous, pale brown, simple or irregularly branched.

Asci contain eight spores which are 22 to 26 μm in length × 12 to 14 μm in width. Coyier (13) showed heterothallism in mildew cultures collected in Oregon. The shortest interval for cleistothecial production was 24 days and longest 109 days. Production of cleistothecia is not common in California, but in 1974 and 1975 they were detected in trees in the University farm at Davis.

Disease development. The fungus overwinters in leaf and flower buds infected during the summer. The fungus is located on the apices of the inner bud scales, and attacks leaves as they emerge in the spring. Older leaves are less susceptible. Susceptibility of leaves was suggested as being dependent on the amount of kinetin in the tissue (18).

There is considerable difference of opinion regarding development of secondary leaf infection from the primary leaf lesion. Woodward (27) claimed that no secondary leaf infection occurs, but Petherbridge and Dillon-Weston (20) claimed that it occurs commonly. In any event, fruit infection occurs after the fruit form and thus is secondary. Coyier showed that reduction occurred in conidial germination with increases in temperature (11), and that a relationship existed between seasonal increase in temperature and a reduction in the severity of mildew (12).

Burchill (4) related the severity of leaf infection only to subsequent infection of the growing shoot apex.

The principal inoculum for infection is the conidia. Some workers believe that ascospores play little or no role in the disease cycle; others believe that they play a minor part. In California, cleistothecial production is usually rare, but in 1976 it was abundant in diseased Rome Beauty trees at Davis.

Control. Early work on control of apple mildew was done by Ballard and Volk (1) in the Pajaro Valley of California, and by Fischer (16) at Wenatchee, Washington. These workers developed spray programs based on sulfur.

Sprague (22, 23, 24) developed fungicidal spray schedules for apple orchards in central Washington. For sulfur-tolerant cultivars such as Jonathan and Rome Beauty he recommended the following schedule:

> 1) Pink stage, 2½ percent liquid-lime-sulfur or 3 lb/100 gallons dried sodium polysulfide; 2) when 75 percent of the petals have fallen, 2 percent liquid-lime-sulfur or 2½ lb/100 gallons of dried sodium polysulfide; 3) 2 weeks later, 2 to 4 lb/100 gallons wettable sulfur. For the sulfur-sensitive varieties such as Golden Delicious, Delicious, Stayman Winesap, and McIntosh, he recommended that 2-(1-methylheptyl)-4,6-nitrophenyl crotonate (formulated under the trade name of Karathane) should be used at the rate of 1 lb/100 gallons of water. A commercial wetting agent is added to this preparation in an amount recommended by the manufacturer.

Byrde and co-workers (7, 8) in England made extensive tests of organic fungicides, including dinocap (Karathane) (0.008) percent, the benzoates and dimethyl acrylates of eight phenols, against the powdery mildew of apple. Butt (5), also in England, found that high-volume sprays of dinocap (0.019 percent) controlled powdery mildew on Cox's Orange Pippin the current year and reduced blossom infection the following year. Ward (25) in Australia reported that a new fungicide binapacryl (dinitro-alkyl-phenyl-acrylate) at 1 and 2 lb/100 gallons of water gave better control than dinocap.

Delp and Klopping (14) reported in 1968 that benomyl acts as a preventive fungicide, is resistant to rainfall and eradicates the fungus in leaves 4 days after they are infected. Systemic uptake of benomyl sufficient to control mildew on 1-year-old apple trees in clay pots occurred when the soil was drenched with benomyl (9). On older trees, however, control was not possible from soil applications.

On susceptible cultivars a typical spray recommendation may be as follows: A prepink application of Benlate 4-6 oz/100 gallons of water, or Karathane 1 lb to 100 gallons followed by a pink (prebloom), then one of the same materials as a calyx application, followed by a first cover spray 15 days after petal fall and a second cover spray 15 or more days after first cover spray. To protect buds from infection, Butt (6) recommended repeated sprays at 10-day intervals from postbloom until new leaf production ceases.

For mildew control, sprays should be applied with reference to new leaf development. Usually, however, the sprays are timed for control of both mildew and scab. In California, the first spray is applied at the pink-bud stage, the second at petal-fall, and cover sprays as needed. The chemicals used are benomyl, sulfurs and dinocap.

Eradication of mildew in the buds during the winter was shown to occur with the use of 0.1 percent 4,6-dinitro-o-cresol (DNOC) in 3 percent petroleum oil at bud burst (4) or 45 percent mixture of methyl esters of fatty acids applied in the autumn (17). These treatments have not been tested in California.

References

1. Ballard, W. S., and W. H. Volk. 1914. Apple powdery mildew and its control in the Pajaro Valley. U.S. Dept. Agr. Bul. No. 120. 26 pp.
2. Bennett, M., and M. H. Moore. 1963. The relative merits of DNOC/petroleum spray in the field control of apple mildew. Dept. E. Malling Res. Sta. for 1962. pp. 105-08.
3. Berwith, C. E. 1936. Apple powdery mildew. Phytopathology 26:1071-1073.
4. Burchill, R. T. 1960. The role of secondary infections in spread of apple powdery mildew, *Podosphaera leucotricha* (Ell. & Ev.) Salm. J. Hort. Sci. 35:66-72.
5. Butt, D. J. 1971. The role of the apple spray programme in the protection of fruit buds from powdery mildew. Annals Applied Biol. 68(2): 149-57.
6. _____ 1972. The timing of sprays for the protection of terminal buds on apple shoots from powdery mildew. Ann. Appl. Biol. 72: 239-48.
7. Byrde, R. J. W., G. M. Clark, and C. W. Harper. 1963. Spraying experiments against apple mildew and apple scab at Long Ashton, 1963. Rept. Agric. Hort. Research Station, Bristol 1962:98-102.
8. Byrde, R. J. W., D. R. Clifford, E. D. Evans, and D. Woodcock. 1965. Potential fungicides for apple mildew. Progress report 1964. Rept. Agric. Hort. Research Station, Bristol 1964:135-42.
9. Cimanowski, J., A. Masternak, and D. F. Millikan. 1970. Effectiveness of benomyl for controlling apple powdery mildew and cherry leaf spot in Poland. Plant Dis. Rep. 54:81-83.
10. Covey, R. P. 1971. The effect of methionine in the development of apple powdery mildew. Phytopathology 61:346.
11. Coyier, D. L. 1968. Effect of temperature on germination of *Podsphaera leucotricha* conidia. Phytopathology 58:1047-48. (Abstr.)
12. _____ 1971. Control of powdery mildew on apples with various fungicides as influenced by seasonal temperature. Plant Dis. Rep. 55: 263-66.
13. _____ 1974. Heterothallism in the apple powdery mildew fungus, *Podosphaera leucotricha*. Phytopathology 64:246-48.
14. Delp, C. J., and H. L. Klopping. 1968. Performance attributes of a new fungicide and mite ovicide candidate. Plant. Dis. Rep. 52:95-99.
15. Ellis, J. B., and B. M. Everhart. 1888. New species of fungi from various localities. J. Mycol. 4:49-59.
16. Fischer, D. F. 1928. Control of apple powdery mildew. U. S. Dept. Agr. Farmer's Bul. No. 1120. 14 pp.
17. Frick, E. L., and B. T. Burchill. 1972. Eradication of apple powdery mildew from infected buds. Plant Dis. Rep. 56:770-72.
18. Kirkham, D. S., R. C. Hignett, and P. J. Ormerod. 1974. Effects of interrupted light on plant disease. Nature 247:158-60.
19. Lawrence, W. H. 1905. The powdery mildews of Washington. Washington State College Agr. Exp. Sta. Bul. No. 70. 16 pp.
20. Petherbridge, F. R., and W. A. R. Dillon-Weston. 1928-29. Observations on the spread of the apple mildew fungus *Podosphaera leucotricha* (Ell. & Ev.) Salm. Trans. British Mycol. Soc. 14:109-11.
21. Salmon, E. S. 1900. A monograph of the Erysiphaceae. Torrey Bot. Club Mem. 9.
22. Sprague, R. 1953. Powdery mildew of apples. *In:* Plant Diseases. U.S. Dept. Agr. Yearbook 1953:667-70.
23. _____ 1955. Study of apple powdery mildew. Western Fruit Grower 9:17.
24. _____ 1955. Fungus disease control. Western Fruit Grower 9:34-36.
25. Ward, J. R. 1965. Binapacryl: a new fungicide for the control of apple powdery mildew *(Podosphaera leucotricha)*. Australian J. Exp. Agric. Anim. Husb. 4(12):52-54.

26. Wieneke, J., R. P. Covey, and N. Benson. 1971. Influence of powdery mildew infection on ^{35}S and ^{45}Ca accumulations in leaves of apple seedlings. Phytopathology 61:1099-1103.

27. Woodward, R. C. 1927. Studies on *Podosphaera leucotricha* (Ell. & Ev.) Salm. I. The mode of perennation. Trans. Brit. Mycol. Soc. 12:173-204.

28. Yarwood, C. E., and L. Jacobsen. 1955. Accumulation of chemicals in diseased areas of leaves. Phytopathology 45:43-48.

Replant Problems of Apple

Apple trees planted in soil in which apple trees have been grown for a few years often fail to grow normally. In Germany, it is said that nurserymen encounter such a problem after growing apple trees in soil for only 2 years (2, 3). A similar problem in replanting stone fruit orchards is discussed under "Replant problems of stone fruit."

Cause. Fastabend (2) showed that apple-root residues are toxic to young apple trees when added to soil in which young trees are growing. According to Börner (1) five phenolic compounds found in soils to which apple-root residues are added produce marked growth retardation in young apple trees. These are phlorizin, phloretin, phloroglucinol, P-hydroxyhydrocinnamic acid, and P-hydroxybenzoic acid. Only phlorizin is a normal constituent of apple bark, and so it is thought that the others are breakdown products of phlorizin.

References

1. Börner, H. 1959-60. The apple replant problem. I. The excretion of phlorizin from apple root residues. Contrib. Boyce Thompson Inst. 20: 39-56.

2. Fastabend, H. 1955. Über die Ursachen der Bodenmüdigkeit in Obstbaumschulen Landwirtschaft—Angewandte Wissenschaft. Sonderheft Gardenbau IV, Landwirtschaftsverlag, Hiltrup/Mainster.

3. Grümmer, G. 1955. Die gegenseitige Beeinflussung höheren Pflanzen-Allelopathie. 162 pp. Fisher-Verlag, Jena.

Rusts of Pear

Gymnosporangium fuscum DC.
Gymnosporangium libocedri (P. Henn.) Kern
Gymnosporangium kernianum Bethel
Gymonsporangium nelsoni Arth.

Rust on pears caused by *Gymnosporangium fuscum* DC. 1805 (*Gymnosporangium sabinae* Dicks. ex Wint.) is considered to be serious in Europe, Asia Minor, and North Africa. The disease is also called "trellis rust." It was first reported in North America in Victoria, British Columbia (13) and in Lafayette, California in the same year (9). Possibly, the fungus was introduced into California on juniper from Germany or Netherlands between 1952-53 (9). The rust has been eradicated from the British Columbia mainland (3), but in California extensive control programs have limited spread, and today only occasional samples of the disease are found on juniper in the San Francisco Bay area.

Damage is confined to leaves, fruit, twigs and branches of pear. No appreciable damage is shown on the alternate host, *Juniperus sabina* var. *tarmariscifolia,* known to the nursery industry as "Spanish," "Tam," and "Tamarix" junipers. The host for the pycnial and aecial (roestelia) stages are the common commercial cultivars of pears as well as the commonly used rootstocks. Telial hosts are the *Juniperus* species commonly found as landscaping plants. The juniper hosts bearing the telial stage of the fungus has sometimes been identified on nursery stock entering U.S. and Canada (9, 13).

Causal organism. The fungus, *Gymnosporangium fuscum* DC. = *G. sabinae* Dicks. ex. Wint. is described by Ziller (13) as follows: Pycnia and aecia develop on yellow to bright-orange tuberculate leaf spots (fig. 9A), on swollen twigs, and on pear fruit. Pycnia are 170 to 190 μm wide by 150 to 170 μm high. Aecia are acorn-shaped (balanoid), rupturing along the sides, the apex remaining conic, 0.5 to 1 mm in diameter and up to 6 mm high; side-walls of peridial cells verrucose; aeciospores 20 to 28 μm in width × 25 to 35 μm in length light chestnut brown. Telia are conic or laterally compressed, dark-brown, up to 5 mm wide and 5 mm high, on spindle-shaped enlargements of the larger branches of juniper (fig. 9B).

Disease development. In spring basidiospores are windborne and may infect young pear leaves of trees within a radius of 1000 feet from the juniper host. Within 13 to 17 days after infection, pycnia appear as yellow blotches on the upper leaf surface. Later in the summer aecial horns develop and aeciospores are disseminated from these in late summer and fall. Aeciospores infect the juniper and not the pear. Unlike basidiospores, aeciospores are relatively resistant to temperature and moisture changes and may be carried for miles by wind currents. Infected areas on juniper remain inconspicuous and may escape detection for many months until the first telial horns develop in spring. Infected areas may subsequently produce a new crop of telial horns every spring without apparent damage to the juniper host. Thus the fungus requires a 2-year period to complete its life cycle.

Control. Eradication of the junipers is considered the only practical method of control in a recently infected area. Copper and carbamate fungicides such as ferbam and maneb (13) can act as protectants.

Of the remaining nine species of rust reported to occur on pear, *G. libocedri* occurs in California, and *G. kernianum* and *G. nelsoni* occur in Arizona and Colorado, respectively.

Pacific Coast pear rust. This had been reported in Oregon and northern California (4, 5, 10). Although pear, quince, and apple are attacked, the disease has been most serious on pear. Pear fruit are malformed while still young and drop from the tree. Yellowish spots with numerous cupshaped aecia at their center develop over the surface of affected fruit. Green shoots and leaves are also attacked but not so frequently as fruit.

The aecial stage also occurs on *Pyrus fusca* Doug. (*Malus rivularius* Roem.), a flowering crab known to nurserymen as *Malus floribundus* Sieb., *Sorbus sambucifolia* Roem., *S. spuria* Pero., *Amelanchier alnifolia* Nutt., *A. pallida* Greene, *Chaenomeles japonica* (Thumb.) Lindl., and *Crataegus douglasii* Londl.

The telial host of the fungus is *Libocedrus decurrens* Torr., on the leaves of which the fungus produces small dark pustules but no marked distortion. A witches'-broom condition, however, commonly develops on affected Libocedrus trees.

The pathogen. The fungus is now known as *Gymnosporangium libocedri* (P. Henn.) Kern, and the following binomials are considered to be synonymous: *Phragmidium libocedri* P. Henn., *Aecidium blasdaleanum* Diet. & Holw., *Gymnosporangium blasdaleanum* (Diet. & Holw.) Kern, and *Gynotelium blasdaleanum* (Diet. & Holw.) Arth.

Uredia are wanting. Reddish-brown pulvinate telia develop chiefly on leaves and green stems of *L. decurrens,* Teliospores are brown, linear-oblong, 2 to 5-celled, 19 to 30 μm broad by 35 to 87 μm long, and blunt at both ends. Cup-shaped aecia are produced on the fruit, leaves, and green stems of the host. Aeciospores are globoid 12 to 20 μm in width and 14 to 32 um in length.

Varietal susceptibility. Both Oriental and European cultivars of pears are affected (10). Winter Nelis is severely affected, but Bartlett is said to be little affected (6).

Disease development. The fungus attacks fruit and occasionally the leaves. Jackson (5) believed that infection occurs at blossoming time. Symptoms develop 2 to 4 weeks after infection and aecia mature about a week later. By July, after affected fruit have fallen, it is difficult to find the disease in the orchard.

Control. Little has been published on control of this disease. Jackson (6) suggested Bordeaux mixture applied as pear flowers emerged from winter buds. Destruction of the alternate host should reduce the disease, although such a procedure would not be practical in some areas.

Kern's pear rust. The aecial stage of *Gymnosporangium kernianum* Bethel (2) occurs on pears in certain western states. Another aecial host is *Amelanchier alnifolia.* The geographic range of this fungus is from Idaho and Oregon to New Mexico and Arizona. The telial stage of the fungus occurs on *Juniperus utahensis* (Englem.) Lemm., *J. occidentalis* Hook. and *J. pachyphlea* Torr. On *J. utahensis* it produces a compact, globose witches'-broom, 5 to 60 cm in diameter. The dark-brown telial sori are hemispherical in shape, scattered and solitary. Teliospores are 2-celled, narrowly ellipsoid, 21 to 26 μm broad by 55 to 74 μm long, slightly restricted at septem, yellowish, and smooth. The pedicels are long, hyaline, and cylindrical.

The inconspicuous aecia are cylindrical and 2 to 2.5 mm high. The cinnamon-brown aeciospores are globose and 21 to 32 μm in diameter. As with other species of *Gymnosporangium,* the uredial stage has not been found.

Rocky Mountain Pear Rust. The rust fungus *Gymnosporangium nelsoni* Arth. (*G. durum* Kern.) (7) occurs in the Rocky Mountain states, producing its telial stage on several species of juniper including *Juniperus utahensis* and *J. scopulorum,* and its aecial stage on the native service berries, *Amelanchier* spp.; mountain ashes, *Sorbus* spp.; hawthorns, *Cratagegus* sp.; and wild crabapple, *Malus* sp. (1, 12).

On pear leaves and fruit the aecia arise from the surfaces of yellowish lesions. The peridial walls are cylindrical, 2 to 4 mm high, splitting at the apex and more or less down the sides. The aeciospores are globoid, 19 to 26 μm broad by 21 to 29 μm long, with chestnut brown finely verrucose walls pierced by 6 to 8 pores. On juniper, the irregularly flattened telial horns arise from woody globose galls which vary from ¼ to ½ inch in diameter. Teliospores are ellipsoid, more or less pointed at each end, 18 to 22 μm broad by 50 to 65 μm long, and with cinnamon-brown walls. The pedicels are long and cylindrical.

References

1. Arthur, J. C. 1934. Manual of rusts in the United States and Canada. P. 376. Science Press. Lancaster, Pa.
2. Bethel, Ellsworth. 1911. Notes on some species of *Gymnosporangium* in Colorado. Mycologia 3:156-60.

3. Creelman, D. W. 1966. Summary of the prevalence of plant diseases in Canada in 1965. Can. Pl. Dis. Survey 46(2):37-79.
4. Dietel, P. 1895. New North American Uredineae. Erythea 3:77.
5. Jackson, H. S. 1914. A new pomaceous rust of economic importance, *Gymnosporangium blasdaleanum*. Phytopathology 4:261-70.
6. _____ 1915. A Pacific Coast rust attacking pears, quince, etc. Oregon Agr. Expt. Sta. Second Bien. Crop. Pest Hort. Rept. 1913-14: 202-12.
7. Kern, F. D. 1907. New Western species of *Gymnosporangium* and *Roestelia*. Bul Torrey. Bot. Club 34:459-63.
8. _____ 1908. Studies on the genus *Gymnosporangium* and *Roestelia*. Bul. Torrey Bot. Club 35:499-571.
9. McCain, A. H. 1961. *Gymnosporangium fuscum* found on pears in California. Plant Dis. Rep. 45:151.
10. O'Gara, P. J. 1914. A rust new on apples, pears and other pome fruits. Science 39:620-21.
11. Smith, R. E. 1941. Diseases of Fruits and Nuts. California Agr. Ext. Serv. Cir. 120. 168 pp (out of print).
12. Weier, J. R., and E. E. Hubert. 1917. Recent cultures of forest tree rusts. Phytopathology 7:106-09.
13. Ziller, W. G. 1961. Pear rust *(Gymnosporangium fuscum)* in North America. Plant Dis. Rep. 45:90-94.

Sappy Bark of Apple
Polystictus versicolor Fr.
Coriolus versicolor (L. ex. Fr.) Quēl.

The disease known as "sappy bark" and "papery bark" is occasionally troublesome in apple trees growing in the Pajaro and Sonoma valleys of California. According to Wormald (4) the disease was widespread some years ago in Australia and Tasmania but is unknown in Great Britain. The causal fungus, however, is found in England on dead stumps of orchard trees. Hotson (2) reported it to be associated at times with a collar rot disease of apple trees in central Washington.

Symptoms. The causal fungus infects larger branches and limbs, causing areas of the bark to become discolored, spongy, and moist and the underlying wood to become discolored. According to Smith (3) the fungus attacks the hemicellulose and cellulose of the xylem elements. The affected areas, which commonly occur at cuts made when branches are removed, sometimes exudes a dark-colored sap. The phelloderm (corky bark) over such areas peels away, exposing the disorganized spongy cortex and phloem.

Under some conditions the brackets of *Polystictus* develop over these areas.

Causal organism. *Coriolus versicolor* (L. ex. Fr.) Quēl. *(= Polypara versicolor* L. ex. Fr.) is said to be the causal fungus (1, 4).

Control. Remove the diseased bark and wood.

References
1. Anonymous. 1924. Plant Pathology. Univ. California Agr. Exp. Sta. Ann. Rept. 1922-23:179-87.
2. Hotson, J. W. 1920. Collar-rot of apple trees in the Yakima Valley. Phytopathology 10:465-86.
3. Smith, R. G. 1924. A chemical and pathological study of decay of the xylem of the apple caused by *Polystictus versicolor*. Fr. Phytopathology 14:114-18.
4. Wormald, H. 1955. Diseases of fruit and hops. C. Lockwood & Son Ltd., London. 325 pp.

Scab of Apple
Venturia inaequalis (Cke) Wint.

Apple scab, also called "black spot" in some countries, occurs wherever apples are grown but it is much more severe where springs and summers are moist and cool. For example, in the northeastern U.S., including New England and states bordering the Great Lakes, apple scab is more damaging than in the southeastern part of the country. Similarly, outbreaks are more common in the coastal areas of California than in the interior. Apple scab probably was known in Europe soon after the commercial apple was introduced, and the fungus was first called *Spilocaea pomi* in Sweden by Fries (6) in 1819. Botanists noted its presence in the eastern U.S. as early as 1834. It was undoubtedly introduced to the Pacific Coast states soon after that region was settled.

Economic importance. When not controlled, scab is responsible for almost total destruction of an apple crop. Loss comes about principally through fruit infection. Some of the infected young fruit drop; those remaining on the tree become so malformed and unsightly as to be unmarketable. On highly susceptible cultivars, damage to the tree may be caused by defoliation following heavy leaf infection.

Symptoms. Some of the first symptoms of apple scab appear on the flower sepals as dark green velvety spots. Later, similar lesions may appear on leaves which surround the flower clusters. As the fruit develops, additional lesions appear on the sides of the fruit adjacent to the infected sepals. As the lesions expand and coalesce they produce large dirty green scabby patches beneath which the host-tissue stops growing, resulting in a misshapened fruit (fig. 10A).

Leaf lesions are of two types: 1) well-defined, more or less circular greenish scabby areas, which generally occur on the upper side of the leaf (fig. 10B); and 2) wefty lesions with indefinite margins which may cover most of the lower surface of the leaf.

Twig infection occurs occasionally on some cultivars of apple but this phase of the disease is usually of minor importance. The scabby patches are composed of largely fungal tissue in the form of stromatic cushions from which arise short unbranched conidiophores bearing conidia shaped like an elongated pear. On leaves, the stromatic cushion extends between the cuticle and the outer walls of the epidermis. Rarely do hyphae from the stroma penetrate into the interior of the living leaf.

The causal organism. Apple scab is caused by the ascomycetous fungus *Venturia inaequalis* (Cke.) Wint. In early reports of the disease the causal fungus was listed according to its conidial stage, *Fusicladium dendriticum*.

As stated earlier, conidia of the fungus are produced successively on short unbranched conidiospores. The conidia (50 to 60 μm long × 4 to 6 μm broad) are one- or two-celled and club-shaped (obclavate).

Ascospores are produced in leaves in flask-shaped pseudothecia. An ostiolum from the pseudothecium projects through to the leaf surface. Eight ascospores (11 to 15 μm long × 4 to 8 μm broad) are produced in cylindrical asci. The ascospores have two cells, one cell being broader and shorter than the other. In *V. inaequalis,* the shorter, broader end of the ascospore is uppermost in the ascus. This feature distinguishes it from *V. pirina* in which the reverse arrangement is true.

Life cycle of the pathogen. Primary infection in spring is caused almost entirely by ascospores developed in pseudothecia in dead leaves on the ground. Conidia are present in early spring only where twig infection occurs. Fruit and leaf lesions produce conidia causing infection after the ascosporic inoculum is exhausted.

Requirements for infection were investigated by Keitt and Jones (11), who found that the optimum temperature for this process is 20 °C, whereas infection will occur at a temperature as low as 5 °C. The fungus spore germinates only if surrounded by a film of water. The length of time moisture must be present to produce germination and penetration of the host tissue is a minimum of 6 hours at 20 °C and 18 hours at 6 °C. Temperatures above the optimum are unfavorable to infection; at 27.8 °C, for example, little infection was found to occur even under optimum moisture conditions (10). A table for calculation of infection periods was developed by Mills and La Plante (14).

Once the germ tube has established itself in the tissue of the fruit or leaf, the fungus is no longer dependent on an external water supply as it can obtain this from the host tissue. It is, however, influenced in its further development by temperature. Keitt and Jones (11) reported that whereas at 20 °C to 24 °C, 8 to 12 days elapsed between infection and appearance of the lesion, at 7.2 °C the incubation process required 17 days.

Dependence of the fungus on favorable temperature and moisture conditions restricts infection to the cooler moisture periods of the growing season. Consequently, little disease will develop during the warmer drier part of the summer. Leaf- and fruit-age also influence infection: young leaves are subject to infection on both surfaces, but as they become older the cuticle on the upper surface becomes resistant to penetration by the fungus, whereas the lower surface remains susceptible much throughout the life of the leaf. Thus one frequently finds abundant infection of the lower surfaces of leaves following rainy periods when the temperature has moderated in early autumn. This type of infection greatly increases the abundance of pseudothecial development.

Although fruit is most susceptible to infection when young, even mature fruit develop small multiple infections when prolonged rains occur in autumn. This type of infection may develop after the fruit is picked and stored.

In addition to providing moisture for spore germination, rain is important as a vehicle of dissemination. Even strong air currents do not detach conidia from the conidiophores, but water does and consequently spattering and wind-blown raindrops spread the conidia about. Striking evidence of rain dissemination is the development of numerous secondary lesions below infected sepals. For a time after fruit is set the calyx end of the fruit remains uppermost, and rainwater running down over the infected sepal can carry conidia to the cheek of the fruit.

As long as the leaf is alive the scab fungus is restricted to the subcuticular position. Soon after the leaf falls to the ground in autumn, fungus hyphae from the stromatic layer penetrate between the epidermal cells and grow into the leaf's interior. This process, which occurs only if the leaf remains moist, is soon followed by the initiation of pseudothecia in the interior of the leaf (20).

Because hyphae from a single lesion are relatively limited, its extension through the leaf interior and the number of lesions per leaf, play an important part in determining the number of pseudothecia developing in the leaf. The well-defined circular lesions resulting from early infection of the upper surface of the leaf may produce pseudothecia only in the area immediately beneath the periphery of the lesion. In contrast the diffuse lesions on the lower surface of the leaf, in which the subcuticular stromata or the fungus grows out extensively from the point of infection, produce psuedothecia scattered over larger areas (20). Thus, when autumnal infection of the lower surfaces of leaves is abundant, pseudothecial development may likewise be abundant.

The optimum temperature for pseudothecial initiation is about 12.8 °C, as compared to 25.5 °C for spore germination and mycelial growth. Pseudothecia consequently are initiated during the autumn and early winter. They develop more or less rapidly depending on temperature in winter, and the ascospores mature in spring about the time the blossom buds begin to open on apple trees (20).

After maturation, the ascospores are forcibly discharged into the air through the pseudothecial neck (ostiolum) which extends to the surface of the leaf. Discharge occurs when the leaves are wetted, and is repeated at each rain as long as ascospores are produced in the pseudothecium. In Wisconsin, Keitt and Jones (11) found that the period of ascospore discharge lasted 7 to 9 weeks in April and May, while in New York the discharge period was through July (17). Ascospores were therefore present in the orchard air at the time the apple blossomed and early foliage was appearing.

Susceptibility of apple cultivars. Schneiderhan and Fromme (16) reported that under Virginia conditions, Winesap, Rome Beauty, Stayman, and Delicious cultivars were highly susceptible to scab infection, and Jonathan, York Imperial, and Grimes somewhat so. In California the various red Delicious mutants and the Rome Beauty seem somewhat more susceptible than Jonathan, Golden Delicious, or Gravenstein. All, however, may suffer loss during years when the disease is severe.

Shay, Dayton, and Hough (16) have made a search for resistance among various species of Malus. Wil-

liams *et al*. (19) found the Priscilla, a fall apple, to be resistant to scab. Aldwinckle, Gustafson and Lamb in 1976 (1) reported two major genes for resistance to *V. inaequalis* derived from *Malus floribunda* and *M. pumila*. Using their technique of forced flowering of seedlings in 16 to 20 months, they have developed numbered selections such as New York 55140-19 and Prima which are immune to scab and resistant to mildew (2).

Control. Preventing infection of flower sepals is one of the most important steps toward successful control of later fruit infection. As the flower buds open in the spring the first green surfaces exposed are those of the flower sepals. These become infected by ascospores, which are ordinarily mature by this time. Within 10 to 14 days after infection, depending upon temperature, lesions appear on the sepals and produce abundant conidia which wash down over the young fruit.

Once sepal infection occurs it is difficult to prevent this secondary fruit infection. Thus it is important that a spray be applied at the so-called green tip stage of blossom-bud opening, which occurs just as the tips of the bud scales separate. A second spray is applied after the blossom cluster has fully emerged from the bud and the individual blossoms have separated in the cluster. During this stage the first leaves (those which surround the blossom cluster) open; the spray therefore protects these leaves as well as the entire blossom. A third spray is applied towards the end of the blossoming period when most of the petals have fallen. The number of later sprays to be applied depends upon weather conditions. Where rains may occur at any time during late spring and summer, a number of fruit-cover sprays may be necessary. In California, where protracted rains (those lasting more than 12 to 24 hours) do not ordinarily occur in late spring, one or two more sprays are generally sufficient and are applied 20 to 40 days after the blossoming period.

Fungicides providing good protection against infection by the scab fungus are captan and benomyl. Dodine which previously gave good results has proved less effective in western New York state. According to Gilpatrick and Blowers (7) ascospores of the fungus developed tolerance to that chemical. Benomyl-tolerance has also been reported, first in Australia and then in Michigan.

Keitt and coworkers (10, 12) in Wisconsin earlier studied the so-called eradicant method for combating apple scab. This consisted of a chemical applied to apple leaves which prevented development of the pseudothecial stage. In earlier tests the spray was applied to the trees in the autumn after harvest but before leaf fall. Later, however, the spray was applied in early spring to overwintered leaves on the ground. The first successful chemical to be employed was monocalcium arsenite. This material was later replaced by a proprietary dinitro cresol compound (Elgetol Extra). Workers in England (4, 8) have reported the successful use of phenylmercuric chloride applied to the trees before leaf fall. Workers in the U.S. (12, 13) reported that phenylmercuric chloride like dinitro cresole suppresses the development of ascospores. Benomyl and thiophanate methyl were effective in controlling apple scab because they suppressed ascospore development (15).

References

1. Aldwinckle, H. S., H. L. Gustafson, and R. C. Lamb. 1976. Early determination of genotypes for apple scab resistance by forced flowering of test cross progenies. Euphytica 25:185-91.
2. Aldwinckle, H. S. and R. C. Lamb. 1977. Controlling apple diseases without chemicals. New York's Food & Life Sciences 10(2):12-14.
3. Aderhold, R. 1900. Die Fusicladien unserer Obstbaume II. Tiel. Landw. Jahrb. 29:541-88.
4. Burchill, R. T. and K. E. Hutton. 1965. The suppression of ascospore production to facilitate the control of apple scab [Venturia inaequalis (Cke.) Wing.]. Ann. Appl. Biol. 56:285-92.
5. Clinton, G. P. 1901. Apple scab. Illinois Agr. Exp. Sta. Bul. 67:109-56.
6. Fries, E. 1819. Spilocaea pomi Fr. Nov. fl. Svec. 5:79.
7. Gilpatrick, J. D. and D. R. Blowers. 1974. Ascospore tolerance to Dodine in relation to orchard control of apple scab. Phytopathology 64:649-52.
8. Hutton, K. E. 1954. Eradication of Venturia inaequalis (Cooke) Winter. Nature (London) 174:1017.
9. Keitt, G. W. 1953. Scab of apples. U.S. Dept. Agr. Yearbook of Ag., p. 646-52.
10. Keitt, G. W., C. N. Clayton, and M. H. Langford. 1941. Experiments with eradicant fungicides for combating apple scab. Phytopathology 31:296-322.
11. Keitt, G. W. and L. K. Jones. 1926. Studies of the epidemiology and control of apple scab. Wisconsin Agr. Exp. Sta. Res. Bul. 73:1-104.
12. Keitt, G. W. and D. H. Palmiter. 1937. Potentialities of eradicant fungicides for combating apple scab and some other plant diseases. J. Agr. Research (U.S.) 55:397-438.
13. Latorre, B. A. 1972. Late season fungicide applications to control apple scab. Plant Dis. Rep. 56:1079-82.
14. Mills, W. D., and A. A. La Plante. 1954. Diseases and insects in the orchard. Cornell Ext. Bul. 711:20-2.
15. Ross, R. G. 1973. Suppression of perithecium formation in Venturia inaequalis by seasonal sprays of benomyl and thiophanate-methyl. Canadian J. Sci. 53:601-02.
16. Schneiderhan, F. J., and F. D. Fromme. 1924. Apple scab and its control in Virginia. Virginia Agr. Exp. Sta. Bul. 236:1-29.
17. Shay, J. R:, D. F. Dayton, and L. F. Hough. 1953. Apple scab resistance from a number of Malus species. Proc. Amer. Soc. Hort. Sci. 62:348-56.
18. Szkolnik, M. 1969. Maturation and discharge of ascospores of Venturia inaequalis. Plant Dis. Rep. 53:534-37.
19. Williams, E. B., et al. 1972. Priscilla, a fall red apple with resistance to apple scab. Fruit Variety Horticultural Digest 26:34-35.
20. Wilson, E. E. 1928. Studies of the ascigerous stage of Venturia inaequalis (Cke) Wint. in relation to certain factors of the environment. Phytopathology 18:375-418.

Scab of Pear
Venturia pirina Aderh.

Pear scab, also known as "black spot" in Australia and New Zealand (2, 6), occurs to some extent wherever pears are grown but it is most prevalent in regions of high summer rainfall. Thus, when not controlled, it is occasionally the source of much economic loss in some areas of the Pacific Northwest. It occurs sporadically in the coastal areas of California but seldom in the drier interior valleys (8). Losses from fruit infection occurred in Lake County, California during 1975.

Symptoms. Blossoms, fruit, leaves and, occasionally, twigs are infected (fig. 11). In spring and summer, superficial more or less circular, wefty, olivaceous lesions develop on the leaf blade, leaf petiole, flower peduncle, and cheek of the fruit. Lesions on fruit frequently occur in greater numbers at the stylar end, and coalescence of several lesions results in development of large irregular, dull green, felt-like patches. Growth of fruit tissue under such areas is checked, and fruit becomes malformed and unsalable. The dark felt-like surface of the lesion is composed of numerous conidiophores and conidia.

On living leaves and fruit, the fungus occupies the area between cuticle and epidermis where it develops a stroma from which conidiophores arise.

Twig lesions appear first as small (1 to 2 mm) blister-like pustules. Later the corky periderm breaks away exposing the fungus stroma (5, 6).

Cultivar susceptibility. Most if not all of the commonly grown pear cultivars are susceptible to scab. Fruits of d'Anjou, Bartlett, Comice, Winter Nelis, Easter Beurre, Forelle, Flemish Beauty, and Seckel are highly susceptible. Very young fruits of Beurre Bosc are highly susceptible, but older fruit is comparatively resistant to infection.

Causal organism. *Venturia pirina* Aderh., the causal fungus of pear scab, produces the conidial stage on fruit, leaves, and twigs in summer and the pseudothecial stage in dead leaves on the ground in winter.

V. pirina conidia are light-yellowish green, pyriform, at first nonseptate, becoming septate with age, 28 to 30 µm long by 7 to 9 µm wide; they are produced on short wavy conidiophores. After each conidium is liberated, the end of the conidiophore to one side of the conidial scar elongates slightly, leaving the conidial scar as a knee-shaped protrusion (1).

Pseudothecia are almost completely immersed in the leaf, with only the neck projecting through the cuticle. They are globose and 120 to 160 µm in diameter. The cylindrical asci produce eight yellowish-green, two-celled ascospores, and are 14 to 20 × 5 to 8 µm in dimension. The cells of the ascospores are unequal in length, the longer cell being oriented toward the base of the ascus. This feature, distinguishes *V. pirina* from *V. inaequalis,* which produces ascospores with the short cell oriented upward in the ascus.

Langford and Keitt (8) found that the pathogen is a species of many strains that differ in cultural characteristics and pathogenicity. For example, none of their isolates infected Bartlett and Keiffer, although neither of these cultivars is immune or even highly resistant to scab.

According to Shabi, Rotem and Loebenstein (9), physiological races of the fungus occurring in Israel are specific to differential hosts of *Pyrus communis* and *P. syriaca* origin. Environmental conditions did not change the specific pathogenic properties of the races tested.

Disease development. The fungus can survive from one season to the next on twig lesions or in diseased leaves on the ground. Some investigators (5, 6) assert that twig lesions are often the more important overwintering sites. Conidia are produced on twig lesions and these are largely disseminated by rain. After leaves fall, the fungus penetrates from its subcuticular position into the interior and initiates pseudothecia. Ascospores mature in early spring; they are forcibly ejected into the air during wet weather and are blown to susceptible parts of the tree. Thus, the inoculum for primary infection in spring may be both conidia and ascospores.

As with apple, among the first parts of the pear to be infected in spring are the sepals of the emerging flowers; the fruit, leaves, and new shoots are then in turn infected. Kienholz and Childs (6) state that while twigs may be attacked at any time of the growing season infection is most frequent in spring.

Temperature and moisture play important roles in development of the disease. Rain disseminates the conidia about the tree, and provides the moisture necessary for ascospore ejection and spore germination. The fungus can attack the host over a relatively wide range of temperatures, but variations in this factor greatly influence both the amount of infection and the length of the incubation period. For example, infection will occur at 23.9 °C when the host part remains continually wet for only 5 hours, whereas at 4.4 °C a continually moist period of 48 hours is necessary for infection. The incubation period also varies from 10 to 25 days, depending on temperature (6).

Although the saprophytic stage of the fungus has not been studied in detail, the pseudothecia apparently develop similarly to those of *V. inaequalis* and are influenced by similar conditions.

Control. The most effective control of pear scab is attained from fungicidal sprays. Kienholz and Childs (6) showed that liquid lime-sulfur, 4 gallons in 100 gallons water or above, was highly effective in destroying the conidia in twig lesions. They therefore recommend an application of 6 to 8 gallons of liquid lime-sulfur in 100 gallons water at the delayed dormant stage of flower bud development; to suppress this source of inoculum, a second application of ferbam or ziram is applied at the pre-pink stage. This application might be delayed until the pink stage if the weather is dry. If the weather is unusually wet, both pre-pink and pink treatment is advisable. The next treatment using ferbam or ziram, is given at the calyx stage (after most of the petals have fallen). Other treatments at 10 to 20 day intervals are given in regions where rains extend into late spring and summer.

Kienholz and Childs (6) and later Coyier and Mellenthin (2) reported that lime-sulfur applied after the buds open is injurious to the d'Anjou cultivar.

Williamson and Burchill (11) reported that as with the apple scab fungus, relatively low amounts of phenylmercuric chloride, benomyl, thiabendazole, and urea applied to scab-infected pear leaves in autumn prevent ascospore formation the following spring. Applied to scab-infected twigs in autumn or spring, however, these materials failed to prevent conidial development.

In California, at least three sprays were applied: 1) at the green-tip stage of bloom, 2) at the cluster-bud stage, and 3) as a cover spray. Chemicals which have been recommended are benomyl, captan, and dodine. Liquid lime-sulfur plus wettable sulfur has been used only during green tip to cluster-bud stage of bloom. Both benomyl and dodine in addition to protective action, provide eradicative properties if used within 24 to 48 hours after infection occurs. (See "Scab of Apple" for method of determining infection periods.)

References

1. Aderhold, R. 1896. Die Fusicladien unserer obstbaum. Landw. Jahrb. 25:875-914.

2. Coyier, D. L., and W. M. Mellenthin. 1969. Effect of lime-sulfur oil sprays on d'Anjou pear. Hortscience 4(2):91.

3. Cunningham, G. H. 1925. The fungous diseases of fruit trees. Brett Printing Co., Auckland, New Zealand. 382 pp.

4. Kienholz, J. R. 1953. Scab on the pear. *In:* Plant Diseases. U.S. Dept. Agr. Yearbook of Agriculture 1953:674-77.

5. Kienholz, J. R., and L. Childs. 1937. Twig lesions as a source of early spring infection by the pear scab fungus. J. Agr. Research 55:667-81.

6. _____ 1951. Pear scab in Oregon. Oregon State Coll. Agr. Exp. Sta. Tech. Bul. No. 21, 31 pp.

7. Kirk, J. W. 1913. Pear scab. New Zealand J. Agr. 7:1-59.

8. Langford, M. H., and G. W. Keitt. 1942. Heterothallism and variability in *Venturia pirina*. Phytopathology 32:357-69.

9. Shabi, E., J. Rotem, and G. Loebenstein. 1973. Physiological races of *Venturia pirina* on pear. Phytopathology 63:41-43.

10. Smith, R. E. 1905. Pear scab. Calif. Univ. Agr. Exp. Sta. Bul. 1963 (out of print).

11. Williamson, C. J., and R. J. Burchill. 1974. The prevention and control of pear scab (*Venturia pirina* Aderh.). Plant Path. 23:67-73.

NONPARASITIC DISEASES OF APPLE AND PEAR

Apple Measles or Internal Bark Necrosis of Apple

The name "measles" was first applied to a disorder of apple trees in northwestern Arkansas by Hewitt and Truax (11), who observed the disease in 1908 and described it in 1912. Two types of branch symptoms were associated with this disease. The more prevalent were scattered red papular excrescences; the less prevalent were scurfy cankers. In 1914, Rose (18) in Missouri discovered a disorder of apple bark which he called "pimple canker." His descriptions and illustrations show this disorder to have many characteristics of the papular type of measles mentioned by Hewitt and Truax.

Up to 1922, according to Haskell and Wood (10), a similar apple disorder was found in Arkansas, Missouri, Pennsylvania (1), New Mexico (4), Maryland, Virginia, Alabama, Michigan, Illinois, and Kansas. According to Ark and Thomas (5) California has been added to this list, the disease being found in both young and old orchards near Sebastopol. The disorder is also known to occur in Australia (14) and Italy (15).

Although the disease has been found in several cultivars, notably Jonathan, Gano, and Stayman Winesap, Delicious and its mutants are most often affected. Grimes Golden, Rome Beauty, and Golden Delicious are seldom affected.

Symptoms. The description of measles (fig. 12) furnished by Hewitt and Truax (11) follows:

> Scattered red pycnidia-like pustules occur on otherwise smooth bark of young twigs. The pustules are 0.3 to 1 mm in diameter and 0.3 to 0.5 mm high, dark red at their centers and light red at the periphery. The latter feature suggested the name "measles." Pustules may become so numerous as to cause the bark to be very rough. The necrotic centers of these pustules are located either in the cortex or, at times, deep in the phloem.

The less prevalent scurfy type of canker involves a considerable area of bark and is produced by an irregular thickening of the bark periderm, which is dark red to nearly black in color. The thickened scurfy condition is relatively shallow, whereas the papular condition extends into the phloem regions of the bark.

Rhoads (16), who gave an extensive account of the symptoms of measles in Missouri, said there are three more or less distinct types. For convenience he designated these as a) the isolated pustular type, b) the aggregate pustular or scurfy type, and c) the canker type. Various gradations exist between the first and second and, less frequently, between the second and third types, depending upon the stage of their development and the variety of apple affected. Judging from his description, the macroscopic aspects of the isolated pustular type are similar to those of the pustular type described by Hewitt and Truax, except the pustules are not so deep-seated.

Descriptions of measles from other parts of the U.S. conform to those occurring in Arkansas and Missouri. After his studies in West Virginia, Berg (6) distinguished two types of measle-like disorders which appeared to be nonparasitic. A third disease, black pox, is caused by a fungus, he stated. The two other diseases he tentatively named "internal bark necrosis" and "measles"—the latter he believed to represent true measles as described by Hewitt and Truax.

Berg (6) stated that in time, the number of dead areas in the bark increases, radial development of the bark is retarded, and numerous short cracks appear in affected areas. Cracking of the bark and sloughing of the periderm may continue for several years, thereby producing a characteristic scaly, cracked, and roughened condition of the surface.

Berg (6) distinguished internal bark necrosis from measles as it occurred in West Virginia on the basis of size, color, and distribution of papules. The papules of measles were, he said, smaller and redder in color than those of internal bark necrosis and occurred in closely aggregated groups, while those of internal bark necrosis were more or less uniformly distributed over the surface of the affected branch. However, Hewitt and Truax (11) did not mention aggregate patches of pustules as a feature of the disease they described, although they mentioned a scurfy bark canker as a type of measles. Rhoads (16) mentioned both the scattered and aggregate type of pustule distribution in his description of measles.

In view of the many similarities, therefore, internal bark necrosis should not be separated from measles on the basis of symptoms alone. Although Berg was inclined to believe that several distinct and widely distributed papular diseases have been called measles, he realized that until the cause or causes of all measles-like symptoms were known such a separation as he proposed was tentative.

Cause. None of the numerous attempts to isolate a pathogenic organism from measles-affected branches proved successful, though some of the organisms obtained were, for a time, considered possibly the cause of the disorder. Rose (19), for example, described *Pseudomonas papulans* as the probable cause of a papular canker condition of apple bark in Missouri. Although he did not specifically associate this condition with measles, which in an earlier report he had called pimple canker, others began to do so. This bacterium is no longer considered to have any causal connection with measles. Berg (6) found a condition of apple twigs characterized by well-defined, scattered, papillate lesions to be caused by the fungus *Helminthosporium papulosum* Berg, but failed to connect this organism or any other fungus or bacterium with internal bark necrosis or measles.

Experiments conducted in New Mexico (4), Ohio (22), and Illinois (3) indicate that the condition is not transmissible by budding or grafting diseased scions into healthy trees. Berg (6) reported that internal bark necrosis was not contracted by young apple trees planted around badly infected orchard trees. In the New Mexico studies (4) young apple trees planted in soil taken from affected orchards developed the disorder, whereas those planted in soil taken from noninfected orchards remained free of the disorder. Soils in which trees developed measles were abnormally high in soluble salts.

Young and Winter (23) of Ohio and Hildebrand (12) of New York reported that symptoms similar to those described by Berg for internal bark necrosis were produced in Delicious grown in sand cultures from which boron was omitted. Hildebrand, also, reported that orchard trees were cured of the disorder by applying borax to the soil. However, Berg and Clulo (7) were "...unable to produce any necrotic lesions or other symptoms typical of internal bark necrosis on the bark of Red Delicious trees growing in boron-free sand cultures. Other symptoms of boron deficiency, such as stunting of the trees, procumbent growth of the twigs, and rosetting were in evidence. The application of boron to the soil of diseased trees in orchards did not correct the disease."

Berg and Clulo (7) obtained evidence that the disease they called internal bark necrosis was induced by an excess of manganese in the soil, but in this connection they did not mention the disorder which Berg had called measles. Later, Clulo (8) published additional evidence on internal bark necrosis but failed to mention measles; she reported that the former was induced by adding 64 ppm of manganous sulfate to sand and soil cultures. Furthermore, the addition of manganous sulfate to soil around Delicious that had grown normally for 20 years was followed by a marked development of internal bark necrosis.

Hildebrand (12) observed an orchard in which internal bark necrosis of Delicious was not benefited by boron treatment. Soil in this orchard was of a different type than that of orchards which responded to boron treatment.

The bark of trees having internal bark necrosis is abnormally high in manganese and iron, thereby indicating a possible causal relationship between an excess of one or both of these elements and the disorder. However, leaf analyses reported by Thomas, Mack and Fagan (22) afforded no evidence that an excess of either of these elements is a causal factor; nor do they support the viewpoint that boron deficiency is involved. Later, Eggert and Hayden (9), Rogers, Thompson and Scott (17), and Shelton and Zeiger (21), presented additional strong evidence that an excess of manganese causes symptoms of internal bark necrosis to develop, and Sheldon and Zeiger (21) found manganese accumulated in the necrotic bark areas.

Little is known about the relation of measles to other soil conditions. Although the incidence of measles is not constantly associated with any particular topography, drainage condition, or soil structure, it often varies from one area of the orchard to another. There seems to be some relation between soil acidity and severity of the disorder, as measles-producing soil in West Virginia was found to give a pH reaction of 6.3, and one in New York a pH reaction of 4.4 and below. Application of ammonium sulfate or other acidifying fertilizers to such soils is said to have increased the incidence of the disorder, whereas the application of alkalizing materials such as calcium hydroxide or magnesium carbonate is said to have suppressed the disorder. In New York a measles-producing soil was found to be low in calcium and magnesium, which probably accounted for its low pH. The potassium, nitrogen and phosphorus contents apparently were neither excessive nor deficient. The manganese, iron, and aluminum contents, however, were very high. The disorder in that orchard was not alleviated by boron treatment. According to Hildebrand (12) soils on which trees responded to boron treatments had a pH well over 5.0.

Studies reported by Shannon (20) in 1954 are interpreted as meaning that both a deficiency of boron and an excess of manganese result in the development of histologically indistinguishable symptoms in young apple trees.

Except for one report (5), bark measles in apple trees has not been described as a prominent feature of symptoms known to be caused by boron deficiency. Symptoms most commonly mentioned in connection with the boron deficiency disorder are corky areas in the flesh or on the skin of the fruit, dwarfing, yellowing, and rosetting of the foliage, and necrosis of the smaller branches. In severely effected branches the larger branches or even the entire tree may die. All these symptoms may be concurrent in a given orchard but not often are they concurrent on the same trees. Such variations in symptoms on trees have come to be regarded as the identifying features of boron deficiency. However, they have not been identified as a part of the syndrome of the internal bark necrosis-type of disorder.

Control. According to Clulo (8) the application of calcium hydroxide or other alkaline materials to the soil suppressed internal bark necrosis for 5 years.

References

1. Adams, J. F. 1919. Notes on plant diseases in Pennsylvania in 1916. Pennsylvania Agr. Exp. Sta. Ann. Rept. 1916-17, 329-36.
2. Anderson, H. W. 1931. Apple measles. Illinois Agr. Exp. Sta. Ann. Rept. 1931, 68-70.
3. _____ 1933. Apple measles. Illinois Agr. Exp. Sta. Ann. Rept. 1933:44.
4. Anonymous. 1927-28. Apple measles. New Mexico Agr. Exp. Sta. Ann. Repts. 30:18, 1918-19; 36:18, 1924-25; 37:17, 1925-26; 38:20, 1926-27; 39:18, 1927-28.
5. Ark, P. A., and H. E. Thomas. 1940. Apple dieback in California. Phytopathology 30:148-54.
6. Berg, A. 1934. Black pox and other apple-bark diseases commonly known as measles. West Virginia Agr. Exp. Sta. Bul. 260:1-24.
7. Berg, A., and G. Clulo. 1946. The relation of manganese to internal bark necrosis of apples. Science 104:265-66.
8. Clulo, G. 1949. The production of internal bark necrosis of apple in sand and soil cultures. Phytopathology 39:502. (Abstr.)
9. Eggert, D. A., and R. A. Hayden. 1970. Histochemical relationship of manganese to internal bark necrosis of apple. J. Amer. Hort. Soc. 95:715-19.
10. Haskell, R. J., and Jessie I. Wood. 1922. Diseases of fruit and nut crops in the United States in 1921. U.S. Dept. Agr. Bur. Pl. Indus. Plant Disease Bul. Supplement 20:51-52.
11. Hewitt, J. L., and H. E. Truax. 1912. An unknown apple disease. Arkansas Agr. Exp. Sta. Bul. 112:481-91.
12. Hildebrand, E. M. 1939. Internal bark necrosis of Delicious apples, a physiogenic "boron-deficiency" disease. Phytopathology 29:10. (Abstr.)
13. _____ 1947. Internal bark necrosis (measles) of Delicious apples in New York in relation to pH, minor element toxicity, and nutrient balance of soil. Plant Dis. Rep. 31:99-106.
14. Holbreche, J. A. 1946. Boron deficiency in apples. Observations at New England Experiment Farm. New South Wales Agr. Gaz. 57:17-21.
15. Refatti, E., and R. Ciferri. 1952. Defoliation, measles, stunting, bark necrosis of apple trees due to boron deficiency in the region of Trentino-Alto Adige. (Trans. title). Notiz. Malattie Piante 18:1-20.
16. Rhoads, A. H. 1924. Apple measles with special reference to the comparative susceptibility and

resistance of apple varieties to the disease in Missouri. Phytopathology 14:289-314.

17. Rogers, B. L., A. H. Thompson, and L. E. Scott. 1965. Internal bark necrosis (measles) on Delicious apple trees under field conditions. Proc. Amer. Soc. Hort. Sci. 86:46-54.
18. Rose, D. H. 1914. Report of the pathologist. Pimple canker. Missouri State Fruit Exp. Sta. Bienn. Rept. 1913-14 (Bul. 24):29-30.
19. _____ 1917. Blister spot of apples and its relation to a disease of apple bark. Phytopathology 7:198-208.
20. Shannon, Leland M. 1954. Internal bark necrosis of the Delicious apple. Proc. Am. Soc. Hort. Sci. 64:165-74.
21. Shelton, J. E., and D. C. Zeiger. 1970. Distribution of manganese[54] in 'Delicious' apple trees in relation to the occurrence of internal bark necrosis (IBN). J. Am. Hort. Sci. 95(6): 758-62.
22. Thomas, W., W. B. Mack, and F. N. Fagan. 1947. Foliar diagnosis: Internal bark necrosis in young apple trees. Proc. Amer. Soc. Hort. Sci. 50:1-9.
23. Young, H. C., and H. F. Winter. 1937. The effect of boron, manganese, and zinc on the control of apple measles. Ohio Agr. Exp. Sta. Bi-Mon. Bul. 22:147-52.

Bitter Pit of Apple

This disease was first described in Germany under the name "stippen", and it so appears in some earlier American literature. Other names are "fruit spot" and "Baldwin spot." Cobb, who reported the disease in Australia, probably was the first to call it "Bitter pit" (21, 22, 23, 39, 40, 41, 53).

Bitter pit was formerly confused with the internal cork manifestion of boron deficiency, Jonathan spot, and Phoma fruit spot (11, 12). The disorder has received much attention by investigators throughout the world. Early in this century it was extensively studied by a commission composed of Australian federal and state agencies. This commission, under the leadership of McAlpine, published five reports totaling more than 900 pages (46, 47, 48, 49, 50).

Before 1914, the disease received little attention in the U.S. but in that year Brooks and Fisher (12) began investigations in the Wenatchee Valley of central Washington. Their studies proved a close relationship between orchard practices, especially irrigation methods, and the incidence of the disorder.

Other investigations pertinent to this subject were conducted in Great Britain and published under the auspices of the Imperial Bureau of Fruit Production and Food Investigation Board of the Department of Scientific and Industrial Research (6, 7, 8, 43, 58, 63). These studies were mainly concerned with storage aspects of the disorder in apples from overseas. Contemporary studies on field aspects of bitter pit were conducted in Australia, New Zealand, and South Africa (1, 5, 15-20, 26, 27). Other studies which contributed information on bitter pit were made at Cornell University (59, 60, 61).

Symptoms. Bitter pit shows as brown spots in the fruit flesh (fig. 13). Many of the spots occur in the outer cortex and are visible as dark colored pits in the skin, 2 to 6 mm in diameter, more or less circular in shape, and sharply delimited in outline. The affected areas are globular in shape, brown, and spongy in texture. Some have a distinctly bitter taste; frequently, they are more numerous in the flesh around the calyx half of the fruit.

Affected spots in the fruit are located around vascular bundles, commonly near the end of one of these elements. Slight plasmolysis of the cells first develops in such a location, and then the walls of some of these cells collapse. By this time the discoloration is visible to the unaided eye as a small brown spongy area. There is little evidence of suberization, cutinization, or other chemical changes in the cell walls, though some changes in pectin content occur in the middle lamellae. A striking microscopic feature of the cells is the presence of starch grains, which have disappeared from the surrounding non-affected cells but are retained in cells affected by bitter pit. In early stages of bitter pit development the skin is not visibly affected, but as the underlying flesh cells collapse the skin becomes somewhat distorted although seldom broken. Some workers have thought that histological differences exist between bitter pit, which develops while the fruit is on the tree, and bitter pit, which develops after the fruit is stored. Others, however, have disagreed (16-18, 19, 44, 61).

Cultivar susceptibility. Notable for their susceptibility to bitter pit in most apple regions of North America are: Baldwin, Northern Spy, Gravenstein, York Imperial, and Stayman Winesap. Fameuse, Grimes Golden, Yellow Bellflower, Rhode Island Greening, Delicious, McIntosh, Jonathan, and Rome Beauty exhibit the disorder more commonly in some apple-growing regions than in others. In certain years, few if any of the better cultivars remain free of the disorder. There is little information with respect to newer cultivars, although Haralson, Lawfam, Lobo, Red Gravenstein, and Stonetosh are said to be less susceptible than are some of the older cultivars (12, 25, 40, 41, 60).

Development of the disorder. Before discussing etiology, it is well to consider how this puzzling disorder is affected by certain factors.

Bitter pit develops either before or after fruit is picked: the preharvest outbreaks occur when fruit is ripening; the postharvest outbreaks occur in the first 6 or 8 weeks after fruit is stored. Fruit with no visible symptoms of the disorder when picked become severely affected after a period in storage. Symptoms which develop while the fruit is on the tree become more pronounced in storage.

The disorder varies greatly from year to year. In the same year, it may be more severe in one orchard than in another, more prevalent on some trees than on others, and may even vary greatly between fruits in the same cluster. Fruits borne at the ends of fruit clusters may develop less bitter pit than those borne laterally (32).

Factors influencing the development of bitter pit are conveniently divided into those affecting the plants in the orchard before the fruit is picked, and those affecting the fruit in storage. Judging from variations in the incidence of the disorder from one season to the next, one would expect to find certain climatic factors to be influential in its development. One such factor having a measurable effect on the disorder is soil moisture. A high soil moisture throughout the growing season, or during the latter part of the growing season, increases the incidence of bitter pit; high soil moisture accompanied by a large fluctuation in temperature is also said to increase it. Evidence concerning the effects of fluctuation in temperature alone is conflicting, however. Some believe the fruit to be disposed to bitter pit development when the diurnal temperature varies greatly, whereas others failed to find such a relationship (11, 12, 60, 63).

Fruit from trees high in vegetative vigor develop bitter pit more severely than does fruit from low-vigor trees. A high level of nitrogen in the tree is said to predispose fruit to the disorder. Potassium is believed to have somewhat the same effect as nitrogen, but phosphorus and sulfur apparently counteract the effects of these elements (13, 14, 35, 53, 54, 60).

At one time bitter pit was thought to be associated with a boron deficiency in the soil, but injection of boron, iron, and certain other minor elements has not affected the development of the disorder. Internal cork, as the boron deficiency disorder is called, differs significantly from bitter pit (5, 63).

Bitter pit is more serious when the crop is light than when it is heavy. Fruit produced in the more shaded parts of the tree are more prone to develop the disorder than fruit produced in less shaded parts of the tree. Apparently this is not a temperature effect, as the cheek of the apple exposed to direct sunlight is no more liable to develop bitter pit than is the opposite cheek (47, 56, 59, 60).

Severely pruning the tree in late summer increased the susceptibility of the fruit to bitter pit (6, 7, 58).

Fruit picked before it is mature often becomes more severely affected than fruit allowed to ripen before being picked. The first fruit to mature on a tree develops more bitter pit in storage than fruit which ripens later (1, 2, 11, 16, 17, 58).

Storage conditions influence development of the disease. Fruit held for long periods is usually stored at a temperature of 0° to 1.1°C, but before being sold to the retailer it is held at about 21°C for further ripening. Bitter pit develops more slowly at the storage than at the ripening temperatures. However, fruit held for a time in storage and then placed at 21°C until ripe may develop more of the disorder than fruit held constantly at 21°C until ripe (1, 2, 17, 58, 60). An initial period of precooling, in which the temperature of the fruit is quickly lowered to 1.1°C prior to storage at that temperature, suppresses bitter pit development more than storage at 1.1°C (58, 60).

A high relative humidity of the air surrounding the fruit, or a high carbon dioxide content, inhibits development of bitter pit. Removal of these conditions is followed by development of the disorder (60).

Coating fruit with certain types of waxes delays the appearance of bitter pit, the delay being somewhat greater at ripening temperatures than at storage temperatures. Waxing retards ripening and reduces water loss and so it is not known whether one or both of these effects are responsible for the delay (60).

Cause. Numerous views as to the cause of bitter pit have been entertained. Those pertaining to microorganism or insect causation have long since been abandoned. Fungi isolated from bitter pit tissue proved to be secondary invaders (30, 40, 41). Stigmonose, a malformation of fruit caused by feeding of the apple aphid, which at one time was considered identical with bitter pit, differs from it in important respects (11, 12).

In 1934 bitter pit was reported to be a virus disease transmissible by budding (3, 4). In 1962, Jackson

(37) reported that of numerous chemical elements tested only calcium as calcium nitrate significantly altered the incidence of bitter pit when applied as a spray to the trees in the postharvest period. A few years later Hilkenbaumer (34) reported that bitter pit was closely related to low calcium levels in the fruit. Areas of calcium deficiency in fruit were affected by bitter pit symptoms. Calcium applied to fruit reduced the incidence of the disorder.

Control. That a shortage of calcium can cause bitter pit has been confirmed by more recent investigations (37, 45, 52); therefore, the control recommended is application of calcium nitrate or calcium chloride (38, 52, 57, 62) to the trees. Calcium nitrate at a concentration of 6-100 or 10-100 is recommended (38, 52, 57). The spray is applied shortly after the trees are through blooming and again 1 to 2 months later (38, 52).

References

1. Adam, D. B. 1924. Experiments in the storage of fruit bitter-pit. J. Dept. Agr. Victoria, Australia 22:577-90.

2. Allen, F. W. 1932. Maturity and rate of ripening of Gravenstein apples in relation to bitter pit development. Proc. Amer. Soc. Hort. Sci. 28:639-45.

3. Atanasoff, D. 1933-34. Bitter pit of apples. A virus disease? Yearbook Univ. Sofia Faculty Agr., Bulgaria 12:31-67.

4. _____ 1934-35. Bitter pit of pome fruit is a virus disease. Yearbook, Univ. Sofia Faculty Bulgaria 13:1-8. (Also Phytopathology Zeitschrift 7:145-68, 1934.

5. Atkinson, J. D. 1935. Progress report on the investigations of corky pit of apples. New Zealand J. Sci. and Tech. 16:316-19.

6. Barker, J. 1928. Wastage in Australian fruit exported to England. J. Counc. Sci. and Indus. Res., Australia 1:261-67.

7. _____ 1932. The prevention of wastage in New Zealand fruit. Dept. Scientif. and Indus. Res. Food Invest. Bd. (England) Special Rept. 39.

8. _____ 1934. Annotated bibliography on bitter pit. Imperial Bur. Fruit Prod. Occasional Paper 3:1-28.

9. Bowles, E. A. 1912. Bitter pit in apples. J. Roy. Hort. Soc. 37 (part 3).

10. Breidahl, H. C., and A. C. H. Rothera. 1914-15. Bitter pit and sensitivity of apples to poisons. Proc. Roy. Soc., Australia, N.S. 27:191-97.

11. Brooks, C., and D. F. Fisher. 1914. Jonathan spot, bitter pit and stigmonose. Phytopathology 4:402-03.

12. _____ 1918. Irrigation experiments on apple-spot diseases. J. Agr. Research 12:109-37.

13. Burrell, A. B. 1938. Control of internal cork of apple with boron. Phytopathology 28:4. (Abstr.)

14. Butler, O. R., and S. Dunn. 1941. Studies on the bitter pit disease of apples. New Hampshire Agr. Exp. Sta. Tech. Bul. 78:1-10.

15. Carne, W. M. 1927. A preliminary note on a theory as to the origin of bitter pit in apples. J. Dept. Agr. Western Australia. Second Ser. 4:382-85.

16. _____ 1928. Bitter pit in apples: some recent investigations. J. Counc. Sci. and Indus. Res., Australia 1:358-65.

17. Carne, W. M., H. A. Pittman, and H. G. Elliott. 1929. Studies concerning the so-called bitter pit of apples in Australia; with special reference to the variety Cleopatra. J. Council Sci. and Indus. Res., Australia Bul. 41:1-88.

18. _____ 1930. Notes on wastage of non-parasitic origin in sorted apples. J. Council Sci. and Indus. Res., Australia 3:167-82 and 193-203.

19. Care, M. H., and A. S. Horne. 1927. An investigation of the behavior of pectic materials in apples and other plant tissues. Ann. Bot. 41:193-237.

20. Carne, W. M. and D. Martin. 1934. Apple investigations in Tasmania. Miscellaneous notes. I. The virus theory of bitter pit. J. Council Sci. and Indus. Res. Australia 7:203-14.

21. Cobb, N. A. 1892, Another obscure disease of the apple. Agr. Gaz., New South Wales 3:1004.

22. _____ 1895. Bitter pit of apples. Agr. Gaz., New South Wales 6:859.

23. _____ 1898. Bitter pit. Agr. Gaz., New South Wales 9:663.

24. Crabill, C. H., and H. E. Thomas. 1916. Stippen and spray injury. Phytopathology 6:51-54.

25. Cummings, M. B., and R. G. Dunning. 1940. Bitter pit of apples. I. In orchard and in storage. Vermont Agr. Exp. Sta. Bul. 467:3-30.

26. Evans, I. B. P. 1909. Bitter pit of apple. Transvaal Dept. Agr. Pretoria Tech. Bul. 1:1-18.

27. _____ 1911. Bitter pit of the apple. South African Dept. Agr. Tech. Bul. 2.

28. Ewart, A. J. On bitter pit and the sensitivity of apples to poisons. Proc. Roy. Soc. Victoria, Australia N. S. 24:367-419, 1911-12; 26:12-44, 1913-14; 26:228-42, 1913-14; 27:342-49, 1914-15.

29. _____ 1917. Cause of bitter pit. Proc. Roy. Soc. Victoria, Australia N. S. 30:15-20.

30. Farmer, J. B. 1907. Bitter pit in cape apples. Kew Bul. Misc. Inform. 6:250.

31. Greig-Smith, R. 1911. Note on bitter pit of apples. Proc. Linn. Soc., New South Wales 36:158.

32. Heinicke, A. J. 1921. The seed content and the position of the fruit as factors influencing stippen in apples. Proc. Amer. Soc. Hort. Sci. 17:225-32.

33. Herbert, D. A. 1922. Bitter pit in apples. The crushed cell theory. Phytopathology 12:489-91.

34. Hilkenbaumer, F. 1970. The present position of bitter pit investigations. Qualitas Pl. Mater. Veg. 19(1-3):267-74.

35. Hill, H., and M. B. Davis. 1936-37. Physiological disorders of apples. Scientif. Agr. 17:199-208.

36. Hutton, K. E. 1947. Bitter pit of pome fruit. Agr. Gaz., New South Wales, 58:205-08.

37. Jackson, D. J. 1962. The effect of calcium and other minerals on incidence of bitter pit in Cox's Orange apples. New Zealand J. Agr. Res. 5:302-09.

38. _____ 1967. Bitter pit and calcium nitrate. Orchard New Zealand 40:395.

39. Jaeger, G. 1869. Ueber das Pelzig- odor Stippigwerden der Kernostfrucht. Illustr. Monatschafte fur Obst- und Weinbau, pp. 318-19.

40. Jones, L. R. 1891. A spot disease of the Baldwin apple. Vermont Agr. Exp. Sta. Ann. Rept. 5:133-34.

41. Jones, L. R., and W. A. Orton. 1899. The brown spot of the apple. Vermont Agr. Exp. Sta. Ann. Rept. 12:159-64.

42. Kaiser, P. 1923. Die stippfleckenkrankheit der apfel. Gartenwelt. 57:204-05.

43. Kidd, F., and C. West. 1923. Brown heart, a functional disease of apples and pears. Dept. Scientific and Indus. Res. (England) Food Invest. Bd. Spec. Rept. 12:34-36.

44. MacArthur, Mary. 1940. Histology of some physiological disorders of the apple fruit. Canadian J. Agr. 18 (Sect. C):26-34.

45. Martin, D., G. C. Wade and K. Stockhouse. 1962. Bitter pit in the apple variety Sturmer in a pot experiment using low levels of major elements. Australian J. Exp. Agr. Anim. Husb. 2(5):92-96.

46. McAlpine, D. 1911-1912. The past history and present position of the bitter pit question. Bitter pit investigation. First Progress Rept. Pp. 1-197. Melbourne, Australia.

47. _____ 1912-1913. The cause of bitter pit: its contributing factors together with an investigation of susceptibility and immunity in apple varieties. Bitter pit investigation. Second Progress Rept. p. 1-124., Melbourne, Australia.

48. _____ 1913-1914. The control of bitter pit in the growing fruit. Bitter pit investigation. Third Progress Rept. pp. 1-176, Melbourne, Australia.

49. _____ 1914-1915. The experimental results in the relation of bitter pit and a general summary of the investigation. Bitter pit investigation. Fourth Progress Rept. pp. 1-178. Melbourne, Australia.

50. _____ 1915-1916. The cause and control of bitter pit with the results of the investigation. Bitter pit investigation. Pp. 1-144. Melbourne, Australia.

51. _____ 1921. Bitter pit in apples and pears. The latest results in preventive measures. Phytopathology 11:366-70.

52. Melville, F., S. E. Hardisty, and N. S. Shorter. 1964. The control of bitter pit in apples. J. Agr. West Australia Ser. 4, 5:938-40.

53. Mix, A. J. 1916. Cork, drought spot and related diseases of the apple. New York (Geneva) Agr. Exp. Sta. Bul. 426:473-522.

54. Mulder, D. 1951. Bitter pit in apples as cultural phenomenon (Trans. title). Meded. Direct. Tuinb. (Wageningen) 14:26-27.

55. O'Gara, P. J. 1911. Absorption of arsenic by apples from spray. Better Fruit. P. 28. February.

56. Palmer, R. C. 1943. The influence of amount of crop and harvesting maturity on bitter pit on Okanagan-grown Newtown apples. Proc. Amer. Soc. Hort. Sci. 43:63-68.

57. Raphael, J. D., and R. R. Richards. 1962. Bitter pit-control with calcium nitrate spray. Tasmanian J. Agr. 33:60-63.

58. Smith, A. J. M. 1926. Bitter pit in apples. A review of the problem. Dept. Scientif. and Indus. Res. (England). Food Invest. Bd. Special Rept. 28:1-24.

59. Smock, R. M. 1936. Bitter pit of Gravenstein apples. I. The effect of environmental temperature during the growing season. Proc. Amer. Soc. Hort. Sci. 34:179-86.

60. _____ 1941. Studies of bitter pit of the apple. New York (Cornell) Agr. Exp. Sta. Mem. 234:1-45.

61. Smock, R. M., and A. Van doren. 1937. Histology of bitter pit in apples. Proc. Amer. Soc. Hort. Sci. 35:179.

62. Stiles, W. C. 1964. Influence of calcium and boron tree sprays on York spot and bitter pit of York Imperial apples. Proc. American Soc. Hort. Sci. 84:39-43.

63. Wallace, T., and J. O. Jones. 1939. Pot experiments on bitter pit of apples. Univ. Bristol (England) Agr. & Hort. Res. Sta. Ann. Rept. 1939:79-84.

64. White, J. 1910. Bitter pit and the enzymes of the apple. J. Dept. Agr., Victoria, Australia 8:805.

65. Wortmann, J. 1892. Ueber die sogenannte "Stippen" der Apfel. Landw. Jahrb. 21:663-75.

Black-End of Pear

"Black-end" or "hard-end" are names given to a pear fruit disorder in which the tissue of the calyx-end of the ripe fruit is hard and dry and the pH of the tissue is higher than that of normal fruit (3). In advanced stages of the disorder the tissue becomes dark in color. This disorder has been reported from California (2), Oregon (1), South Africa (5), and Japan (8).

Black-end occurs chiefly in fruit (fig. 14) of horticultural cultivars when these are grown on such rootstocks as *Pyrus serotina, P. ussuriensis, P. betulaefolia,* and Keiffer and under water stress. It is of little importance when cultivars are grown on French *(P. communis)* rootstock.

Causal factors. Aside from influence of the rootstock no other causal factor is known. Tests have indicated (8) that the disorder is not caused by a virus, nor does it spread from tree to tree in the orchard (6). Soil and tree injections have failed to reveal any chemical or combination of chemicals that affect the development of the disorder (6).

Control. Inarching of affected trees to rootstocks known not to cause the disorder have been tried with varying success. Only when the original rootstock is severed and the tree is allowed to grow on the inarches is the disease controlled (2). The only practical way of avoiding the disease is to start the trees on the French rootstock *(P. communis).* Beurre Hardy cultivar interstock was ineffective in counteracting the rootstock influence (4).

References

1. Barss, H. P. 1921. Physiological disorders of developing fruit. Oregon Agr. Exp. Sta. Third Crop Pest and Hort. Rept. 164.
2. Davis, L. D. 1948. Black-end of pear. California Agriculture 6:10, 15.
3. Davis, L. D., and N. P. Moore. 1938. Black-end of pear. Seasonal changes in pH of the fruit. Proc. American Soc. Hort. Sci. 35:131-38.
4. Davis, L. D., and K. Ryugo. 1968. The influence of Buerre Hardy interstock on the occurrence of black-end of 'Bartlett' pears. Proc. American Soc. Hort. Sci. 92:167-69.
5. Davis, L. D., and W. P. Tufts. 1931. Black-end and its occurrence in selected pear orchards. Proc. American Soc. Hort. Sci. 29:634-638.
6. _____ 1936. Black-end of pears II. Proc. American Soc. Hort. Sci. 33:304-15.
7. Heppner, M. L. 1927. Pear black-end and its relation to different rootstocks. Proc. American Soc. Hort. Sci. 24:139.
8. Ryugo, K., and L. D. Davis. 1968. Yuzuhada, a physiological disorder of Oriental pear, and its possible relation to black-end and hard-end of Bartlett. Hort. Science 3.

Water Core of Apple

This disorder, known as "water core" or "glassiness" ("vitrescenza" in Italy), occurs worldwide but is particularly prevalent in arid and semi-arid regions (4, 6, 7, 13, 15). Water core is a misnomer because, except for a few varieties, the disorder is usually manifested only in the fruit cortex (3). Some have called it "glassiness" but this name has not been widely accepted.

Symptoms. The fruit cortex becomes water-soaked in separate areas or more or less uniformly throughout the flesh (fig. 15). The condition is due to the presence of water and soluble materials in the intercellular spaces and first appears around the vascular bundles. The influx of water into affected areas may increase the moisture content as much as 20 percent and produce sufficient pressure to cause excretion of liquid through the lenticels.

The water-soaked condition is rarely discernible from the exterior. Affected fruit transmit light more readily than nonaffected ones, the water-soaked areas being visible as bright luminous spots, particularly where such areas occur near the surface of the fruit (10).

In initial stages the disorder causes few if any histological changes in the apple flesh (12)—there is little collapse, discoloration, or abnormal growth of affected cells. Reports vary regarding the comparative rate at which starch is converted into sugar in affected apples (3, 8, 9, 12).

Susceptibility of cultivars. Summer and fall cultivars are more susceptible to water core than are winter cultivars. Tompkins King, Fall Pippin, Yellow Transparent, Early Harvest, Rambo, Winesap, and Stayman Winesap are notable for their susceptibility to this disorder. Cultivars ordinarily not affected by the disorder may develop it if exposed to a prolonged period of high temperature (8, 9).

Cause. Some workers believe that the influx of water into intercellular spaces is a consequence of an abnormally high osmotic concentration produced by a rapid conversion of starch to sugar (starch conversion is a normal process in ripening fruit). According to the proponents of this theory, starch conversion occurs prematurely in affected tissue and proceeds at an accelerated rate when the fruit is exposed to high temperature when ripening. After development of the watersoaked condition, the osmotic concentration remains high but soluble sugars decrease and ethyl alcohol appears (8, 9). Brown (3), however, did not regard the rapid conversion of starch to sugar to be the basic cause of water core. He believed that something happening elsewhere in the tree (probably in the spur or in the fruit cluster base) causes an influx of water and solutes into the fruit under sufficient pressure to fill the intercellular spaces of the cortex or sometimes even the core tissue. He found the juice from affected tissue to be abnormally high in soluble solids and low in acidity.

Development of the disorder. Water core begins to develop as fruit approaches maturity. It increases as the fruit ripens, and reaches its maximum stage of development in fruit that is left on the tree until fairly ripe. It seldom if ever develops after the fruit is picked, and the disorder will gradually disappear in fruit which develops water core before harvest. The rate of disappearance is faster at moderate than at low temperatures. Severely affected fruit held too long at storage temperatures (0° to 1.1°C) will undergo secondary breakdown (3, 10).

Environmental conditions in the orchard exert a marked influence on water core. Its incidence is increased if the fruit is exposed to high temperatures while growing. Fruit exposed to direct sunlight and thus subjected to high temperatures develop the disorder more often than does fruit shaded by leaves. Low soil moisture during the latter part of the growing season tends to increase the number of fruit affected by the disorder (8, 10).

Conditions which increase vegetative growth tend to intensify the disorder. Harley (9) reported a correlation between water core intensity and the ratio of leaf area to the number of fruit, the disorder being most prevalent when leaf area is large in proportion to the number of fruit. Fruit produced on young trees, which normally develop few fruits but abundant foliage, is more prone to water core than is fruit produced on older trees where the leaf-fruit ratio is lower. Consequently, the forcing of leaf growth by heavy nitrogen applications may result in an increase of the disorder. This increase is associated with an increase in the ability of the leaves to synthesize and transport carbohydrates to the fruit (9).

Control. Though no highly effective method of controlling water core is known, over-fertilization with nitrogenous fertilizers should be avoided. Where irrigation is practiced, trees should be supplied with adequate soil moisture throughout the growing season.

References

1. Birmingham, W. A. 1925. An uncommon water core condition in apples. Agr. Gaz. New South Wales 36:59-62.
2. Brooks, C., and D. F. Fisher. 1926. Water-core of apples. J. Agr. Research 32:223-60.
3. Brown, D. S. 1943. Notes and observations on a study of water core in Illinois apple during the 1942 season. Proc. Amer. Soc. Hort. Sci. 42:267-69.
4. Campbell, A. G. 1905. Constitutional diseases of fruit trees. J. Victoria Agr. Dept. Australia 3:463-65.
5. Carne, W. M., H. A. Pittman, and H. G. Elliott. 1930. Notes on wastage of non-parasitic origin in stored apples. J. Australian Counc. Sci. and Indus. Res. 3(3):167-82. R.A.M. 10:114-15. 1931.
6. Clinton, G. P. 1914. Report of the Botanist. Water Core. Conn. Agr. Exp. Sta. Ann. Rept. 1913:8-9.
7. Cobb, N. A. 1891. Water core in apples. New South Wales Agr. Gaz. 2:286-87.
8. Fisher, D. F., C. P. Harley, and C. Brooks. 1931. The influence of temperature on the development of watercore. Proc. Amer. Soc. Hort. Sci. 28:276-80.
9. Harley, C. P. 1939. Some associated factors in the development of watercore. Proc. Amer. Soc. Hort. Sci. 36:435-39.
10. Kemp, H. K. 1939. Detection of water core in apples. J. Australian Inst. Agric. Sci. 5:227-29.
11. Kemp, H. H., and J. A. Beare. 1939. The effect of water core on the keeping quality of apples. J. Dept. Agr. South Australia 43:22-28.
12. MacArthur, Mary. 1940. Histology of some physiological disorders of the apple fruit. Canad. J. Res. Sect. C. 18:26-34.
13. Norton, J. B. S. 1911. Water core of apples. Phytopathology 1:126-28.
14. O'Gara, P. J. 1913. Studies on the water core of apples. Phytopathology 3:121-28.
15. Petri, L. 1926. La 'vitrescenza' dell Mele. Boll. R. Staz. Pat. Veg. 6(3):253-60.

POSTHARVEST DISEASES OF APPLE AND PEAR

Nonparasitic Disorders of Apples and Pears in Storage

Each year millions of bushels of apples and pears are stored until they can be released for consumption. Storage time ranges from a few weeks to several months and the temperature of the storage area must be held low, or the fruit will quickly deteriorate. Even at the lowest temperature at which fruit can be held without freezing, apple and pear are subject to a number of disorders; some of these are parasitic, others are nonparasitic. The parasitic disorders are discussed under "Parasitic diseases of apples and pears in storage." The nonparasitic disorders to be discussed here are peculiar to stored fruit and, except for Jonathan spot, rarely develop while fruit is on the tree. In this respect these diseases differ from a disease such as bitter pit, which develops both on the tree and in storage. Where the cause of such a disorder is known, it is found usually to be associated with the effect of storage conditions on the metabolic processes (which continue at a slow rate even though the fruit is held at low temperature).

The nomenclature of these disorders is confusing. Not only have certain disorders been given several names each, but different disorders sometimes have been given similar names. Reducing them to synonymy is made more difficult by the fact that the causes of several are either unknown or in doubt. The nomenclature and classification employed here are, for the most part, employed by Plagge, Maney, and Pickett (37) and by Kidd and West (24).

Blackskin of Pear

This disorder, which is characterized by the black discolored blotches over large areas of the skin, develops most severely in overripe fruit stored at 1.1 to 2.8 °C. Kieffer, Beurre Bosc, and Vicar of Winkfield are more prone to this disorder than are others. Blackskin is thought to be caused by hydrolysis of the phenol glucoside, arbutin to glucose and hydroquinone, and subsequent oxidation of the latter compound to quinone and water (1).

Brown Heart of Apple

Fruit affected by brown heart seldom exhibit external symptoms. The flesh of the fruit is discolored—in mild cases the discoloration occurs in patches scattered through the fruit tissue. These patches are usually associated with vascular bundles, especially the larger ones. In severe cases large areas of the fruit are discolored, sometimes involving all the flesh around the core. Discolored areas are firm in texture and sharply delimited from the surrounding normal-appearing tissue. If the fruit is removed from storage the affected areas become dry and shrunken, producing cavities which are lined with brown leathery collapsed tissue (23, 24, 26, 37).

Brown heart is caused by an accumulation of carbon dioxide in the storage area and is of importance only where aeration is restricted. It formerly caused extensive losses of apples shipped from Australia to England. During the long sea voyage in poorly aerated holds of the ship, the fruit evolved sufficient carbon dioxide to cause this type of disorder. Susceptibility of fruit to injury from carbon dioxide is greatest at the low temperature commonly used for storage. It is estimated that when the carbon dioxide content of the storage air reaches 13 percent, brown heart is likely to occur, and it is almost certain to occur when the content reaches 15 percent (15, 22, 23, 24, 34, 44, 45).

Control of brown heart consists in providing the storage area with sufficient ventilation to prevent a large increase in carbon dioxide (10, 34, 45).

Ethylene Injury of Apple

When fruits in different stages of maturity are stored together in a restricted area, the more mature fruit sometimes develop brown spots about the lenticels. These spots differ from Jonathan spot and lenticel infection by rot fungi, and are attributed to ethylene chlorohydrin gas produced during the ripening processes of less mature fruit. The spots have been produced experimentally by storing ripe apples with apples that are in the process of ripening, and also by exposing fruit to ethylene chlorohydrin.

Freezing Injury of Apple

Minimum safe storage temperature is 0 °C. If the temperature falls to − 1.1 °C or below some injury may occur. Bruised areas may become frozen even above 0 °C temperature. Slight injury from freezing is noticeable only in the peripheral tissue and is manifested as a mealiness without browning. Somewhat more severe injury is evidenced by diffuse browning of the flesh, sometimes localized, sometimes general, accompanied by mealiness and disfigurement of the surface. This condition may resemble internal browning or the early stages of mealy breakdown. When fruit is severely frozen, the tissues become water-soaked and brown (13, 21, 47).

Internal Breakdown of Apple

Internal breakdown, internal browning, soft scald, brown dry rot, flesh collapse, Jonathan scald, Jonathan breakdown, and physiological decay are terms applied to softening and discoloration of the pulp of apple fruit under storage conditions. Some authorities (20) include all such disorders under the name of internal breakdown, but others (35) recognize two principle types: mealy breakdown and soggy breakdown.

Mealy breakdown. The flesh of the fruit becomes brown and dry and mealy in consistency. Symptoms vary with cultivars. In Grimes Golden, York Imperial, and Delicious, the disorder appears first in the area around the core; in Jonathan and McIntosh it develops first in pulp tissue just below the skin. In the late stages of mealy breakdown, the skin cracks and the outer portions of the flesh readily break away from the underlying core tissue. Plagge and Gerhardt (34) consider the disorder known as Jonathan breakdown (12) to be a type of mealy breakdown.

Mealy breakdown develops in fruit which have been held too long in storage or have been stored at too high a temperature. Believed to be due to senescence of the fruit tissues, it develops late in the storage season. Some fruit may undergo a year or more of storage before manifesting this condition; others develop it after only a few months of storage. Early cultivars are more prone to develop it than are late cultivars; large fruits are more inclined to develop it than are small ones. Immature or overripe fruit develop the disorder more quickly than crisp-ripe fruit (12, 34).

To prevent mealy breakdown, fruit should be picked at the proper stage of ripeness and promptly stored at a temperature of 1.1°C to 2.2°C (34). It is important to know the approximate storage life of each and to gauge the length of storage period accordingly.

Soggy breakdown. The symptoms of this disorder, like those of mealy breakdown, vary greatly between cultivars. The first symptom, which appears even before changes in color or consistency, is the development of an alcoholic flavor. Then, small brown areas develop in the cortical region of the flesh and enlarge rapidly until most of the cortical tissue is involved. In advanced stages, the soft, brown, spongy condition may extend entirely around the fruit. The inner limits of the affected area are sharply delimited and seldom extend into the core region. Although the skin usually does not become discolored until the final stages of soggy breakdown, it becomes lusterless, and a slight pressure on it will reveal the spongy texture of the tissue beneath (31, 32, 36).

According to Plagge and Gerhardt (34) the disorder known as "soft scald" (46, 48), which is particularly severe on fruit of Jonathan, Northwestern Greening, Rome Beauty, Wealthy, and Golden Delicious, is a form of soggy breakdown. The scald form is visible on the surface of the fruit as elongated, irregularly shaped sunken areas 1/8 to 1/2 inch wide. The flesh is soft and watery to a depth of 1/4 inch or more, and such areas of collapsed cells may partially or completely surround normal tissue. In early stages only the skin is discolored and resembles apple scald. In soft scald, however, the pulp tissue soon collapses (this does not occur in apple scale). When exposed to the air the affected tissue loses moisture rapidly and soon become dry and corky

Typical soggy breakdown is most common in the cultivars most prone to develop soft scald. It is less important than apple scald because it is limited to fewer important cultivars. Common sorts which seldom develop soggy breakdown are Winesap, Stayman Winesap, Delicious, Willow Twig, York Imperial, Baldwin, Rhode Island Greening, McIntosh, Ben Davis, Fameuse, and Mammoth Black Twig (35).

Soggy breakdown has been called "low temperature breakdown" because it develops at 0° and 1.1°C and little if at all at 2.2°C and above. According to Harding (19) it is caused by some disturbance in the fruit incident to the interruption of respiration by storage at low temperature. The initial high respiration rate followed by cold storage resulted in soggy breakdown. For this reason, fruit held for a few days at a moderate temperature before storage, develops more soggy breakdown than does fruit stored immediately after picking. According to Harding, fruit produced on heavily nitrated trees respire at a higher rate and are somewhat more susceptible to soggy breakdown than fruit produced on trees not so fertilized.

Soggy breakdown is prevented by prompt storage at a temperature not lower than 2.2°C (36) or holding apples in storage in an atmosphere containing 20 to 30 percent carbon dioxide for 2 days during the cooling period.

Internal Browning of Apple

Apples grown in the Pajaro Valley of California exhibit an unusual tendency to develop a brown condition of the flesh when held at certain storage temperatures. Although the condition occurs to some extent in most cultivars of apples grown in this valley, it is of economic importance only in Yellow Newtown (3, 20, 51).

Internal browning, as this disorder is called, is a condition which develops in the large isodiametric cells of the fruit pulp. In a cross-sectional view of an affected fruit, the disease is first noticeable as more or less elongated brown streaks radiating outward from the core. The areas first to become brown are adjacent to the primary vascular bundles, the bundles themselves becoming discolored only in late stages of the disorder. Once begun, the brown discoloration spreads rapidly in the region of the secondary vascular bundles and advances towards the calyx end of the apple before it begins to involve the pulp. In late stages, the discoloration spreads to all parts of the apple and sometimes to the thick-walled cells of the epidermis, thus producing a scalded appearance of this tissue. Most frequently, however, the skin retains its natural color and luster and the flesh remains firm.

Although internal browning in a severe form is restricted to Yellow Newtown fruit produced in the Pajaro Valley, it occurs to some extent in Yellow Newtown in other localities. Apparently, the disorder is due to some peculiarity of the cultivar and to some condition peculiar to the Pajaro Valley. An outstanding climatic feature of the Pajaro Valley is the prevalence of cool foggy weather in late July and early August when fruit is growing most rapidly. In this locality, fruit produced in the most shaded locations on the tree develops more of the disorder than does fruit produced in the less shaded locations, and artificially shaded fruit develops more than does unshaded fruit. Winkler (51) believed that temperature rather than sunlight is involved in the phenomenon because enclosing the fruit in black cloth bags, which restricted sunlight but increased the temperature, reduced the incidence of internal browning.

Fruit allowed to remain on the tree until the skin color changes from green to yellow are more susceptible to internal browning than is fruit picked before the skin undergoes this change. Apparently, the increase in susceptibility which accompanies ripening is not directly the result of increase in sugar content or changes in acidity of the fruit.

Regardless of the time of harvest, the onset of internal browning occurs 2 or 3 months after the fruit is first stored. Storage temperature greatly influences the rate and extent of the disorder's development: fruit stored at 0°C, for example, develops the disorder earlier and more severely than does fruit stored at 4.4°C or above. In fact, it is said that the disease was relatively unknown before low temperature storage was practiced (46). Yellow Newtown was then regarded as one of the better storage cultivars.

In these and other respects, internal browning resembles apple scald, but the disorders differ with respect to the tissues affected. With apple scald, the skin is the first tissue to exhibit injury, and next is the pulp tissue immediately beneath the skin. With internal browning, the tissue first to exhibit injury is that around the core, and next is the tissue over the pulp cells. In histological aspects, however the two disorders resemble each other closely. Winkler (51) found they appeared almost simultaneously when fruit was exposed to the proper conditions, with scald developing first on the skin and then extending inward, and internal browning developing first at the core and then extending outward. He suggested that internal browning was, like scald, caused by a product of metabolism, possibly essential oils which are known (39) to be produced by ripening fruit. With regard to the differences in symptoms between scald and internal browning, he stated:

> The generally-observed appearance of scald on the surface without the internal browning and the reverse condition would then seem to indicate that these two regions (the core tissue and the skin) of the fruit are most susceptible to the essential oils, or that these substances accumulate more pronouncedly in these than in any other region of the apple. The disease seemingly appears first in that region which is most susceptible. In the Yellow Newtown,

apparently the region of greatest susceptibility is in the flesh, while in those varieties that scald readily, it is at the surface.

Winkler (51) found that the presence of the essential oils, in concentrations even lower than those reported for ripening fruit by Powers and Chestnut (39), caused a marked increase in the permeability of the cell protoplasm, as determined by the resistance to passage of an electric current. He believed that as a result of the increased permeability the cell enzymes are no longer prevented from acting upon the substrate. For example, the tannins of the apple cells are oxidized by oxidase, thereby producing the brown discoloration of affected tissue.

Knowledge of the effect of air movement and temperature on internal browning has enabled the operators of storage warehouses to avoid the disorder by storing Yellow Newton fruit at a higher temperature than fruit of other cultivars, and by maintaining proper aeration of the stored product.

Jonathan Spot of Apple

Jonathan spot, one of the most troublesome functional disorders of the Jonathan apple, was described and its nonparasitic nature proved over 50 years ago. For a time it was thought to be caused by injury from lead arsenate which was then used widely for the control of codling moth (43, 44).

Symptoms. Though the disorder may appear while the fruit is on the tree, it usually develops after the apples have been placed in storage. It is characterized by circular, sharply defined spots 1/16 to 1/8 inch in diameter and frequently, but not always, centering around the lenticels. On light-colored portions of the skin the spots are greenish; on dark-colored portions of the skin, they are dark-red to black. In early stages, the spots are shallow, involving only the color-bearing cells of the skin, but later they may extend through the skin to the pulp tissue beneath. Adjacent spots often coalesce into extensive dark-colored blotches. Though affected fruit are not damaged for culinary purposes, they are unsightly and not readily sold. Also they are liable to infection by rot fungi which quickly destroy them (6).

Varietal susceptibility. The disorder is chiefly a disease of Jonathan, but it also occurs on Yellow Newtown, Wealthy, Rome Beauty, Gravenstein, Golden Delicious, King David, and others. Jonathan is believed to be one of the parents of the King David. Crossing these two cultivars has produced hybrids which were especially susceptible to the disorder (35).

Cause. The factor or factors which cause Jonathan spot are not understood, although it is known that the initial darkening of the skin tissue in the affected areas is due to low acidity of the cells. Anthocyanins, which are the pigments producing the red color in apple skin, are red under acid conditions and blue under alkaline conditions. The spots are most numerous and develop most conspicuously on red portions of the skin and it is known that the pulp cells immediately beneath the spots in the skin are of lower acidity than the surrounding cells. Under such conditions the anthocyanins assume a blue color, thus giving to the spot its initial dark color. Spots typical to those of Jonathan spot are produced by exposing the fruit to ammonia fumes; the spots disppear when the fruit is aerated. Jonathan spot behaves in a similar manner: spots change from black to brown when the affected fruit is aerated. The brown color persists because the cells in the affected area are injured (31, 35, 37).

The above suggests that Jonathan spot develops because of a physiological difference between affected cells and unaffected surrounding cells. What this physiological difference might be and what causes it is unknown.

Development of the disorder. When Jonathan spot occurs before harvest, it usually develops just before fruit is ripe enough to be picked. Fruit which has fallen from the tree tends to develop the disorder more severely than does fruit remaining on the tree.

The rate at which Jonathan spot develops in storage is influenced by temperature. It develops rapidly between 10° and 15.5°C and consequently will appear in a short time if fruit is not placed in cold storage soon after picking. At 0° to 1.1°C, however, it develops very slowly and is not likely to appear until late in the storage season.

At relative humidities around 70 percent, Jonathan spot develops less extensively than at higher relative humidities. Neither aeration nor oil-wrappers prevent its development, so Jonathan spot is apparently not a disorder of the scald type (4, 35).

Environmental factors in the orchard have little effect on the proneness of apples to develop Jonathan spot. Excessive fertilization with nitrogen and potash is suspected of increasing the tendency for fruit to develop the disorder, but this has not been proved. Though Jonathan spot varies greatly from season to season, no relation is apparent between its severity and the amount of rainfall or level of atmospheric temperature during the growing season.

Jonathan spot develops to a greater degree in storage on apples that are well colored and matured when picked than it does on apples picked when not fully mature. The relatively high acid content of immature fruit, is thought to be at least one reason why such fruit is less prone to develop the disorder in cold storage. If immature fruit is picked and held at moderate temperature until its acid content decreases, it develops the disorder as readily as does fruit picked when fully ripe.

Control. Picking fruit before it is fully ripe and storing it immediately at temperatures between 0° and 1.1°C reduces the incidence of the disorder. When taken from storage, fruit should be consumed as quickly as possible (34).

Scald of Apple and Pear

Scald, or apple scald, is the most prevalent and consequently the most widely known functional disorder of stored fruit. It probably has occurred since apples were stored in bulk because it is not strictly a cold storage disorder, but develops in ordinary storage as well. In 1897, Jones (21) remarked on its prevalence in Vermont apples. It was more fully described in 1898 by Jones and Orton (22), who recognized it as nonparasitic in character. With the rapid development of commercial apple production, it became the cause of much loss.

Symptoms. In its early stages, scald only appears as a discoloration of the fruit skin (fig. 16). The affected areas vary in size from small dots to large brown, irregularly shaped, and often confluent patches. At this time the flesh beneath the affected areas is normal in appearance and texture. Later, however, the flesh may become discolored for a short distance below the skin. The margins of this discolored area are sharply delimited and, except in very late stages, seldom extend very deep into the fruit. Although the quality of the fruit is not materially damaged by a few scalded areas, the attractiveness of the fruit is. The scalded areas, however, are readily invaded by rot organisms.

The disease differs from other functional disorders in being more prevalent on the greener or nonblush side of the fruit. Red fruit surfaces are seldom affected, and yellow surfaces are somewhat less affected than green surfaces.

Cause. At one time a shortage of oxygen or an excess of carbon dixoide was thought to be the cause of scald, but a relatively high percentage of carbon dioxide in the storage area was shown to reduce the severity of the disorder (4, 7).

It is now known that scald is caused by other volatile materials produced by the metabolic activities of the fruit tissue. Under normal conditions of aeration these materials escape and are dissipated, but in confined storage areas they accumulate in such amounts as to be injurious. Soon after harvest, respiration in the fruit begins to increase. At moderate temperatures this process reaches a climacteric a week or so later. This is followed by an increase in emanation of volatile substances. Although typical scald has been produced by exposing the fruit to vapors of ethyl malonate, ethyl and amyl acetate, and methyl butyrate, it is believed that acetaldehyde is largely responsible for the injury. The accumulation of this material in the apple tissue parallels the emanation of total volatile materials, and is concurrent with development of scald (4, 7, 25, 35, 39).

Development of the disorder. Environmental conditions which promote growth of the tree and the crop tend to favor scald development. Abundant soil moisture (during the latter part of the growing season especially) and possibly nitrogenous fertilization increase the incidence of the disorder (4, 7). The greater tendency for scald to develop on large fruit, on fruit produced on young trees, and the seasonal variations in the disorder, are indicative of the influence of soil and climatic factors. It may be, as Brooks (4) suggested that the basic cause for development of more scald in large than in small fruit is some forcing agency such as heavy irrigation. Fruit which is forced could attain mature size but remain physiologically immature, and it is well-known that physiologically immature fruit is more prone to develop scald than is physiologically mature fruit (4, 7, 24, 26, 38). When immature fruit is held for a time at moderate temperatures before placing in storage, scald development is reduced.

Conditions which decrease the metabolic activities in the stored fruit reduce scald development. For example, scald develops more slowly at 0° to 1.1°C than at 4.4° or 10°C, and more slowly at low than at high relative humidity. A high carbon dioxide content of the air reduces scald development, probably because it restricts metabolic activity in the fruit (6).

Because scald is produced by the accumulation of volatile materials such as acetaldehyde, removal of these materials prevents the disorder. Proper aeration of the stored fruit is one method of preventing scald. It is, of course, difficult to attain proper aeration of fruit which is packed and stored in the warehouse or refrigerator cars. Brooks and his co-workers (5, 8) developed an oil-impregnated paper wrapper which effectively prevents scald. According to these writers, the oil removes these odorous substances by absorption in the same manner as butter and other fats take up various odors. Oiled wrappers as they come from the package of packed fruit are heavily charged with the various odorous materials given off by the apples. The oil also has a retarding effect upon the activities of the apple skin, slightly delaying the development of yellow in the ground color and probably at the same time checking the development of scald. Stevens and Nance (46) estimated that between 1922 and 1930 the use of oiled wrappers reduced scald development in Washington-grown apples about 80 percent.

Control. Workers in Australia (28, 42) and the U.S. (14, 17, 18) have successfully used chemical dips and chemically impregnated paper fruit wraps to prevent scald. Ethoxyquin (6-ethoxy-1,2-dihydro-2-2-4-trimethyl-guinoline) at 2000 ppm as a dip or 2.5 mg per wrap and diphenylamine (DPA) at 2000 ppm as a dip have been found effective.

References

1. Adam, D. B. 1923. Experiments in the storage of fruits. J. Dept. Agr., Victoria, Australia, 21:178-86, 234-41, 371-82.
2. Anonymous. 1940. New Zealand Dept. Sci. and Ind. Research. New Zealand Ann. Rept. 14:1-100.
3. Ballard, W. S., J. R. Magness, and L. A. Hawkins. 1922. Internal browning of the Yellow Newtown apple. U.S. Dept. Agr. Bul. No. 1004.
4. Brooks, C. 1919. Nature and control of apple-scald. J. Agr. Research 18:211-40.
5. Brooks, C. 1923. Oiled wrappers, oils, and waxes in the control of apple scald. J. Agr. Research 26:513-36.
6. Brooks, C., and J. C. Cooley. 1917. Effect of temperature, aeration and humidity on Jonathan spot and scald of apples in storage. J. Agr. Research 11:287-317.
7. Brooks, C., J. S. Cooley, and D. F. Fisher. 1919. Apple-scald. J. Agr. Research 16:195-217.
8. Brooks, C., and J. S. Cooley. 1924. Oiled paper and other oiled materials in the control of scald on barrel apples. J. Agr. Research 29:129-35.
9. Brooks, C., and C. B. Harley. 1934. Soft scald and soggy breakdown of apples. J. Agr. Research 49:55-69.
10. Carne, W. M., and D. Martin. 1938. Apple investigations in Tasmania: Miscellaneous notes. 8. The influence of carbon dioxide concentration on brown heart and other storage disorders. J. Council Sci. and Indus. Research, Australia 11:47-60.

11. Carrick, D. B., and J. Oskamp. 1925. Storage scald of apples. Cornell Univ. Agr. Exp. Sta. Bul. No. 128:1-10.

12. Daley, P. M. 1924. The relation of maturity to Jonathan breakdown. Proc. Am. Soc. Hort. Sci. 286.

13. Diehl, H. C., and R. C. Wright. 1924. Freezing injury of apples. J. Agr. Res. 29:99-127.

14. Dilley, D. R., and D. H. Dewey. 1963. Dip treatment of apples in bulk boxes with diphenylamine for control of storage scald. Quart. Bul. Michigan Agr. Exp. Sta. 46(1): 73-79.

15. Eaves, C.A. 1938. Physiology of apples in artificial atmospheres. Sci. Agr. 18:315-38.

16. Gerhardt, G., and B. D. Ezell. 1938. Respiration and emanation of volatiles from Bartlett pears as influenced by ripening and storage. Proc. Am. Soc. Hort. Sci. 35:423-26.

17. Hansen, E., and W. M. Mellenthin. 1967. Chemical control of superficial scald on Anjou pears. Proc. Amer. Soc. Hort. Sci. 91:860-62.

18. Hardenburg, R. E., and R. E. Anderson. 1965. Postharvest chemical, hotwater and packaging treatment to control apple scald. Proc. Amer. Soc. Hort. Sci. 87:93-99.

19. Harding, P. L. 1935. Physiological behavior of Grimes Golden apples in storage. Iowa Agr. Exp. Sta. Res. Bul. 182:317-52.

20. Harley, C. P., and D. F. Fisher. 1927. The occurrence of acetaldehyde in Bartlett pears and its relation to pear scald and breakdown. J. Agr. Res. 35:983-93.

21. Jones, L. R. 1897. Report of the botanist. II. Apple scald. Vermont Univ. Agr. Exp. Sta. Ann. Rept. 10:55-59.

22. Jones, L. R., and W. A. Orton. 1898. Report of the botanist. II. Apple scald. Vermont Univ. Agr. Exp. Sta. Ann. Rept. 11:198-99.

23. Kidd, F., and C. West. 1923. Brown heart—a functional disease of apples and pears. Dept. Scientific and Indus. Res. Great Britain Food Invest. Bd. Special Rept. 12:1-53.

24. _____ 1925. Functional diseases of apples in cold storage. G. Brit. Dept. Scientif. Indus. Research. Food Invest. Bd. Special Rept. 23:1-15.

25. _____ 1938. Spotting and other effects on apples in storage due to volatile products from ripening apples of other varieties stored with them. J. Pomol. 16:274-79.

26. Kidd, F., C. West, and M. N. Kidd. 1927. Gas storage of fruit. Chapter V. Functional diseases and their control. G. Brit. Dept. Scientif. Indus. Research. Food Invest. Bd. Special Reptr. 30:29-33.

27. McClelland, N., and L. W. Tiller. 1924. Flesh collapse in apples, season 1923. Cawthorn Institute, Nelson, N. Z.

28. Melville, F. 1967. Ethoxyquin for the control of scald of Granny Smith apples. J. Agr. West Australia 8(1):16-20.

29. Miller, E. V., and H. A. Schomer. 1940. A physiological study of soft scald in Jonathan apples. J. Agr. Research 60:183-92.

30. Overhalser, E. L., A. J. Winkler, and H. E. Jacob. 1923. Factors influencing the development of internal browning of the Yellow Newtown apple. California Univ. Agr. Exp. Sta. Bul. 370:3-40 (out of print).

31. Pentzer, W. T. 1925. Color pigment in relation to the development of Jonathan spot. Proc. Am. Soc. Hort. Sci. 22:66-69.

32. Plagge, H. H. 1925. Cold storage investigations with Wealthy apples. Iowa State Coll. Agr. Exp. Sta. Bul. 230:58-72.

33. _____ 1930. A study of soggy breakdown and some related functional diseases of the apple. Proc. Am. Soc. Hort. Sci. (1929) 26:315-18.

34. Plagge, H. H., and F. Gerhardt. 1930. Acidity changes associated with the keeping quality of apples under various storage conditions. Iowa State Coll. Agr. Exp. Sta. Res. Bul. 131.

35. Plagge, H. H., and T. J. Maney. 1924. Apple storage investigations. I. Jonathan spot and soft scald. II. Apple scald and internal breakdown. Iowa State Coll. Agr. Exp. Sta. Bul. 222:1-64.

36. _____ 1928. Soggy breakdown of apples and its control by storage temperature. Iowa State Coll. Agr. Exp. Sta. Res. Bul. 115.

37. Plagge, H. H., T. J. Maney, and B. S. Pickett. 1934. Functional diseases of apple in storage. Iowa State Coll. Agr. Exp. Sta. Res. Bul. 115.

37. Plagge, H. H., T. J. Maney, and B. S. Pickett. 1935. Functional diseases of apple in storage. Iowa State Coll. Agr. Exp. Sta. Bul. 329:35-79.

38. Powell, G. H., and S. H. Fulton. 1903. The apple in cold storage. U.S. Dept. Agr. Bur. Plant Ind. Bul. 48:1-66.

39. Powers, F. B., and V. K. Chestnut. 1920. The odorous constituents of apples. Emanation of acetaldehyde from the ripe fruit. J. Am. Chem Soc. 42:1509-26.

40. Ramsey, H. J., A. W. McKay, E. L. Markell, and H. S. Bird. 1917. The handling and storage of apples in the Pacific Northwest. U.S. Dept. Agr. Bul. No. 587:1-32.

41. Rose, D. H. 1924. Diseases of apples in the market. U.S. Dept. Agr. Bur. Plant Indus. Bul. 1253.

42. Scott, K. J., and E. A. Roberts. 1966. The relative effectiveness of diphenylamine and ethoxyquin in inhibiting superficial scald of Granny Smith apples. Australian J. Exp. Agr. Anim. Husb. 6:445-47.

43. Scott, W. M. 1911. A new fruit spot of apple. Phytopathology 1:32-34.

44. Scott, W. M., and J. W. Roberts. 1913. The Jonathan fruit spot. U.S. Dept. Agr. Bur. Plant Ind. Circ. 112:11-16.

45. Smith, A. J. 1925. Brown heart in Australian apple shipments. Gr. Brit. Dept. Scientif. Indus. Res. Food Invest. Bd. Special Rept. 22:1-28.

46. Stevens, N. E., and N. W. Nance. 1932. Efficiency of oiled wraps in the commercial control of apple scald. Phytopathology 22:603-07.

47. Sutherland, R. 1936. Factors relating to the control of soft scald in Jonathan apples. New Zealand J. Agr. 53:161-66.

48. Thomas, M. 1931. The production of ethyl alcohol and acetaldehyde by fruits in relation to the injuries occurring in storage. Part II. Injuries to apples and pears occurring in the presence of oxygen and in the absence of accumulation of carbon dioxide in the storage atmosphere. Ann. Appl. Biol. 18:60-74.

49. Trout, S. A., G. B. Tindale, and F. E. Huelin. 1940. Investigation on the storage of Jonathan apples grown in Victoria. Council Sci. Indus. Res. (Australia) Bul. 135:1-96.

50. Whitehouse, W. E. 1919. Cold storage of Iowa apples. Third Progress Report. Iowa State Coll. Agr. Exp. Sta. Bul. 192:179-216.

51. Winkler, A. J. 1923. A study of the internal browning of Yellow Newtown apples. J. Agr. Research 24:165-84.

52. Wright, J. R. 1953. Physiological Disorders. *In* Plant Diseases. U. S. Dept. Agr. Yearbook 1953:830-34.

53. Wright, R. C., and G. F. Taylor. 1923. The freezing temperature of some fruits, vegetables and cut flowers. U.S. Dept. Agr. Bur. Plant Ind. Bul. 1133.

PARASITIC DISEASES OF APPLE AND PEAR IN STORAGE

Nonparasitic disorders of stored apple and pear fruit are discussed under the title "Nonparasitic diseases of apple and pear in storage." The diseases to be discussed here are all caused by fungi.

Alternaria Rot of Apple
Alternaria alternata (Fries) Keissler

Infection of apples by *Alternaria* is most frequently found on fruit held in ordinary storage, but it seldom causes extensive loss of fruit in cold storage. This type of rot (fig. 17) was described by Cook (4) in 1913. *Alternaria mali* Roberts is the common cause of apple fruit rot in northeastern U.S. (5, 13), and in Illinois (19) it causes about 1 percent loss of Jonathan and Delicious apple crops each year. The disease caused by *A. mali* was named "cork rot" to distinguish it from that caused by *A. tenuis* (19). Another phase of the disease is a carpel discoloration and decay described by Miller (8) on Wagener and Red Delicious apples and by Ceponis, Kaufman, and Butterfield (3) during surveys of apples in New York City. The open calyx tube in the fruit allows *Alternaria* and other fungi to enter the carpel area; as much as 5 percent of the Pacific Northwest shipments sampled had moldy carpels and 2.9 percent developed *Alternaria* core rot. Susceptible cultivars of apples have deep calyx-sinuses or pits (8).

The causal organism is a fungus classified by Neergaard (9) as *Alternaria tenuis* Auct., and more recently by Simmons (16) as *A. alternata* (Fries) Keissler (= *A. tenuis* Nees). The species *A. mali* was established by Roberts (13) because the spores of that species had minute pointed spines on their surfaces. According to later concepts, the many biotypes reported as characteristic of *A. mali* are embraced in the *A. alternata* description.

A. alternata is described by Simmons (16) as follows: "Conidiophores and conidia dilute yellow brown to medium golden brown in color. Conidiophores simple, straight or curved, smooth, 1 to 3 septate, 20 to 46 μm long by 4 to 6 μm wide, apically uniperforate, sometimes with basal cell slightly swollen. Conidia ovoid, obclavate, obpyriform, or rarely simple ellipsoidal in shape, usually with an easily visible basal pore; beakless when ellipsoidal or with a short conical, narrowly tapered, or cylindrical beak 2 to 3 μm in diameter, the apex of the beak may be narrow and rounded without a terminal pore, or abruptly blunt with a well-defined pore; beak length 25 μm, never equalling the length of the conidium body but commonly representing one-fourth to one-third of the total conidium length; the beak is usually lighter in color than the body. Conidium body $(10-)$ 18 to 47 $\times$ $(5-)$ 7 to 18 μm, av. 30.9 $\times$ 12.6 μm; $1/w = 1.7$ to 3.4, av. 2.4; with $(1-)$ 3 to 8 transverse septa, one or two longitudinal septa in each of the 1 to 6 transverse divisions, and commonly, a strongly oblique septum occurs in the basal division, distinctly but not deeply constricted at major transverse septa. The conidium wall is smooth or very minutely roughened."

Several types of Alternaria rot symptoms are found on apples grown in the Pacific Northwest. In cold storage, small, firm, slightly sunken areas, brown around the edge but covered by a black crust, will sometimes occur. Another type which develops on apples after removal from cold storage is characterized by firm, slightly sunken, rotted areas which commonly are dark brown to black (but sometimes light yellowish brown to gray) and which may show mold growth on the surface if stored in high relative humidity. The third type is the development of a black rot on areas of the fruit affected by scald. A *Cladosporium* may also cause a black rot which is indistinguishable from that produced by *Alternaria* (14). Rick (11) characterized *Alternaria* as a weak pathogen which develops slowly on immature apples and produces a brown dry rot. The lesions commonly occur at the calyx and in the depression around the stem, and occasionally can be found within the fruit core. Spores of the fungus commonly occur as contaminants on the fruit and leaf surfaces (7). This fungus grows saprophytically on dead or weakened plant tissues and sporulates abundantly.

Effective control is achieved by careful handling of fruit during harvest. Prompt washing, packing, and storage at −0.6 to 0.6 °C, reduces this rot to negligible amounts. Chemicals such as maneb, captan, dodine or benzimidazoles have not proved effective (18), but washes in chlorine solution reduce the numbers of contaminating spores (15).

References

1. Adams, R. E., and S. E. Tamburo. 1957. The West Virginia spot-rot complex of apple in 1956. Plant Dis. Rep. 41:760-65.
2. Brooks, C., J. S. Cooley, and D. F. Fisher. 1935. Diseases of apples in storage. U.S. Dept. Agr. Farmer's Bul. 1160. 20 pp.
3. Ceponis, M. J., J. Kaufman, and J. E. Butterfield. 1969. Moldy carpels in Delicious apples on the greater New York markets. Plant. Dis. Rep. 53:136-38.
4. Cook, M. T., and G. W. Martin. 1913. Alternaria rot of apples. Phytopathology 3:72.
5. English, H. 1944. Notes on apple rots in Washington. Plant Dis. Rep. 28:610-22.
6. Heald, F. D., and G. D. Ruehle. 1931. The rots of Washington apples in cold storage. Wash. Agr. Expt. Sta. Bul. 253. 48 pp.
7. Kuss, F. R., and W. N. Harnish. 1972. *Alternaria* species associated with apple leaf spot. Plant Dis. Rep. 56:721-22.
8. Miller, P. M. 1959. Open calyx tubes as factor in contributing to carpel discoloration and decay of apples. Phytopathology 49:520-23.
9. Neergaard, P. 1945. Danish species of *Alternaria* and *Stemphylium*. Oxford University Press. London. 560 pp.
10. Pierson, C. F., et al. 1971. Market diseases of apples, pears, and quinces. USDA, ARS, Agricultural Handbook No. 376. 112 pp. illus. 17 color plates.
11. Rick, A. E. 1970. Calyx-end rot of apples. Phytopathology 60:1152.
12. Roberts, J. W. 1914. Experiments with apple leaf-spot fungi. J. Agr. Research 2:57-66.
13. _____ 1924. Morphological characters of *Alternaria mali* Roberts. J. Agr. Research 27:699-708.
14. Rose, D. H., D. F. Fisher, and C. O. Bratley. 1933. Market diseases of fruit and vegetables: apples, pears, quinces. U.S. Dept. Agr. Misc. Publ. 168. 70 pp.
15. Segall, R. H. 1968. Fungicide effectiveness of chlorine as influenced by concentration, temperature, pH and spore exposure time. Phytopathology 58:1412-14.
16. Simmons, E. G. 1967. Typification of *Alternaria, Stemphyllium,* and *Ulocladium*. Mycologia 59:67-92.
17. Stakman, E. C., and R. C. Rose. 1914. A fruit spot of the Wealthy apple. Phytopathology 4:333-35.
18. Szkolnik, M. 1968. Apple fruit rots (*Botrytis* sp. and *Penicillium* sp.) Fungicide-Nematicide Tests, Results of 1968, 24:26.
19. Tweedy, B. G., and D. Powell. 1962. Cork rot of apples and its causal organism, a pathogenic strain of *Alternaria mali*. Phytopathology 52:1073-79.
20. Wiltshire, S. P. 1933. the foundation species of *Alternaria* and *Macrosporium*. Trans. Brit. Mycol. Soc. 18:135-60.

Blue-Mold Decay or Soft Rot of Apple and Pear
Penicillium expansum (Link) Thom

Blue-mold decay is the most common and important storage rot of apples, quinces, and pears in the U. S. In Washington State alone, the loss from the mold decay is said to have been well over a million dollars per year. The disease is also the cause of serious loss of apples in England (11, 22, 37). Recent studies showing mycotoxin production by certain strains of *Penicillium* make decay control highly desirable (21).

Jonathan and Delicious are the most susceptible apple varieties grown on the Pacific Coast. Baker and Heald (4) stated that the storage life of such cultivars as Jonathan, Delicious, and Winesap is related to their susceptibility to blue mold. Winesap, which is less susceptible than the other two cultivars has the longest storage life. In the eastern U. S. such cultivars as McIntosh, Fameuse, York Imperial, Stayman Winesap, Winesap, Rome Beauty, and Baldwin are frequently affected by blue mold (4).

Among pear cultivars the Winter Nellis, d'Anjou, and Comice are highly susceptible, while Columbia, Doyenne, d'Alencon, and Seckel are said to be relatively immune (4).

Infection is first visible as pale brown to brown, sunken, more or less circular lesions. The maceration of the tissue is caused by pectolytic enzyme produced by the fungi (13). The lesions not infrequently are located at lenticels or at mechanically caused breaks in the skin. The lesion expands rapidly; the affected tissue which is at first yellowish-brown or dark-brown in color is soft and watery, with a strong musty odor and an unpleasant taste. The apple skin becomes wrinkled as the underlying tissue collapses. If fruit is held under humid conditions the fungus produces numerous bluish to greenish-blue tufts of spores over the skin (fig. 18).

Although blue mold decay may be caused by several species of *Penicillium, P. expansum* (Link) Thom is the most common. Synonyms of the fungus are *P. glaucum* Link, *Coremium glaucum* Link, *Floccaria glauca* Grenville, and *Coremium vulgare* Corda. The fungus grows rapidly on Czapek's medium and attains a diameter of 40 to 50 mm in 8 to 10 days at room temperature. Sporulation is heavy throughout, with conidiophores regularly arising from the substrate. Small colonies are white but turn quickly to yellow-green shades with maturation of conidia. Conidiophores are mostly 150 to 700 μm in length and 3.0 and 3.5 μm in diameter, with walls smooth or finely roughened and terminating in large penicilli commonly measuring up to 75 to 100 μm in length. These bear long tangled chains of spores 150 to 200 μm in length. Conidia are elliptical when first formed and continue to show some ellipticity with measurements of 3.0 to 3.5 μm in diameter (30).

Although this fungus cannot penetrate uninjured fruit skin, it gains entrance through lenticels and through breaks sustained during harvesting and packing (2, 3). Lenticel infection is common in such cultivars as Jonathan and Delicious. The susceptibility of these openings is influenced by a variety of factors and increased if the fruit skin is subjected to pressure bruising during harvesting and packing. Pressure bruising ruptures the layer of cutinized cells in the lenticel basins (2, 3, 18).

Washing fruit with alkaline or acid solutions, such as were employed for the removal of arsenical residues, increase the infectibility of lenticels. The lenticels on fruit that have been washed are often found to be ''open''—that is, lacking a compact cutinized and suberized layer of cells in the lenticel basin. The open lenticels develop a distinct stained halo when fruit is immersed in a methylene blue solution; the closed lenticels remain uncolored. Exposure of fruit to warm dry air is effective in closing lenticels. Storing fruit at 0 °C also tends to close the lenticels (17, 18).

Susceptibility of lenticels increases with fruit maturity, probably because those of ripe fruit are more easily injured by pressure and because changes occur in the composition of cells in the lenticel basin.

Mechanical injures sustained when one fruit strikes the stem of another fruit or the sharp edge of a box during grading and packing, or from small breaks made by sand particles, are also common avenues for entry of the fungus. Susceptibility to bruising is greatest with ripe fruit (39). Newly-made bruises are more susceptible to infection than are old bruises. With pears, the fruit stem is one of the most important sites of infection.

Because the fungus is an ubiquitous saprophyte, the fruit can become contaminated either in the orchard or in the packing shed. Favorable conditions for contamination and infection occur when the fruit is handled after it is wetted by rain or stored in boxes that had contained rotting fruit.

Improvement in handling of fruit to reduce mechanical injuries has resulted in a marked reduction in blue mold decay. Some growers periodically steam-sterilize the fruit boxes used in the orchard. Others employ in the orchard the same boxes in which the fruit is to be packed; because these are new, they are rarely contaminated with rot fungus spores (36).

In the large apple-growing regions of the northwestern U.S. there has been a great increase in treatment of fruit to destroy unwanted mold spores. One of the first chemical washes employed was sodium hypochlorite. Sodium chloro-orthophenylphenate (Dowicide C) was replaced by 0.6 percent solution of sodium orthophenylphenate with a water rinse to prevent injury. Benomyl and thiabendazole dips have recently offered decay control superior to other treatments (7, 9, 12, 14, 15). These fungicides, in combination with hot water dips (3 min at 45 °C), have provided better control of decay on wounded apple fruit than did unheated fungicide treatments (32, 33). On pears, stem-end decay is more effectively controlled by the heat-fungicide dip treatment, while the cold fungicide dip treatments control the flesh decay (27).

Prompt cooling to storage temperatures near 0 °C and maintaining such temperatures will arrest mold infections (28), but spores not chemically treated continue to grow and will produce lesions within 30 days; these will enlarge from 3/4 to 1 inch in diameter in 60 days (34).

Other treatments used with some effectiveness are applications of 5000 ppm 2-aminobutane (16, 26) to the fruit, and gamma radiation of 100,000 rep (roentgen equivalent physical) which arrest progress of decay (8, 18).

References

1. Baker, K. F., and F. D. Heald. 1932. Some problems concerning blue mold in relation to cleaning and packing of apples. Phytopathology 22:879-98.

2. _____ 1934. An investigation of factors affecting the incidence of lenticel infection of apples by *Penicillium expansum*.

3. _____ 1934. Investigations on methods of control of blue-mold decay of apples. Washington Agr. Exp. Sta. Bul. 304:1-32.

4. _____ 1936. The effect of certain cultural and handling practices in the resistance of apples to *Penicillium expansum*. Phytopathology 26:932-48.

5. Beattle, B. B., and W. L. Outhred. 1970. Benzimidazole derivatives as postharvest fungicides to control rotting of pears, cherries, and apricots. Aust. J. Exp. Agric. Anim. Husb. 10:651-56.

6. Ben-Arie, R., and S. Guelfat-Reich. 1969. Postharvest heat treatment to control storage rots of Spadona pears. Plant Dis. Rep. 53:363-67.

7. _____ 1973. Preharvest and postharvest applications of benzimidazoles for control of storage decay of pears. Hort. Sci. 8:181-83.

8. Beraha, L., G. B. Ramsey, M. A. Smith *et al.* 1961. Gamma radiation in control of decay in strawberries, grapes, and apples. Food Technol. 15:94-98.

9. Blanpied, G. D., and A. Purnasiri. 1968 Thiabendazole control of Penicillium rot of McIntosh apples. Plant Dis. Rep. 52:867-71.

10. Brooks, C., and J. S. Cooley. 1917. Temperature relations of apple rot fungi. J. Agr. Research 8:139.

11. Brooks, C., J. S. Cooley, and D. F. Fisher. 1935. Diseases of apples in storage. U. S. Dept. Agr. Farmer's Bul. 1160:1-20.

12. Cargo, C. A., and D. H. Dewey. 1970. Thiabendazole and benomyl for the control of postharvest decay of apples. Hortscience 5:259-60.

13. Cole, M., and R. K. S. Wood. 1961. Types of rot, rate of rotting, and analysis of pectin substances in apples rotted by fungi. Ann. Bot. (N.S.) 25:417-34.

14. Crivelli, G. 1966. Investigations on the utilization and commercialization of citrus fruits V., Evidence for the fungistatic action of 2-(4-thiazolyl) benzimidazole on *Penicillia* of oranges. (in Italian, English summary). II. Freddo 20 (3).

15. Daines, Robert H., and Ronald D. Snee. 1969. Control of blue mold of apples in storage. Phytopathology 59:792-94.

16. Eckert, J. W., M. J. Kolbenzen, and R. L. Sleesher. 1962. Control of postharvest fruit decay with 2-aminobutane. Phytopathology 52:730.

17. English, Harley. 1948. Disinfectant washes for the control of decay in apples and pears. Phytopathology 38:914. (Abstr.)

18. English, Harley, A. L. Ryall, and E. Smith. 1946. Blue mold decay of Delicious apples in relation to handling practices. U.S. Dept. Agr. Circ. 731:1-20.

19. Eustace, H. J. 1908. Investigations on some fruit diseases. New York Agr. Exp. Sta. Bul. 297:31-48.

20. Fisher, D. F. 1942. Handling apples from tree to table. U.S. Dept. Agr. Circ. 659:1-39.

21. Harwig, J., Y. K. Chen, and B. P. C. Kennedy. 1973. Occurrence of patulin and patulin-producing strains of *Penicillium expansum* in natural rots of apple in Canada. Can. Inst. Food Technol. J. 6:22-25.

22. Kidd, M. N., and A. Beaumont. 1924. Apple rot fungi in storage. Trans. British Mycol. Soc. 10:98-118.

23. Kienholtz, J. R., R. H. Robinson, and E. S. Degman. 1949. Reduction of pear rots in Oregon by the use of chemical washes. Oregon Agr. Exp. Sta. Inf. Circ. 160. 7 pp.

24. Maas, J. L., and I. C. MacSwan. 1970. Postharvest fungicide treatments for reduction of Penicillium decay of Anjou pears. Plant Dis. Rep. 54:887-90.

25. Maxie, E. C., N. F. Sommer, C. J. Muller, and H. L. Rae. 1966. Effect of gamma radiation on the ripening of Bartlett pears. Plant Physiology 41:437-42.

26. Pierson, C. F. 1966. Fungicides for the control of blue-mold rot of apples. Plant Dis. Rep. 12:913-15.

27. Pierson, C. F., M. M. Ceponis, and L. P. McColloch. 1971. Market diseases of apples, pears, and quinces. USDA, ARS, Agricultural Handbook No. 376. 112 pp. 17 color plates.

28. Pierson, C. F., and H. M. Couey. 1970. Control of decay in Anjou pears with hot water and with heated and unheated suspensions of benomyl or thiabendazole. Phytopathology 60:1308. (Abstr.).

29. Ramsey, H. J., A. W. McKay, and E. L. Markell. 1917. The handling and storage of apples in the Pacific Northwest. U.S. Dept. Agr. Bul. 587:1-32.

30. Raper, K. B., and C. Thom. 1949. A manual of the *Penicillia*. The Williams and Wilkins Company, Baltimore, Md. 875 pp.

31. Rose, D. H., D. F. Fisher, and C. O. Bratley. 1933. Market diseases of fruits and vegetables:

apples, pears, quinces. U.S. Dept. Agr. Misc. Publ. 168. 70 pp.

32. Spalding, D. H., and R. E. Hardenburg. 1971. Postharvest chemical treatments for control of blue mold of apples in storage. Phytopathology 61:1308-09.

32. Spalding, D. H., H. C. Vaught, R. H. Day and G. A. Brown. 1969. Control of blue mold rot development in apple treated with heated and unheated fungicides. Plant Dis. Rep. 53:738-42.

34. United States Department of Agriculture, Agr. Res. Serv. 1965. A review of literature on harvesting, handling, storage and transportation of apples. ARS 51-4. 215 pp.

35. Walker, J. R. L. 1970. Phenolase inhibitor from cultures of *Penicillium expansum* which may play a part in fruit rotting. Nature 227:298-99.

36. Wellman, R. F., and F. D. Heald. 1938. Steam sterilization of apple boxes for blue mold. Washington Agr. Exp. Sta. Bul. 357:1-16.

37. Wiant, J. S., and C. O. Bratley. 1948. Spoilage of fresh fruits and vegetables in rail shipments unloaded at New York City, 1935-1942. U.S. Dept. Agr. Circ. 773:1-62.

38. Wilson, D. M., G. J. Nuovo, and W. B. Darby. 1973. Activity of o-diphenol oxidase in postharvest apple decay by *Penicillium expansum* and *Physalospora obtusa*. Phytopathology 63: 1115-18.

39. Wright, J. R., and E. Smith. 1954. Relation of bruising and other factors to blue mold decay of Delicious apples. U.S. Dept. Agr. Circ. 935:1-15.

Bull's-eye Rot of Apple
Pezicula malicorticis (Jacks.) Nann.

This disease can be serious on apples grown in Washington, Oregon, and British Columbia (Canada). In California it occurs only occasionally in the central and northern coast districts (6); total decay in experimental lots was a fraction of a percent in the Watsonville area in 1975 (1). The causal organism is *Pezicula malicorticis* (Jacks.) Nann. the imperfect stage being *Crytosporiopsis curvispora* (Pk.) Gremmen. The fungus was previously reported as *Neofabrae malicorticis* (Cord.) Jack., and the imperfect stage *Gleosporium malicorticis*. The pathogen has been described as "Anthracnose and perennial canker of apple."

Infection of fruit can occur as early as petal-fall stage of bloom to harvest. The rot usually begins at open lenticels and develops very slowly at cold-storage temperatures of near 0°C. The most susceptible cultivars are Yellow Newtown, Winesap, Delicious and Golden Delicious, although all cultivars can be infected (5).

Symptoms on fruit appear as pale yellowish cream or uniformly brown, but are often brown with a pale center resembling a bull's-eye. The spots are flat to sunken, and the rotted tissues are relatively firm. The skin does not break easily under light pressure. The spore-bearing tufts of the fungus (imperfect stage [*C. curvispora* (Pk.) Gremmen] may or may not develop in storage (5).

Control is accomplished by rapidly cooling fruit after harvest and maintaining it at temperatures of −0.6 to 0°C. A forecast method for determining the presence of the disease is to hold samples of fruits at 18.3 to 21.1°C and a high relative humidity to hasten disease development. Fruit from lots developing the disease are then marketed early in the storage season (2, 3, 4). Field control of anthracnose by application of fungicides reduces the postharvest decay problems but in California such practice is not followed because of a low disease incidence.

References

1. Combrink, J. C., N. F. Sommer, R. H. Tyler, and R. J. Fortlage. 1976. Postharvest Phomopsis rot of apple fruits. Plant Dis. Rep. 60:1060-64.

2. Kienholz, J. R. 1951. The Bull's-eye rot *(Neofabraea)* problem of apples and pears. Oregon State Hort. Soc. Proc. 66:75-77.

3. _____ 1956. Control of Bull's-eye rot on apple and pear fruits. Plant Dis. Rep. 40:872-77.

4. Pierson, C. F. 1958. Forecasting Bull's-eye rot in Northwest-grown apples in storage. Plant Dis. Rep. 42:1394-96.

5. Pierson, C. F., M. J. Ceponis, and L. P. McColloch. 1971. Market diseases of apples, pears, quinces. USDA-ARS Agr. Handbook No. 376, p. 21-23.

6. Smith, R. E. 1941. Disease of fruits and nuts. Calif. Agr. Ext. Serv. Circ. 120, p. 22 (out of print).

Gray Mold Rot of Apple and Pear
Botrytis cinerea Pers. ex Fr.

Gray mold rot occurs whenever pears are stored for extended periods in cold storage; it is considered second in importance to Penicillium rot. The disease is not a problem of stored apples in the Pacific Northwest but has been a problem in the Eastern U.S., where the climate is more humid during the growing season. Generally, the disease has been less of a problem during the last few years and this has been attributed to use of better fungicide treatments in the field before harvest (14).

The decay caused by *B. cinerea* Pers. originates at the calyces or at punctures in the skin. A water-soaked spot on the fruit turns grayish and then becomes light-brown with darker brown areas. The decaying tissue is at first firm, but later becomes soft and readily crumbles when rubbed between the fingers (5). Sporulation of the fungus occurs under high moisture conditions but may not be evident when stored under low-moisture conditions. Decaying tissue does not separate easily from the healthy as with *Penicillium* decay. The fungus moves from one fruit to the next causing a "nesting effect" (7) and at this stage of decay small black sclerotia, the resting bodies of the fungus, may be detected. The decaying tissue usually has a pleasant fermented odor rather than the musty odor given off by *Penicillium*. Symptoms vary according to cultivars and stage of fruit maturity. On red apple cultivars a reddish-brown ring (2 to 3 mm in diameter) around the lenticels amid the light-brown decaying areas has been described as "spot rot" (1, 11). Only certain strains of *Botrytis* cause spot rot, and this symptom is found only when apples are stored at low temperatures. In 1932 Cooley (5) reported that in pears a high percentage of stem infection started as blackened areas with a definite line of demarcation. The infected areas later spread into the fruit and to adjacent fruit. *Botrytis* infection on pears has been observed only on fruit taken from an orchard in which abundant spores of the fungus occurs on infected covercrops such as vetch and clover. Severe sepal infection on Rome Beauty apples was reported from Hudson River Valley, New York (12) in 1951 when rains fell for 28 to 34 hours and the temperature was 7.8 to 8.9 °C during the end of bloom. Blanpied and Purnasiri (2) found that with an increase in spore concentration in the wash water there was increase in number of punctured fruit infected.

The causal organism of gray mold is *Botrytis cinerea* Pers. ex Fr. The perfect stage is *Botryotinia fuckeliana* (de Bary) Whetezel, [= *Sclerotinia fuckeliana* (de Bary) Fuckel (21)]. The only other species occurring on apple was reported from Washington by Ruehle (17), who named it *Botrytis mali* Ruehle in 1931. This species produces exceptionally large sclerotia in culture.

Colonies of *B. cinerea* on potato-dextrose agar appear at first as a colorless mycelial growth. Later, erect fasiculate conidiophores develop; these are 2 mm or more in length, mostly 16 to 30 μm thick, and olive-colored. They turn darker in color with exposure to light. Conidiophores form open clusters of short branches which are smooth, clear, and brown below and paler near the apex, with ends often quite colorless. These conidiophores, which are usually hyaline and terminally swollen, bear dense clusters of conidia on sterigmata. Conidia are smooth, unicellular, hyaline to light brown, ovate to subglobose or subpyriform. They are usually more profuse when the atmosphere is dry than when it is high in humidity. They are 6 to 18 × 4 to 11 μm (mostly 8 to 14 × 6 to 9 μm in dimension). Older cultures form a stroma at the edges of the Petri dish—these are black sclerotia and are characteristically flattened, loaf-shaped, or hemispherical. Spermatia are formed on branching spermatiophores with the entire structure enveloped in a mucilaginous matrix. Apothecia, rare in California, are cupulate, stalked, and brown-colored. Ascospores are hyaline, unicellular, and ellipsoidal (9, 21).

The fungus develops in stored apples and pears from incipient infections around the stem or calyx end. Of particular significance is the fact that gray mold infections can continue to develop in storage temperatures of −0.6° to 0°C (16, 18). As an example, healthy fruit stored at the above temperature in the fall of the year may be completely decayed by the following February or March. The fungus forms a nest rot by moving from infected to adjacent healthy fruit. It infects by forming masses of appressoria on the mycelial tips.

Control of fruit rot is related to the reduction of inoculum or infection in the orchard and the prevention of injures to the fruit at harvest and during the handling and packing operations. Prompt cooling of fruit below 0 °C and maintenance of low temperature throughout storage is essential (14). Control of *Botrytis* in the orchard can be obtained with benzimidazole sprays. The initial scab sprays are certainly a benefit if tolerant strains of *Botrytis* are not present. Postharvest treatments with benzimidazoles provide fair to good control. Thiophanate and thiabendazole provide better control than does benomyl (19). Thiabendazole is an excellent protectant but not an eradicant; however, it is compatible with storage scald inhibitors such as diphenylamine and ethoxyquin (20). Sodium chlororthophenylphenate can reduce decay effectively (8), but it has been replaced by sodium orthophenylphenate as an standard fungicide used in the wash-water (13).

References

1. Adams, R. E. and S. E. Tamburo. 1957. The West Virginia spot-rot complex of apple in 1956. Plant Dis. Rep. 41:760-65.
2. Blanpied, G. D. and A. Purnasiri. 1968. Penicillium and Botrytis rot of McIntosh apples in water. Plant Dis. Rep. 52:865-67.
3. Brooks, C. and J. S. Cooley. 1917. Temperature relations of apple-rot fungi. USDA J. Agr. Res. 8:139-64.

4. Brooks, C., Cooley, J. S., and D. F. Fisher. 1935. Diseases of apples in storage. U.S. Dept. Agr. Farmers' Bul. 1160. 20 pp.

5. Cooley, J. S. 1932. Botrytis stem infection of pears. Phytopathology 22:269-70.

6. Cooley, J. S., and J. H. Crenshaw. 1931. Control of Botrytis rot of pears with chemically treated wrapper. U.S. Dept. Agr. Cir. 177. 10 pp.

7. Daines, R. H. 1968. Soft rot (blue mold) and nest rot (*Botrytis* sp.) of apples and their control in storage. Proc. Mass. Fruit Growers' Assoc., Inc. 74:85-89.

8. English, H. 1948. Disinfectant washes for the control of decay in apples and pears. Phytopathology 38:914. (Abstr.)

9. Ellis, M. B., and J. M. Waller. 1974. CMI descriptions of pathogenic fungi and bacteria. No. 431. *Sclerotinia fuckeliana.* Commonwealth Mycological Institute, Ferry Lne, Kew, Surrey, England.

10. Heald, F. D., and G. D. Ruehle. 1931. The rots of Washington apples in cold storage. Wash. Agr. Expt. Sta. Bul. 253. 48 pp.

11. Heald, F. D., and R. Sprague. 1926. A spot-rot of apples in storage caused by *Botrytis.* Phytopathology 16:485-88.

12. Palmiter, D. H. 1951. A blossom-end rot of apples in New York caused by *Botrytis.* Plant Dis. Rep. 35:435-36.

13. Pierson, C. F. 1960. Postharvest fungicide treatments for reduction of decay in Anjou pears. Plant Dis. Rep. 44:64-65.

14. Pierson, D. F., *et al.* 1971. USDA, ARS. Agriculture Handbook No. 376. 112 pp. 15 color plates.

15. Rose, D. H. 1924. Diseases of apples on the market. U. S. Dept. Agr. Dept. Bul. 1253. 24 pp.

16. Rose, D. H., L. P. McColloch, and D. F. Fisher. 1951. Market diseases of fruits and vegetables: apples, pears, quinces. U.S. Dept. Agr. Misc. Pub. 168. 72 pp.

17. Ruehle, G. D. 1931. New apple-rot fungi from Washington. Phytopathology 21:1141-52.

18. Schneider-Orelli, O. 1911. Versuche uber die Wachstumsbedingungen und Verbreitung der Faulnis pilze des Lagerobtes. In Landw. Jahrb. Schweiz, Jahrg. 25, Heft 3:225-46.

19. Sinclair, W. A. 1972. Prevention of Botrytis and Penicillium rots and scald of apples in storage with postharvest dip treatments. Phytopathology 62:500. (Abstr.)

20. Thomas, O. C. N., and G. D. Blanpied. 1971. Further evaluation of thiabendazole as a postharvest fungicide for apples. Plant Dis. Rep. 55:791-94.

21. Whetzel, H. H. 1945. A synopsis of the genera and species of the Sclerotiniaceae, a family of stromatic inoperculate discomycetes. Mycologia 37:648-714.

Phomopsis Rot of Apple
Phomopsis mali Roberts

Phomopsis rot was found in Yellow Newtown apples stored in Santa Cruz County, California, in 1975 and 1976 (1). The disease is thought not to be of concern to the industry because of its low incidence of occurrence. It does not appear in the handbook on market diseases published in 1971 (4). The rot was first reported on Yellow Newtown pippin apple foliage and fruit in Virginia in 1912 (5).

Symptoms. Rot symptoms are first seen in the stem cavity as light-to-dark brown skin discoloration (fig. 19). The tissue below is also discolored and softens as the lesion enlarges. The growing lesion has a well-defined margin, and the decayed area cannot be easily separated from surrounding healthy tissue. In storage near 0 °C the rot does not develop for about 4 months. Aerial mycelium is sparse on rotted fruit and there is no spread of rot from affected to healthy fruit. On Phomopsis-inoculated fruit held at room temperature, black pycnidia developed in about 1½ months.

The causal organism is *P. mali* Roberts; the perfect stage is *Diaporthe perniciosa* Marchal (3). The fungus is easily cultured on potato-dextrose medium where the aerial mycelium is sparse, chalk-white to gray flocculent and darken with age, and the substrate turns to bluish-purple. Pycnidial development was enhanced by exposure to near-UV illumination, and measured 0.14 to 0.22 × 0.12 to 0.16 mm in size. Conidia are produced on linear conidiophore and measure 20 × 2 μm. Alpha spores are spindle-shaped (7 to 10 × 3 to 4 μm) and biguttulate and Beta spores are thread-like, hooked or S-shaped, attenuate, and measure 20 × 36 × 1.5 μm. The fungus grows rapidly at 20 °C, covering a 90 mm Petri dish in 6 days; at 0 °C no growth was observed (1, 5).

In the process of disease development, the *Phomopsis* inoculum comes from the cankers and leaf spots (5, 6) on the tree. The fruit infection comes from 6.5 to 8.0 percent of stems in which 6.5 to 8 percent have incipient infections.

Some control of the decay is possible by cold storage at about 0 °C. Field spraying with benomyl is reported to control Phomopsis canker on peach (2) and could be beneficial. Extended storage definitely is an inducement to development of Phomopsis fruit decay as well as development of other fruit rot pathogens.

References

1. Combrink, J. C., N. F. Sommer, R. H. Tyler, and R. J. Fortlage. 1976. Postharvest Phomopsis rot of apple fruits. Plant Dis. Rep. 60:1060-64.

2. Danes, R. H. and J. L. Peterson. 1976. The occurrence and control of Phomopsis fruit rot of peach. Plant Dis. Rep. 60:141-43.

3. Dunegan, J. C. 1932. The occurrence of the perfect stage of Phomopsis mali in the United States. Phytopathology 22:922-24.

4. Pierson, C. F., M. J. Ceponis, and L. P. McColloch. 1971. Market diseases of apples, pears, and quinces. USDA Agr. Handbook No. 376, 112 pp.

5. Roberts, J. W. 1912. A new fungus on the apple. Phytopathology 2:263-64.

6. Smith, R. E. 1941. Diseases of fruits and nuts. Calif. Agr. Ext. Serv. Circ. 120, 15 pp.

7. Terui, M. and Y. Harada. 1968. On *Phomopsis mali* causing "jikugusare" disease of apples. Bul. Fac. Agric. Hirosaki Univ. 14:43-46. (RAM 46:3151, 1968).

II. STONE FRUITS AND THEIR DISEASES

Stone fruit belongs to the family Rosaceae. The fruit of *Prunus* species is a drupe with the seed surrounded by a hard shell or stone. The stone develops from the inner part of the ovary wall and the soft flesh from the outer part. Blossom parts are located around the single ovary (perigynous). Blossoms are borne singly on peduncles or in clusters. Almond trees start to bloom in early February, followed by the apricots in the latter part of February, then peaches and nectarines, followed by plums, prunes, and finally cherries.

Important considerations for production of stone fruit in California are pruning, fruit thinning, fertilization, pest and disease control, weed control, irrigation, harvest, packaging, postharvest decay control, storage, and shipping. These vary with each crop, and it could differ in regions whether the orchard is located in the warm Sacramento and San Joaquin valleys, the cooler areas of Santa Clara Valley or the North Bay Region. The Sacramento Valley can have 16 inches of rain annually—the southern San Joaquin Valley might have 6 or 8. Humidity and dew occur more in areas adjacent to rivers and lakes. Fog areas are related to the rivers, lakes, and distance close to the ocean.

The Almond (*Prunus amygdalus* Batsch.)

The almond, *Prunus amygdalus* Batsch. (*Amygdalus communis* L.), a native of southwest Asia, was brought to Greece and North Africa in prehistoric times. Almond growing in North America is confined almost entirely to California, with more than 325,000 acres located in the Sacramento and San Joaquin valleys.

Most of the principal cultivars were developed in California in the last half of the nineteenth century from seedlings brought from Europe and northern Africa. These are Nonpareil, NePlus Ultra, Mission (Texas), Drake, and Peerless. About 1938 the U.S. Department of Agriculture and the University of California Agricultural Experiment Station introduced two new cultivars, Jordanolo and Harpareil. Only the Jordanolo, favored because of its large meats, was planted extensively. Later the Experiment Station introduced the Davey, which has been planted to some extent in the central valleys to supply small meats.

Propagation is by budding the desired cultivar onto seedlings of the bitter almond or seedlings of one of the commercial cultivars. The Mission cultivar is frequently used. The peach was formerly used as a rootstock but this practice has declined.

Almonds are self-sterile, so it is necessary to provide proper conditions for cross-pollination among cultivars. This is done by alternating two to three rows of Nonpareil with adjacent rows of other cultivars such as Peerless, NePlus Ultra, or Mission. Because these blossom at different times, some thought is required in planting so that those which overlap in their blossoming periods are continuous.

August, September, and October are harvest months —the nuts are mechanically shaken from the tree and picked up mechanically on preleveled ground.

The Apricot (*Prunus armeniaca* L.)

The cultivated apricot, *Prunus armeniaca* L., originated about 4,000 years ago in China near Peking and reached southwest Asia (Armenia) before the time of Alexander the Great. The famous "Golden Apples" of Greek mythology were actually apricots. The wandering of man to all parts of the globe resulted in the introduction of apricots in Italy by 100 B.C., in England by 1620, and in Virginia about 1629 (although the fruit did not adapt to the climate of the eastern U.S.). The Spaniards brought the apricot to Mexico in the fifteenth century. Seedlings were planted at Californian missions in the eighteenth century, and European cultivars were introduced before 1850.

Commercial growing of apricots in California was started more than 175 years ago, and the first production recorded in 1792 was from an orchard in the town of Santa Clara. Today, apricot production is mainly confined to California, Washington, Utah, and Arizona.

Numerous cultivars have been grown in California, but since 1920 major commercial production has been limited to Tilton and Royal (Blenheim). Moorpark and minor ones make up the remainder. The Royal supposedly originated in France about 1830 and soon after the Blenheim in England. The Royal is highly flavored and used for canning, drying, and fresh shipment. The Tilton was originated in Kings County by J. E. Tilton in 1890, is used primarily for canning, and tends to bear alternate heavy and light crops. Moorpark has a fine quality with a plum-like taste. Derby Royal resembles Royal but sets a lighter crop. It was first planted near Winters, California, in 1895; next to Perfection it is the earliest commercial cultivar for fresh shipment. Perfection originated in the state of Washington in 1911.

California leads both the nation and the world in apricot production. The 27,000 acres of production represents about 97 percent of the U. S. crop. About 70 percent of the crop is used for canning, 18 percent for drying, 6 percent for freezing, and 6 percent for fresh market. Other products made from apricots are wine, brandy, champagne, and nectar. Ground apricot pits are used to clean jet engines, and the kernel oil is used for soaps and perfume. Fresh apricots are high in vitamin A.

Apricots are usually propagated by budding the commercial cultivar on seedling peaches or apricots. Myrobalan plum is sometimes used as a rootstock if the planting is to be made in heavy, poorly drained soils. The apricot does well on the Marianna 2624 plum rootstock. Because apricot is self-fertile, it is not necessary to alternate cultivars in the plantings. The tree starts to bear in its third year and comes to its peak production by the sixth year. Some apricot trees in Solano County are still providing excellent fruits after more than 60 years. Apricots blossom in February, and harvest begins in the middle of June and continues for about a month. Trees can be pruned in late fall before leaves are shed, but this is usually done after leaf fall in winter and before blossoming in spring.

The Cherry (*Prunus avium* L.)

Ancestors of the domesticated cherries of today were native to southwestern Asia around the Caspian and Black seas. They were of three distinct kinds: sweet cherries, *Prunus avium* L.; sour cherries, *P. cerasus* L., and Duke cherries which are thought to be hybrids between sweet and sour cherries.

In California the sweet cherry is grown in the Stockton, San Jose, and Hollister areas. In Oregon they are grown at Hood River and in Washington, at the Dalles and Wentachee. They are also grown in Montana at Flathead Lake and in Utah near Salt Lake City. The cultivars planted on 12,000 acres in California are Early Burlat, Larian, Mona, Van, Lambert, Black Tartarian, Royal Ann (Napoleon), Bing, Chapman, and Republican.

Cross pollination among cultivars is necessary. Examples of pollenizers for the main sorts are Black Tartarian for Bing, Early Burlat, and Mona; Bing serves as a pollenizer for Black Tartarian, Early Burlat, Jubilee, Larian, Mona, and Van.

Rootstocks for new orchards are primarily Mahaleb, but Mazzard and Stockton Morello can be used.

The harvest season starts the middle of May in Stockton and lasts until the end of June in Hollister. This is followed by harvests in Oregon, Washington, Idaho, Montana, and Utah. About three-fourths of the crop is sold fresh and the remainder is brined or canned.

Sour cherries do best where winters are rather cold and summers are cool. Consequently they are not grown commercially in California, but around the Great Lakes and in the Pacific Northwest, including Canada. The most important cultivars are Montmorency, Early Richmond and English Morello.

The Peach (*Prunus persica* [L.] Batsch.)

The peach, *Prunus persica* (L.) Batsch. (*Amygdalus persica* L., *Persica vulgaris* Mill.) was introduced into Europe from Persia, having been brought to Persia from China where it apparently had been cultivated for some 3,000 years (the term ''peach'' is derived from a Latin word meaning Persian). By 330 B. C. the peach had reached Greece and during the Middle Ages its culture spread throughout Europe. By the 1570's it was in Mexico and introduced into Florida by the Spanish, to Louisiana by the French, and to Jamestown and Massachusetts by English settlers. Today about one-fourth of the world's peach supply is produced in the San Joaquin and Sacramento valleys of California.

California fresh peaches for market are harvested from the second week of May to late September. Of more than 125 improved cultivars in California some of the most important are Springtime, Springcrest, Royal May, Merrill Gemfree, Redtop, Suncrest, Fay Elberta, Rio Oso Gem, Summercrest, and Halloween. Those gaining popularity are Armgold, Carnival, Fayette, Angelus, and June Lady. Over 7 million packages are sold fresh, the rest are canned, frozen, or dried.

Clingstone canning peaches total 55,000 acres with an average production of 630,415 tons. Harvest starts in the middle of July and extends to the beginning of September. Important cultivars, grown almost exclusively in California are the extra early Fortuna and Dixon; early, Bowen and Andora; late, Gaume and Halford; and extra late, Everts and Corona. New cultivars which appear promising are Tufts, Herrington, and Merriam. All clingstone peaches are canned. The only freestone peach canned is the Fay Elberta.

The Nectarine (*Prunus persica* var. *nectarina* Maxim.)
The Peach (*Prunus persica* L.)

The nectarine, *Prunus persica* var. *nectarina* Maxim., is identical with peach in all features except in the skin of the fruit, which is without trichomes. Current cultivars are yellow-fleshed rather than white and are highly colored with red blush over-spreading a rich amber-yellow skin. Harvest starts in late May and extends through late September. Principal cultivars of the freestone types are Red June, May Grand, Early Sungrand, Independence, and Sungrand, while clingstone types are Red Grand, Le Grand, Gold King, Late Le Grand, and Autumn Grand. California supplies over 97 percent of the U.S.-grown nectarines, the current production being over 86,000 tons. The 10,000 acres in production are in central San Joaquin Valley.

Peach and nectarine are commonly propagated by budding to seedlings of peach. Seedlings of Lovell and more recently Nemaguard have been used extensively for this purpose. Nemaguard is a strain of peach rootstock that is resistant to root-knot nematodes. The Myrobalan plum and Marianna 2624 are sometimes used as rootstock for planting in heavy, poorly aerated soils but they are not entirely satisfactory.

Peach and nectarine cultivars are self-fertile, so large numbers of trees of the same cultivar are planted together. This fact has considerable influence on the incidence of diseases.

Plums and Prunes
Prunus salicina Lindl. and *P. domestica* L.

Plums are native to almost all land areas of the North Temperate Zone and have been used as food by man since primitive times. Indians of certain parts of North America sometimes added the flesh of plums to venison or buffalo meat in making pemmican, a staple article of food. As with other stone fruits, cultivation of plums undoubtedly began in the ancient civilizations near the Caucasus bordering the Caspian Sea. In fact, the wild progenitor of the cultivated plums of Europe is unknown. Some think that *Prunus domestica* L., the species to which European plums and prunes are assigned, actually arose as hybrids between *Prunus cerasifera* Ehrh. and *P. spinosa* L. Many cultivars of plums are self-sterile.

Fresh California plums are available from early May through the end of August. All the prominent types originated in either Japan or Europe. The Japanese types, *Prunus salicina* Lindl. (*P. triflora* Roxb.), came from stock introduced in the 1870's and are mostly early or midseason types with red or yellow skins. The European cultivars, which are descended from stock apparently introduced into America by the Pilgrims, are generally midseason or late and always blue-to-purple in skin color. Plum cultivars are frequently classified according to skin color. Examples of red ones are Red Beut, Casselman, Santa Rosa, Laroda, and Late Santa Rosa; purple types are Arrosa, New Yorker, Sim-ka, Queen Ann; a blue type is President, green are Kelsy and Wickson; and black-red types are El Dorado and Nubiana. California, with 16,000 acres, produces more than 90 percent of the total U.S. supply of fruit, which is available from early May through August.

Certain European or "domestica" plums can be sundried or dehydrated without fermenting. By definition, a prune is a dried plum. The California prune is an offshoot of La Petite d'Agen, a prune-plum native to southwest France. In 1856 Jean and Pierre Pellier obtained cuttings and brought them to San Jose, California, where their brother Louis grafted them onto the American wild plum rootstocks. Currently California's prune orchards produce approximately 68 percent of the world's prune supply and 98 percent of the nation's crop. In 1973, 226,000 dried tons were produced in California on 84,000 acres (8,000 acres non-bearing). Today the d'Agen prune is known as the California French Prune and constitutes approximately 92 percent of the state's prune production. Other commercial types of importance are Imperials (Imperial Epineuse) which originated in France in 1870, Robe de Sergeant, Sugar and Burton.

Full production of fruit occurs between the eighth and twelfth year after planting and continues on a commercial basis for about 30 years. Harvesting starts in late August and lasts for about a month. Mechanical shakers drop the fruits onto fabric catching-frames, and conveyor belts place them in bins in which they go to the dehydrator. Washed fruits are placed in wooden trays and subjected to a constant flow of warm circulating air (76.6 °C) for 14 to 24 hours, at which time the moisture content has been reduced to 16 to 20 percent of the original. After sorting, the moisture content is restored to 26 to 32 percent. Potassium sorbate is added as a preservative to protect against mold and yeast spoilage.

Rootstocks used for Salicina plum trees are Marianna plum and nematode-resistant varieties of peach. For Domestica plum trees the Myrobalan plum is the most commonly used; Marianna plum and peach are also used.

References

1. Chandler, W. H. 1951. Deciduous orchards. Lea and Febiger. Philadelphia, Pa. 436 pp.
2. Day, L. H. 1951. Cherry rootstocks in California. Univ. California Agr. Exp. Sta. Bul. No. 725. 31 pp.
3. _____ 1953. Rootstocks for stone fruits. Univ. California Agr. Exp. Sta. Bul. No. 736. 76 pp.
4. California Tree Fruit Agreement, 1973. Statistical Report.
5. Foytik, Jerry. 1961. Trends and outlook, California cherry industry. California Agr. Exp. Sta. Cir. 501. 34 pp (out of print).
6. Norton, R. A., C. J. Hanson, H. J. O'Reilly, and W. H. Hart. 1963. Rootstock for peaches and nectarines in California. University of California Agr. Exp. Sta. Leaflet 2157.

BACTERIAL DISEASES OF STONE FRUIT

Bacterial Blast and Canker of Stone Fruit
Pseudomonas syringae van Hall

The bacterial canker organism kills buds in the winter and blossoms (fig. 20) in the spring, and induces canker formation on branches and trunks from fall to spring. The bud-blight phase has been related to infections through leaf scars during the fall months, while the blossom blast phase is most serious in years of cold or freezing temperatures during bloom. Associated with blossom blast has been infection of green fruits especially in low-lying parts of the orchard. The canker phase has been considered one of the most important diseases on young stone fruit trees during the first few years after planting. Mature trees can also be attacked although they are not as susceptible.

Control is possible by use of soil fumigations, chemical sprays, and cultural programs such as time of pruning and keeping the blossoms from freezing.

Details of this disease are discussed in sections I and III of this publication.

Crown Gall of Stone Fruit
Agrobacterium tumefaciens
(Smith & Townsend) Conn.

This disease, caused by *A. tumefaciens,* is important in nursery trees, young plantings, and mature trees. To prevent young seedling infection in the nursery, the seed is soaked in chlorine solution and nursery fields are fumigated with methyl bromide-chloropicrin or a mixture of dichloropropane and dichloropropene. Trees having galls when dug are eliminated.

Root infections occur when trees are planted in the orchard, and galls are commonly found on mature trees. Recent studies in Australia and the U.S. have shown that roots of nursery trees dipped in nonpathogenic strains of certain isolates of the crown gall organism are protected from infections. Rootstocks for stone fruit trees are in general very susceptible. Rootstocks moderately resistant are apricot *(Prunus armeniaca* var Royal) seedlings, mahaleb *(P. mahaleb)* seedlings, and Stockton Morello *(P. cerasus)* softwood cuttings or suckers. Of the plum rootstocks, Myrobalan *(P. cerasifera)* seedlings are less susceptible than peach seedlings while the hardwood cuttings of Myrobalan 29C and Marianna 2624 *(P. cerasifera* × *P. munsoniana)* are considered more resistant than *P. cerasifera.*

Details of the disease are discussed in section III of this publication.

Leaf Scorch of Almond
Bacterial Agent

Almond leaf scorch, also known as "Golden death" and "almond decline," was first noted in 1958 on a few scattered almond trees in the Quartz Hill area of Los Angeles County (5). A survey in 1974 revealed that the disease occurs in 14 counties from San Diego to Glenn counties (7). As yet no other stone fruit trees are affected in California, but in the southeastern U.S. peaches are affected by a disease called "phony peach" which is caused by an organism similar to that causing almond leaf scorch (6). On grapes, a disease, known in California since 1892 (7) as "Pierce's disease," is caused by a similar if not the same pathogen (2, 3, 4).

The distribution of the disease on almonds and its effect on the crop suggests that it could have a significant effect in limiting almond production in certain areas.

Symptoms. The disease is characterized by marginal leaf scorch which initially appears on a single terminal shoot or branch usually after mid-June (figs. 21A, 21B). An increase of these symptoms occurs and after 3 to 8 years leaves of the entire diseased tree show the characteristic golden-brown appearance. Although affected trees produce normal leaves in the spring, they can be recognized by reduced terminal growth, large numbers of dead spurs, and dieback of terminal shoots. Affected leaves do not wilt but the margins suddenly become desiccated at either the edge or tips; this produces a zonate pattern in the dead areas. The leaf tissue between the green and scorched area appears as a bright yellow band on some varieties and this distinguishes the disease from damage caused by excess salt. Affected leaves are shed at the same time as the healthy leaves. In Long IXL and Jordanolo, affected branches develop rough bark symptoms, and the bark on severely affected terminal shoots and secondary branches develops pitting in the outer woody cylinder. Pitting, however, does not occur on large branches, trunks, or roots of affected trees. A test for early detection of the disease is to immerse cut branches for 5 to 20 minutes in acidified methanol, at which time distinct reddish-purple streaks develop only in diseased wood tissue (4, 7) (fig. 21C).

Causal organism. Examination of affected leaf tissue with the electron microscope has consistently revealed bacteria in the water-conducting tissues (4). The bacterial agent of the almond leaf scorch has been transmitted in greenhouse tests by leafhoppers, and by bud and scion grafts (4). The bacterial agent of Pierce's disease can also be transmitted to healthy almond, causing typical leaf scorch symptoms. Both the leaf scorch and the Pierce's disease bacteria have been isolated in culture.

Disease development. The pathogen survives from one year to the next in affected almond trees and perhaps in other woody host plants similar to those reported for Pierce's disease (1). The bacterial agent is transmitted by the same leafhopper (*Draculacephala minerva*) that transmits Pierce's disease (4).

Host susceptibility. The disease has been seen on more than 11 commercially important almond cultivars, including Nonpareil, Mission, Ne Plus Ultra, IXL, Peerless, Drake, Trembath, and Jordanolo.

Control. To plant for future acreage of almonds more information is needed on cultivar suscepti-

bility and on the pattern of disease spread in the various almond-growing areas. Diseased trees should be removed if there are indications of tree-to-tree spread. Injection of the antibiotic oxytetracycline HCl has provided some symptom remission, but effectiveness and economic feasibility of this control measure remain to be experimentally determined.

References

1. Frazier, N. W. (Ed.) 1970. Virus diseases of small fruits and grapevines. Univ. of California, Div. of Agr. Sci., Berkeley, Ca. 290 pp.
2. Goheen, A. C., G. Nyland, and S. K. Lowe. 1973. Association of a rickettsia-like organism with Pierce's diseases of grapevines and alfalfa dwarf and heat therapy of the disease in grapevines. Phytopathology 63:341-45.
3. Hopkins, D. L., and H. H. Mollenhauer. 1973. Rickettsia-like bacterium associated with Pierce's disease of grapes. Science 179:298-300.
4. Mircetich, Srecko M., S. K. Lowe, W. J. Moller, and G. Nyland. 1976. Etiology of almond leaf scorch disease and transmission of the causal agent. Phytopathology 66:17-24.
5. Moller, W. J., R. R. Sanborn, S. M. Mircetich, H. E. Williams, and J. A. Beutel. 1974. A newly recognized and serious leaf scorch disease of almond. Plant Dis. Rep. 58:99-101.
6. Nyland, G., A. C. Goheen, S. K. Lowe, and H. C. Kirkpatrick. 1973. The ultrastructure of a Rickettsialike organism from a peach tree affected with phony disease. Phytopathology 63:1275-78.
7. Pierce, N. B. 1892. The California vine disease. U. S. Dept. Agr. Div. Veg. Pathol. Bul. 2. 222 pp.
8. Sanborn, R. R., S. M. Mircetich, G. Nyland, and W. J. Moller. 1974. "Golden Death" a new leaf scorch threat to almond growers. California Agriculture 28(12):4-5.

FUNGAL DISEASES OF STONE FRUIT

Armillaria Root Rot of Stone Fruit
Armillaria mellea (Vahl.) Quel.

Armillaria root rot, one of the most important soil-borne diseases of stone fruit trees, was first reported on peaches in 1891, on prunes in 1902, almonds in 1918, apricots in 1921, sweet cherries in 1926, and on Japanese plums between 1930 and 1949. *Armillaria* kills trees by attacking the roots and stem at the soil line and moving from one tree to the next by rhizomorphs on root grafts. Confinement of infected areas by trenching and injection of methyl bromide is possible if done each year. It is not possible to completely kill fungus in the soil with methyl bromide, so resistant rootstocks offer the least expensive and most practical method of control. Plum rootstocks Marianna 2624, Myrobalan 29C, *Prunus insititia*, St. Julien, and Damson are considered resistant to *Armillaria*. Marianna 2624 is widely used for plum and apricot orchards.

Nematode-resistant rootstocks such as Nemaguard seedlings (FV 234-1), Rancho Resistant, and S-37 are susceptible to *Armillaria*. However, if nematodes are not a problem, plum rootstocks are available for peaches and nectarine plantings.

Almond cultivars such as Jordanolo, Ne Plus Ultra, Peerless, and Mission may be grown on *Armillaria*-resistant Marianna 2624, but other varieties cannot. Intergrafts of New Havens B with Nonpareil scion are available.

Mahaleb and Stockton Morello cherries are susceptible, but Mazzard is considered moderately resistant after it is well established.

Details of the *Armillaria* disease are given in section III of this publication.

Blossom Rot and Green Fruit Rot of Stone Fruit
Botrytis cinerea Pers.
Whetzelinia sclerotiorum (Lib.) Korf. and Dumont
Monilinia laxa (Aderh. & Ruhl.) Honey
Monilinia fructicola (Wint.) Honey

"Green rot," "jacket rot," "calyx rot" and "blossom rot" are names given to a disease of apricot, prune, plum, almond, and occasionally cherry. Blossom rot is most common in coastal districts of California where protracted rains occur during the trees' blossoming period. Green-fruit rot occurs both in coastal and interior areas of California. The disease is of little importance in most years, but sometimes causes severe loss of crops.

Symptoms. As the names imply, the disease affects both blossoms and green fruit (fig. 22A). The early stage of the disease, blossom rot, becomes apparent during the latter part of the blossom stage as a withering of the calyces. As the fruit sets and starts to grow, a brown lesion commonly develops on fruit to which the calyces have adhered. The lesion expands rapidly involving the entire young fruit.

Causal organisms. *Monolinia laxa* and *M. fructicola*, the two brown rot fungi attacking stone fruit, cause blossom blighting similar to that just described. Occasionally, these fungi attack the green fruit, and symptoms produced by them are distinguishable by development of the conidial stage on the blossoms

and on the rotted fruit. The diseases produced by these fungi are discussed elsewhere.

Nixon and Curry (4) and later Smith (12) first believed that blossom rot and green-fruit rot was primarily caused by both *Botrytis cinerea* (*Sclerotinia fuckeliana* [deBary] Fuckel) and *Sclerotinia sclerotiorum* [earlier identified incorrectly as *S. libertiana* and now classified as *Whetzelinia sclerotiorum* (Lib.) Korf and Dumont (2)]. Smith (11) later believed that the disease was caused almost entirely by *S. sclerotiorum*. Yarwood (14, 15), however, reported both fungi to be involved in blossom and fruit rotting, one being more common than the other in some localities. Yarwood's observations were made principally on apricots in coastal districts of California; in the Sacramento and San Joaquin valleys, blossom rotting is less common.

B. cinerea Pers. is a loosely defined species, containing forms exhibiting a wide range of variability in sclerotial size, conidial production, rate of growth, and production of aerial mycelium. Groves and Drayton (1) obtained an apothecial stage from isolates of the *cinerea* type; hence this fungus belongs, as do other species of *Botrytis,* to the genus *Sclerotinia*. Groves and Drayton did not consider a change in nomenclature to be justified, inasmuch as the morphological differences between apothecia produced by their different isolates had not been determined.

S. sclerotiorum (Lib.) Mass. has well-defined characters (7). Apothecial production from sclerotia (fig. 22B) in the laboratory was described by Purdy (8).

The name *B. cinerea* is reserved for *Botrytis* forms which produce grayish-brown conidiophores and conidia, and large flat sclerotia which adhere close to the substrate. *W. sclerotiorum* produces large elongated, black sclerotia but no conidia. Under some conditions it produces abundant microconidia which, according to Smith (10), germinate.

Disease development. Sclerotia of *W. sclerotiorum* are rarely seen on affected blossoms or fruit on the tree—they form after these affected structures fall to the ground. *Botrytis cinerea* probably survives in a like manner or as mycelia in dead organic material (5). Ascospores from apothecia, which develop from October until spring, are probably the only agents for primary infection by *W. sclerotiorum*. Conidia constitute the principal inoculum for infection by *B. cinerea;* the apothecial stage is rare in the life cycle of this fungus. Both the ascospores of *W. sclerotiorum* and the conidia of *B. cinerea* are disseminated by air currents, the former being forcibly ejected from the apothecia (3). Smith (11) mentioned the wide occurrence of *W. sclerotiorum* in the spring. Infection of green fruit occurs by growth of the mycelia from the infected calyx cup into the flesh of the fruit.

Presumably the germ tubes of both organisms invade the blossom directly by appressoria. Infection of fruit by both organisms probably results from the direct penetration of the surfaces by mycelia established first in the dead flower parts.

Judging from Yarwood's (15) studies, blossom infection occurs from the time the flower is fully open until the petals are shed, and the disease develops rapidly during the latter part of the blossoming period. Fruit infection occurs from the time fruit is set until shucks (floral tube) are shed. The relation between the presence of infected calyces and development of fruit infection was established for both *W. sclerotiorum* (Smith, 11) and *B. cinerea*. All floral parts are susceptible to infection by *B. cinerea;* the pollen grains stimulate spore germination and infection of petals (5). On apricots, stylar infection by *B. cinerea* is conducive to infection of green apricot fruit (5).

Prolonged rains during the blossom periods favor blossom infection by both fungi. After fruit is set and begins to grow, rains which moisten the shucks, (jackets) favor fruit infection. Cool weather prolongs retention of the shucks, and favors fruit infection. Yarwood (15) observed that the disease was less prevalent where the orchard floor was bare than where weeds and grasses covered it. It is a common observation that apothecia of *W. sclerotiorum* are most abundant where grass and weeds protect the soil from rapid drying.

Host susceptibility. All commercial cultivars of apricots, plums, prunes, almonds, and cherries are susceptible to infection by these fungi. Blossoms in dense clusters, such as those produced by NePlus Ultra and Drake, are highly susceptible to infection. Peach and nectarine blossoms, however, are rarely affected.

Control. Clean cultivation of the orchards probably is beneficial in prevention of apothecial development. Forceful removal of the jackets from the young fruit might conceivably reduce infection. Some growers have reported benefits from removing the jackets by shaking the branches or by blowing them off with a helicopter. Such a practice is of limited practicality.

Earlier attempts to prevent green-fruit rot by spraying the fruit soon after it set were unsuccessful. Yarwood (13, 14, 15) succeeded in preventing fruit and blossom infection by sprays applied during the full-bloom period of the tree. Ferbam (ferric dimethyl-

dithiocarbamate) at 1½ lb per 100 gallons of water plus a spreader was recommended. On cherries benomyl provided excellent control when applied at full bloom (6). Botran, however, injured young apricot fruit when applied at petal fall stage of bloom.

References

1. Groves, J. W., and F. L. Drayton. 1939. The perfect stage of *Botrytis cinerea*. Mycologia 31:485-89.
2. Korf, R. P., and K. P. Dumont. 1972. *Whetzelinia,* a new generic name for *Sclerotinia sclerotiorum* and *S. tuberosa*. Mycologia 64:248-51.
3. Leach, L. D., and Wm. B. Hewitt. 1939. Forced ejection of ascospores of apothecia of *Sclerotinia* species. Phytopathology 29:373.
4. Nixon, W. H., and H. W. Curry. 1910. Disease of young apricot fruits. Pacific Rural Press 80:124.
5. Ogawa, J. M., and H. English. 1960. Blossom blight and green fruit rot of almond, apricot and plum caused by *Botrytis cinerea*. Plant Dis. Rep. 44:265-68.
6. Ogawa, J. M., B. T. Manji, and W. R. Schreader. 1975. *Monilinia* life cycle on sweet cherries and its control by overhead sprinkler fungicide applications. Plant Dis. Rep. 59: 876-80.
7. Purdy, L. H. 1955. A broader concept of the species of *Sclerotinia sclerotiorum* based on variability. Phytopathology 45:421-27.
8. Purdy, L. H. 1956. Factors affecting apothecial production by *Sclerotinia sclerotiorum*. Phytopathology 46:409-10.
9. Reidemeister, W. 1909. Die Bedingungen der *Sclerotien*-ringbildung von Botrytis cinerea auf Künstlichen Nährboden. Annales Mycologici 7:19-44.
10. Smith, Ralph E. 1900. *Botrytis* and *Sclerotinia:* their relation to certain plant diseases and to each other. Bot. Gaz. 29:369-406.
11. _____ 1931. Life history of *Sclerotinia sclerotiorum* with reference to the green rot of apricots. Phytopathology 21:407-23.
12. Smith, Ralph E., and E. H. Smith. 1911. California plant diseases. Calif. Agr. Exp. Sta. Bul. 218:1039-1193 (out of print).
13. Yarwood, C. E. 1944. Apricot diseases in the Santa Clara Valley in 1943. Plant Dis. Rep. 28:32-33.
14. _____ 1945. Apricot diseases in coastal California in 1945. Plant Dis. Rep. 29:678-80.
15. _____ 1948. Apricot jacket rot. Phytopathology 38:919-20. (Abstr.)

Brown Rot of Stone Fruit
Monilinia laxa (Aderh. & Rhul.) Honey
Monilinia fructicola (Wint.) Honey

Brown rot is the name given to diseases of deciduous tree fruit caused by species of *Monilinia* (= *Sclerotinia*). In 1900, Woronin showed that two types of brown rot diseases existed in Europe: one largely caused by *Sclerotinia cinerea* Bon. on stone fruit, and one largely caused by *S. fructigena* on pome fruit. It was not until almost 25 years later, however, that the common brown rot diseases of stone fruit in North America were recognized as a third distinct type. Consequently, the earliest literature on the subject names either *S. fructigena* or *S. cinerea* as the causal organism of the American type of brown rot. Such misconceptions, and the tendency to name new fungus species on the basis of slight differences, led to confusion and duplication in the names of the causal organisms.

Even after the identities of the two brown rot fungi on stone fruits were established, few persons attempted to differentiate between the diseases they produce. For obvious reasons it is difficult to find common names that are entirely satisfactory. In this discussion the brown rot disease of stone fruit originally found in Europe is referred to as "European brown rot," and disease of stone fruit originally found in North America is called "American brown rot." Disease caused by *S. fructigena* is not discussed because it has not been reported in the United States.

European brown rot
(*Monilinia laxa* (Aderh. & Ruhl.) Honey,

This disease, also known as "brown rot blossom blight," "apricot brown rot," and "Monilia blossom blight" (67, 81), attacks apricots, almonds, cherries, domesticated plums, nectarines, peaches, prunes, flowering quince, and certain wild species of *Prunus*. It occurs in Australia, Europe, eastern Asia, New Zealand, North America, Manchuria, South America, and Japan (18). In North America, the disease occurs in the states and provinces along the Pacific coast (3). It also occurs in some fruit-growing districts of Michigan and Wisconsin (8) and New York. It was probably introduced into California when the state's fruit industry was being established. In 1898 Bioletti (6) found brown rot on apricot blossoms in the San Francisco Bay area. This strongly suggests that the disease was European brown rot because severe blossom and twig blighting of apricot is one of the principal features of that disease. In 1921, Howard and Horne (33) and in 1925 Rudolph (67) gave similar descriptions of brown rot disease on apricots in San Mateo and Santa Clara counties. It was not until 1939, however, that both European and American types of brown rot were shown to occur in California (31).

Symptoms. As just noted, the principal feature of European brown rot disease is severe blossom and twig blighting. Sudden withering of the flowers occurs during the blossoming period (fig. 23A). For the next 3 or 4 weeks, twigs die in large numbers owing to the growth of the fungus from the infected flower onto the twigs. On apricots, profuse gumming occurs on the twigs. Fruit infection in the orchard is sporadic; in some years it may be quite common, but in most years it is insignificant. Fruit rot begins as small dark spots which expand rapidly. The affected flesh is brown, firm, and fairly dry (as contrasted with the soft watery rots caused by other fungi). The fungus sometimes grows from infected apricot fruit onto the twigs, much as it does from infected blossoms. Somewhat the same symptom has been observed in almonds, where the fungus first colonizes the inner surface of the fruit hull after this structure dehisces. There is evidence, however, that the twig is usually not killed by direct invasion of the fungus, but probably by a toxin (45).

Tufts of conidia (sporodochia) are present on infected blossoms (fig. 23B). In late winter, (December to early January), new conidial tufts develop on the blighted blossoms and twigs. These are pulverulent ash-gray cushions 1 to 2 mm in diameter.

The causal organism. The confused state of the taxonomy of the fungus will not be discussed here. Honey (32) erected a new genus, *Monilinia,* for the monilioid species previously placed in the genus *Sclerotinia,* but Harrison (27) did not favor such a transfer. At the present time most plant pathologists accept Honey's classification and call the fungus *Monilinia laxa* (Aderh. & Ruhl.) Honey. *M. cinerea* Bon., *S. cinerea* (Bon.) Wr., *S. cinerea* (Bon.) Wr. f. *pruni* Wormald, and *M. oregonensis* Barss & Posey, are synonyms. Two biologic forms are reported in Europe (83).

Conidia (moniliospores) of *M. laxa* are hyaline, lemon-shaped, 6.25 to 7.35 × 10.23 to 11.61 µm in diameter, and are produced on branched chains arising from a hypostroma, the whole fruiting structure being regarded as a sporodochium. Conidia are produced in spring and early summer on newly blighted blossoms, and in late winter and early spring on twigs, blossoms, and peduncles blighted the previous growing season, as well as on mummified fruit.

Apothecia of *M. laxa* are extremely rare. Aderhold and Ruhland (1) described the species on the basis of a few apothecia. Wormald (85) and Harrison (28) described apothecial development in England, but no apothecia of this fungus have been reported from North America.

Features indicating the presence of *M. laxa* in the orchard are extensive blossom infection followed by blighting of the twigs, and production of abundant ash-grey conidial tufts (sporodochia) in early winter on the blighted blossoms and twigs. Where fruit infection by *M. laxa* occurs, the fungus produces abundant conidial tufts on the surface of the rotted fruit and these commonly occur in concentric zones. Although in Washington and Oregon, *M. laxa* and *M. fructicola* (the American or peach brown rot fungus) can occur simultaneously in the same orchard, in California the two species exhibit a considerable degree of host selectivity. While *M. fructicola* occurs frequently on peach and nectarine causing blossom blight and fruit rot, *M. laxa* is seldom found on these hosts (11, 56, 72). However, *M. laxa* occurs frequently but *M. fructicola* infrequently on apricot and almond. Both species may be found in cherry, prune, and plum orchards (56).

Growth characteristics on potato-dextrose agar afford a fairly reliable method for distinguishing *M. laxa* from *M. fructicola* (31). On this medium the former grows more slowly than the latter, colonies are characteristically lobed instead of having smooth margins with concentric rings, and there are few rather than many conidia. In continuous light at 21°C both organisms produce numerous conidia.

Mycelial characteristics also serve to identify the two species. *M. laxa* produced geniculate (bent) germ-tubes, and the hyphae seldom anastamose. *M. fructicola* produces relatively straight germ-tubes and its hyphae anastamose frequently (31, 51).

Disease development. *M. laxa* survives from one season to the next in twig cankers, blighted blossoms, peduncles, and in the rotted mummified fruit hanging in the tree. Conidia begin to develop on these parts in late December and continue to develop until April. A single blighted almond twig often bears as many as 25 sporodochia, each of which produces numerous conidia. A high percentage of newly-formed conidia is germinable, and if not exposed to direct sunlight and high temperature they retain their viability for many days. An abundant and timely supply of inoculum, therefore, is strategically located in the tree when blossoms emerge in the spring (11, 12).

The conidia are blown about by wind (11, 12, 79) and washed about by rain (12). When they lodge on susceptible tissue they will germinate in 2 to 4 hours if moisture is present and temperature is favorable.

As noted earlier, *M. laxa* attacks the blossoms of almonds and apricots, producing extensive flower and twig blighting. The critical period for flower infection extends from the time the unopened flowers emerge from the winter buds until the petals are shed. There is evidence that the flowers are most susceptible to infection when fully open. Though some infection through the side of the floral tube may occur, Calavan and Keitt (7) reported that the most frequent sites of infection in some cherry blossoms are the anthers, stigmas, and petals. In almond, stigma infection is most common, with anthers and petals the next most frequently infected (53). In apricot, the sepals are susceptible.

At ordinary springtime temperatures 3 to 6 days elapse between blossom infection and the first evidence of necrosis. This is followed by rapid necrosis of the entire blossom. Infection and development of disease symptoms occur over a relatively wide temperature range (4 to 30°C), the optimum being about 24°C (7). Low moisture conditions limit infection; little or none occurs in rainless weather even if humidity is high (77).

Susceptibility of stone-fruit cultivars. Among almond cultivars, Drake and Jordanolo are highly susceptible to blossom infection, and Ne Plus Ultra and Texas (Mission) is moderately susceptible. Severe blossom infection is uncommon in Nonpareil, Peerless, and Davey.

The commercially important Royal, Blenheim, and Derby Royal cultivars of apricot are highly susceptible to blossom infection, whereas Tilton is noticeably less susceptible (29). Crossa-Raynaud (15) evaluated resistance based on rate of canker development on young branches of apricots and almonds.

In California, Santa Rosa and Wickson plums and Imperial and French prunes may suffer severe blossom infection by *M. laxa*. In Oregon, Italian prune is susceptible to blossom infection by both *M. laxa* and *M. fructicola*, but this is sporadic. In a few nectarine orchards severe blossom blight and fruit rot by *M. laxa* has occurred, but in most orchards only *M. fructicola* has been isolated.

Control. Rudolph (67) developed a protective spray schedule that has proved relatively effective on apricots in California. The trees are sprayed with Bordeaux mixture 16-16-100 when the blossoms are at "red bud" (which is before the white petals are exposed). Where the disease has been severe two sprays are advisable, one at early red bud stage and one at full bloom. On almonds, protective sprays are recommended for application at the early pink-bud stage of bloom.

Later, dormant eradicative sprays were proved effective in reducing brown rot blossom blight in apricots, almonds, prunes, and plums (13, 29, 79, 80, 81). The purpose of the eradicative spray is to destroy the conidial inoculum in the tree. Applications are made in late winter (January 15-February 1) while the trees are still dormant. Monocalcium meta-arsenite at 2 to 3 lb/100 gallons applied at the rate of 300 to 400 gallons per acre penetrated into the blighted blossoms and twigs of apricot trees and killed the fungus. This treatment is no longer approved. A formulation of 79 percent sodium pentachlorophenoxide at the rate of 3 to 4 lbs/100 gallons is now used and may be applied on apricots, almonds, and prunes. Later studies (13, 57) showed that early applications (December) before sporodochial development reduced the numbers of spore pustles formed and their ability to be wind-dispersed. These sporodochia are white in color. Such eradicant fungicides may be applied as concentrate sprays using 100 gallons of spray per acre.

On almonds and apricots, benomyl was found to suppress sporodochial development and to protect the blossoms and fruit (63, 64).

Mixtures of benomyl and oil proved superior to benomyl alone. Early winter application of this combination before sporodochia appear will suppress sporodochial development on twigs and blighted blossoms (63). Spray application of benomyl before opening of blossoms provides protection of anthers and stigma by systemic movement of the chemical (64). Captan, fixed coppers, dichlone, and coordinated mixtures of nabam plus metal salts are applied as protectants at early and full bloom.

American brown rot
Monilinia fructicola (Wint.) Honey

This has been called "peach brown rot" and "fruit brown rot" to distinguish it from the European stone-fruit brown rot, the usual designation in America being simply "brown rot." American brown rot is indigenous to North America, probably occurring on species of wild *Prunus* long before the continent was settled by Europeans. It is found in Australia, New Zealand, Africa, Japan, Argentina, but is unknown in Europe (86).

Although this brown rot disease is present wherever stone fruits are grown in North America, the most frequent and severe outbreaks occur where rainfall and humidity are high during the growing season. It is particularly destructive in the Atlantic Coast states south of New Jersey and in western parts of Washington and Oregon. It is sporadic in California, where summers are usually rainless. Nevertheless, the disease occurs with sufficient frequency to be a major problem (69).

American brown rot affects all species of stone fruits but is particularly severe on peach, nectarine, plum, prune, and cherry. Infections of apricot and almond blossoms are rare. Hull rot of almond is commonly caused by *M. fructicola* (45). The disease has been found at times on apple.

Symptoms. Symptoms occurring on California peaches are included here. Blossom infection is much less prevalent in California than in some parts of the country. Nevertheless, each year peach blossoms are infected during their blossoming period. The first indication of the disease is necrosis of the anthers; this is followed by rapid death of the floral tube, the ovary, and peduncle. The fungus can extend into the supporting spur or shoot and usually does not cause extensive death to these parts, as does European brown rot fungus *(M. laxa)*.

The fungus immediately produces abundant, slightly tan, dusty, buff-colored tufts of conidia on the blighted blossoms and twigs. The fungus remains alive in diseased blossoms and twigs throughout the following fall and winter, and under California conditions, sometimes produces a few new conidial tufts in spring on these parts. It is reported not to produce conidia on these parts in spring (8, 38, 47, 66), but sporodochia have been observed on peduncles and on blighted twigs in California.

During rainy spring weather infection of green shoots is sometimes serious in plum trees in the eastern states, but seldom does this occur in peach.

The most important aspect of the American brown rot is fruit infection. While incipient infection may occur, resulting in some green fruit rot, ripe fruit is much more susceptible. The symptoms appear as dark brown circular spots which spread rapidly over the fruit (fig. 23C). The affected tissues remain relatively firm and dry, in contrast to the soft watery type of rotting produced by a fungus such as *Rhizopus*. Numerous buff-colored masses of conidia are produced over the rotted area.

In some years extensive killing of twigs and even branches follow fruit infection. Although the situation would seem to indicate that the twigs and branches are killed because they are invaded by the fungus from the infected fruit, toxins produced by the fungus may be implicated much as they are in hull rot of almonds by *Rhizopus circinans* (45).

The causal organism is *Monilinia fructicola* (Wint.) Honey. Synonyms are: *Sclerotinia fructicola* (Wint.) Rehm., *S. cinerea* (Bon.) Schroeter, forma *americana* Wormald, and *S. americana* (Wormald)

Norton & Ezekiel (47, 86). Most authorities agree that the American brown rot fungus differs from any of the *Sclerotinias* occurring in Europe. Earlier American writers called this fungus *Sclerotinia cinerea, Monilia fructigena,* or *Sclerotinia fructigenum* (10, 17, 31, 44).

Though some workers have tried to show differences in size, the conidia of *M. fructicola* (moniliospores) are indistinguishable from those of *S. laxa.* These are produced in chains on sporodochia and average about 15 um in length by 10 μm in width Apothecia are smooth, fleshy, brown to reddish-brown, cup-like structures, varying in size from 1/4 to 3/4 inch in diameter and arising by means of a stalk from the mummied fruit on the ground. Some stalks may be 2 inches long if they arise from mummied fruit buried that deep in the soil. The interior of the cup is lined with a hymenial layer consisting of long slender asci averaging 9 μm in width × 155 μm in length. The ascospores are ovoid to ellipsoid, single-celled and 6 × 12 μm. Microconidia are often found in abundance on pseudosclerotia which form on rotted fruit on the ground; these are 2 to 5 μm hyaline spheroid structures produced on short bottle-shaped sterigmata arising from the mycelia (20, 31). Production of apothecia by *M. fructicola* on synthetic media was achieved after exposure to cold temperatures (73).

Disease development. The fungus survives the winter in several ways: 1) As mycelia in rotted fruit hanging in the tree; here conidia are produced on the surface of the fruits in spring. Bertram (5) reports that in Vermont conidia produced in the autumn remained viable throughout winter. When temperatures of − 12 to − 22 °C prevailed, however, few conidia survived. Jenkins (38) showed that in sun or shade reduction in viability of conidia was less than 1 percent. 2) As mycelia in rotted fruit fallen to the ground. On such fruit the fungus produces the typical flat sclerotial mat from which arise the apothecia. Apothecia appear and mature at the time the host blossoms in spring. They discharge their spores into the air for a few weeks and then disappear. 3) As mycelia in blossom parts, peduncles, and twigs killed by the pathogens the previous year (71). Only occasionally do these parts produce conidia in California. Sporulation on peduncles, twig and branch cankers occurs, however, in the eastern U.S. and in Australia (40).

Apothecia develop in areas where the soil is moist in spring but they seldom occur in California where the weather may become dry just as they begin to appear. Under such conditions these structures are found only where soils are protected from drying by weeds or debris. Other factors affecting apothecial development are temperature and soil pH. Moderate spring temperatures (10 to 15.5 °C) favor development, while cold weather deters it. Ezekial (21) reported that a soil with a pH below 7.0 favors apothecial development, whereas an alkaline soil does not.

In California the most important primary inoculum is the conidia produced on mummies and blighted flower parts which remain in the tree. However, in California ascospores can at times be important in initiating primary infection. Apothecia appear about the time the trees begin to blossom. Ascospores are forcibly ejected into the air and are carried by air currents about the orchard. Slight disturbances in the air (which change the humidity) initiate ascospore discharges. Apothecia develop and discharge their spores for 2 to 3 weeks.

In the eastern U.S. and the Pacific Northwest blossom infection is often severe, causing a marked reduction in fruit production. In California, blossom infection is much less abundant. Nevertheless, conidia produced on these infected blossoms are often the only inoculum present in the orchard in mid-summer before fruit infection occurs. Conidia are freely disseminated by moving air, rainwater (37, 41) and insects (72).

A few green fruit may become rotted in early summer. This is thought to be the result of incipient infections (75) or insect wounds (72) because direct infections require over 30 hours of continuous moisture. Infected fruit sporulate and increase the inoculum supply. Fruit infection is more common during the last 4 weeks before harvest. Where the fruit is not picked until fully ripe (for canning or freezing), heavy losses from brown rot infection is experienced in the field. If fresh-market fruit is to be shipped it is picked before it is fully ripe, and consequently loss in the field is relatively light. Loss in shipment, however, may be heavy as the fungus develops rapidly when packaged fruit is removed from cold storage.

Although wounding of fruit may lead to an increase in frequency of infection, the fungus readily infects when no wound is present. It commonly enters the fruit by way of the trichome (hair) sockets—breaking of the trichome increases the likelihood of infection (68). Pathogenicity has been related to production of hydrolytic enzymes (23, 24, 25).

Although the fungus can grow slowly at 1.7 to 4.4 °C, its optimum temperature is 22.2 to 23.9 °C. At 23 °C or above it produces visible symptoms on infected fruit within 2 days and can completely rot the fruit in 4 or 5 days.

Frequent rains and accompanying high humidity favor infection. Thus the disease occurs most frequently and causes the greatest destruction in the more humid fruit-growing areas. In California, where summers are usually rainless, a sudden outbreak of fruit rot may follow a brief shower (70); nevertheless, the disease may also appear during a rainless period. Dew, which forms at night following a sharp drop in temperature, probably provides the moisture for germination of the spores and rot developed from incipient infections (39, 75).

Control. Cultural practices, such as removal of mummies immediately after harvest, would reduce the number of spores available for blossom and fruit infections. The chances for apothecial development may be reduced through cultivation of the orchard just before blossom time. Baur and Huber (4) and Huber and Baur (34, 35) were able to destroy many of the apothecia by dusting the orchard floor in spring with finely ground calcium cyanamide, but they did not determine the degree of control obtainable by such procedure. No cultivars of peaches have been reported as resistant to brown rot infections of the blossom or fruit. Such cultivars as Dixon, Fortuna, Vivian, and Walton show blossom blight more often than do Halford and Stuart.

Chemical prevention has been most widely used and found effective. Eradication of spore pustules with dormant sprays has not been possible, although sodium pentachlorophenate can help control *M. laxa* on apricots, almonds, and prunes. Sodium pentachlorophenate causes severe injury to peach trees. Fungicides for blossom protection on peach should be applied before rains when about 5 percent of the blossoms are open, and again at 70 percent bloom. Chemicals which have been recommended for blossom blight control are sulfur, copper, captan, ferbam, nabam plus salts, dichlone, and benomyl. Liquid lime-sulfur applications on blossoms may result in severe burns. Benomyl and thiophenate-methyl have provided better control (22, 58, 62, 73) and have been applied as early as pink-bud stage of bloom. Aircraft application provided effective spray coverage on peach blossoms and was followed by effective control (87).

Protection of fruits from infection can be achieved only if fungicides such as captan, sulfur, or benomyl are applied before free moisture occurs on the fruit. Aircraft or ground dusting was shown to be effective if applied before rains (70). Repeated ground spray or dust application was shown to be beneficial in sprinkler-irrigated peach orchards but not in prune orchards.

Fruits with incipient infections continued to develop rot during the last month before harvest regardless of application of protective fungicide. Only Botran plus captan or Botran plus benomyl combinations appeared to offer some control at this time.

Eradication of incipient fruit infection following rains during the last 3 weeks before harvest was shown to be possible with ground application of liquid lime-sulfur within 37 hours from the beginning of rain (60). Phytotoxicity to leaves was observed in Fresno County, but not in the Sacramento Valley or as far south in San Joaquin Valley as Stanislaus County. Benomyl was not as effective, although it significantly reduced the rate of decay development (50).

Two preharvest Botran sprays applied to ripe cling peaches prevented fruit decay after mechanical harvest and holding for processing controlled decay during ripening (61). Cling peaches mechanically harvested are more prone to decay than hand-harvested fruit, but may be protected by dipping in Botran suspensions (61). Hand-harvested fruit were protected from brown rot by two preharvest applications of Botran, a single application of benomyl (50), or by heat treatment followed by Botran dip (65). When a disinfestant such as calcium hypochlorite was mixed with protectant fungicides such as captan or Botran, better disease control was obtained in the orchard (55).

References

1. Anderhold, R. and W. Ruhland. 1905. Zur Kenntnis der Ostbaum-skerotinien. Arb. Biol. Abt. Land- und Forstw. Kaiserl. Gesundheitsamte 4:427-42.
2. Barss, H. P. 1923. Brown rot and related diseases of stone fruits in Oregon. Oregon State Coll. Agr. Exp. Sta. Cir. No. 53.
3. ———— 1925. Serious blossom blight in Pacific Northwest orchards due to species of *Monilia*. Phytopathology 15:125, (Abstr.).
4. Baur, K. and G. A. Huber. 1941. Effect of fertilizer materials and soil amendments on development of apothecia of *Sclerotinia fructicola*. Phytopathology 31:1023-30.
5. Bertram, H. E. 1916. A study of the brown rot fungus in northern Vermont. Phytopathology 6:71-78.
6. Bioletti, F. T. 1902. Brown-rot of stone fruits. Pacific Rural Press 60:67, and California Univ. Agr. Exp. Sta. Rept. 1898-1901:330-31.
7. Calavan, E. C., and G. W. Keitt. 1948. Blossom and spur blight *(Sclerotinia laxa)* of sour cherry. Phytopathology 38:857-82.

8. Cation, D., and J. C. Dunegan. 1949. The overwintering of *Monilinia fructicola* in twig cankers under Michigan conditions. Plant Dis. Rep. 33:97-98.

9. Cation, D., J. C. Dunegan, and J. Kephart. 1949. The occurrence of *Monilinia laxa* in Michigan. Plant Dis. Rep. 33:96.

10. Cooley, J. S. 1914. A study of the physiological relation of *Sclerotinia cinerea* (Bon.) Schroeter. Ann. Missouri Bot. Gard. 1:291-326.

11. Corbin, J. B., and J. M. Ogawa. 1974. Springtime dispersal patterns of *Monilinia laxa* conidia in apricot, peach, prune, and almond trees. Can. J. Bot. 52:167-76.

12. Corbin, J. B., J. M. Ogawa, and H. B. Schultz. 1968. Fluctuations in numbers of *Monilinia laxa* conidia in an apricot orchard during the 1966 season. Phytopathology 58:1387-94.

13. Chitzanidis, A. 1971. Tests of eradicant fungicides against *Sclerotinia laxa* on sour cherry trees. Inst. Phytopathol. Benaki Ann. (ns) 10:119-24.

14. Chochriakova, T. M. 1971. Evaluation of cherry resistance to moniliosis, *Monilinia cinerea*. Tr. Prikladnoi Bot. Genet. Selek. 43:231-36. (Eng. Summ.)

15. Crossa-Raynaud, P. H. 1969. Evaluating resistance to *Monilinia laxa* (Aderh. & Ruhl.) Honey of varieties and hybrids of apricots and almonds using mean growth rate of cankers on young branches as a criterion of susceptibility. J. Amer. Soc. Hort. Sci. 94:282-84.

16. Dunegan, J. C. 1953. Brown rot of peach. *In* Plant Diseases. U. S. Dept. Agr. Yearbook 1953:684-88.

17. Dunn, M. S. 1926. Effect of certain acids and their sodium salts upon the growth of *Sclerotinia cinerea*. Amer. J. Botany 13:48-58.

18. English, H., Adriana Pinto de Torres y Joyce Kirk, C. 1969. Reconocimiento de especies del genero *Monilinia* en frutales de carozo y en membrillo de flor en Chile. Agricultura Tecnica 29:54-59.

19. Evans, A. W., and C. E. Owens. 1941. Incidence of *Sclerotinia fructicola* and S. laxa in sweet cherries in Oregon. Phytopathology 31:469-71.

20. Ezekiel, W. N. 1921. Some factors affecting the production of apothecia of *Sclerotinia cinerea*. Phytopathology 11:495-99.

21. _____ 1923. Hydrogen-ion concentration and the development of *Sclerotinia* apothecia. Science 58:166.

22. Gilpatrick, J. D. 1973. Control of brown rot of stone fruits with thiophanate-methyl and a piperazine derivative fungicide. Plant Dis. Rep. 57:457-59.

23. Hall, R. 1971. Pathogenicity of *Monilinia fructicola*. II. Penetration of peach leaf and fruit. Phytopathol. Z. 72:281-90.

24. _____ 1972. Pathogenicity of *Monilinia fructicola*. III. Factors influencing lesion expansion. Phytopathol. Z. 73:27-38.

25. _____ 1971. Pathogenicity of *Monilinia fructicola*. I. Hydrolytic enzymes. Phytopathol. Z. 72:245-54.

26. Harrison, T. H. 1928. Brown-rot of fruits and associated diseases in Australia. Part I. History of the disease and determination of the causal organism. J. Proc. Roy. Soc. N. S. Wales 62:99-151.

27. _____ 1933. Brown-rot of fruits and associated diseases of deciduous fruit trees. I. Historical review and critical remarks concerning taxonomy and nomenclature of the causal organism. J. Proc. Roy. Soc. N. S. Wales 67:132-77.

28. _____ 1934-35. Brown-rot of fruits and associated diseases of deciduous fruit trees. II. The apothecia of the causal organisms. J. Proc. Roy. Soc. N. S. Wales 68:154-76.

29. Hesse, Claron O. 1938. Variation in resistance to brown-rot in apricot varieties and seedling progenies. Proc. Am. Soc. Hort. Sci. 36:266-68.

30. Heuberger, J. W. 1934. Fruit-rotting Sclerotinias. IV. A cytological study of *Sclerotinia fructicola* (Wint.) Rehm. Maryland Agr. Exp. Sta. Bul. 371:167-89.

31. Hewitt, W. B., and L. D. Leach. 1939. Brown-rot *Sclerotinias* occurring in California and their distribution on stone fruits. Phytopathology 39:337-51.

32. Honey, E. E. 1928. The monilioid species of Sclerotinia. Mycologia 20:127-56.

33. Howard, W. L., and W. T. Horne. 1921. Brown-rot of apricots. California Univ. Agr. Exp. Sta. Bul. No. 326:73-88 (out of print).

34. Huber, G. A., and K. Baur. 1939. The use of calcium cyanamide for the destruction of apothecia of *Sclerotinia fructicola*. Phytopathology 29:436-41.

35. _____ 1941. Brown rot on stone fruits in western Washington. Phytopathology 31:718-31.

36. Humphrey, J. E. 1893. On *Monilia fructigena*. Botany Gaz. 8:85-93.

37. Jenkins, P. T. 1965. The dispersal of conidia of *Sclerotinia fructicola* (Wint.) Rehm. Aust. J. Agric. Res. 16:627-33.

38. _____ 1967. The longevity of conidia of *Sclerotinia fructicola* (Wint.) Rehm. under field conditions. Aust. J. Biol. Sci. 21:937-45.

39. Jenkins, P. T., and C. Reinganum. 1965. The occurrence of quiescent infection of stone fruits caused by *Sclerotinia fructicola* (Wint.) Rehm. Australian J. Agric. Res. 16:131-40.

40. Kable, P. F. 1965. The fruit peduncle as an important overwintering site of *Monilinia fructicola* in the Murrumbridgee Irrigation Areas. Aust. J. Exp. Agric. Anim. Husb. 5:172-75.

41. _____ 1965. Air dispersal of conidia of *Monilinia fructicola* in peach orchards. Aust. J. Exp. Agric. Anim. Husb. 5:166-71.

42. _____ 1970. Eradicant action of fungicides applied to dormant peach trees for control of brown rot *(Monilinia fructicola)*. J. Hort. Sci. 45:143-52.

43. _____ 1971. Significance of short-term latent infections in the control of brown rot in peach fruits. Phytopathol. Z. 70:173-76.

44. Matheny, W. A. 1913. A comparison of the American brown-rot fungus with *Sclerotinia fructigena* and *S. cinerea* of Europe. Botan. Gaz. 56:418-432.

45. Mirocha, C. J., and E. E. Wilson. 1961. Hull rot disease of almonds. Phytopathology 51:843-47.

46. Mirocha, C. J., J. E. DeVay, and E. E. Wilson. 1961. Role of fumaric acid in the hull rot disease of almond. Phytopathology 51:851-60.

47. Norton, J. B. S., and W. N. Ezekiel. 1924. The name of the American brown rot *Sclerotinia*. Phytopathology 14:31-32.

48. Norton, J. B. S., W. N. Ezekiel, and R. A. Jehle. 1932. Fruit-rotting Sclerotinia. I. Apothecia of the brown-rot fungus. Maryland Agr. Exp. Sta. Bul. 256.

49. Ogawa, J. M. 1958. The influence of emanations from fruits of *Prunus* species on spore germination of the brown-rot organisms. Phytopathology 48:396. (Abstr.).

50. Ogawa, J. M. 1970. Brown rot control developments. Cling Peach Qtrly. 7:7-9.

51. Ogawa, J. M., and H. English. 1954. Means of differentiating atypical isolates of Sclerotinia laxa and *S. fructicola*. Phytopathology 44:500. (Abstr.).

52. _____ 1960. Relative pathogenicity of two brown rot fungi, *Sclerotinia laxa* and *Sclerotinia fructicola,* on twigs and blossoms. Phytopathology 50:550-58.

53. Ogawa, J. M., and A. H. McCain. 1960. Relations of spore moisture content to spore shape and germination reaction to temperature. Phytopathology 50:85. (Abstr.).

54. Ogawa, J. M., and E. E. Wilson. 1960. Effects of the combinations of sodium pentachlorophenoxide and liquid lime-sulfur on the brown rot fungi. Phytopathology 50:649. (Abstr.).

55. Ogawa, J. M., G. W. Clason, and J. B. Corbin. 1967. Calcium hypochlorite added to selected fungicide sprays improves effectiveness in disease control. Phytopathology 57:824. (Abstr.).

56. Ogawa, J. M., W. H. English, and E. E. Wilson. 1954. Survey for brown rot of stone fruits in California. Plant Dis. Rep. 38:254-57.

57. Ogawa, J. M., D. H. Hall, and P. A. Koepsell. 1967. Spread of pathogens within crops as affected by life cycle and environment. Air-borne Microbes, pp. 247-67. Symposium of the Society for General Microbiology, London.

58. Ogawa, J. M., B. T. Manji, and E. Bose. 1968. Efficacy of fungicide 1991 in reducing fruit rot of stone fruit. Plant Dis. Rep. 52:722-26.

59. Ogawa, J. M., B. T. Manji, and D. J. Ravetto. 1970. Evaluation of pre-harvest benomyl applications on postharvest rot of peaches and nectarines. Phytopathology 60:1306. (Abstr.).

60. Ogawa, J. M., R. Sanborn, H. English, and E. E. Wilson. 1954. Late season protective eradicative sprays as means of controlling brown rot of peach fruit. Plant Dis. Rep. 38:869-73.

61. Ogawa, J. M., J. L. Sandeno, and J. H. Mathre. 1963. Comparisons in development and chemical control of decay-causing organisms on mechanical- and hand-harvested stone fruits. Plant Dis. Rep. 47:129-33.

62. Ogawa, J. M., E. E. Wilson, and J. B. Corbin. 1967. Brown rot of cling peaches in California. Its history, life cycle and control. 10 pp. multi-lith. Department of Plant Pathology, University of California, Davis.

63. Ramsdell, D. C., and J. M. Ogawa. 1973. Reduction of *Monilinia laxa* inoculum potential in almond orchards resulting from dormant benomyl sprays. Phytopathology 63:830-36.

64. _____ 1973. Systemic activity of methyl 2-benzimidazolecarbamate (MBC) in almond blossoms following prebloom sprays of benomyl MBC. Phytopathology 63:959-64.

65. Report of the Research work on brown rot of stone fruits. The brown rot research committee 1957-62. (Australia). 117 pp.

66. Roberts, J. W., and J. C. Dunegan. 1932. Peach brown rot. U. S. Dept. Agric. Bul. No. 328. 59 pp.

67. Rudolph, B. A. 1925. Monilia blossom blight (brown-rot) of apricots. Calif. Univ. Agr. Exp. Sta. Bul. No. 383.

68. Smith, M. A. 1936. Infection studies with *Sclerotinia fructicola* on brushed and nonbrushed peaches. Phytopathology 26:1056-60.

69. Smith, W. L., Jr., and R. D. Bassett. 1963. Hydrothermal and hygrothermal inactivation of *Monilinia fructicola* on *Rhizopus stolonifer* spores. Phytopathology 53:747. (Abstr.).

70. Sonoda, R. M., J. M. Ogawa, R. A. Vertrees, *et al*. 1967. Evaluations of the 1965 and 1966 brown-rot epidemics on cling peaches in California. Department of Plant Pathology, University of California, Davis. 25 pp. Multilith.

71. Sutton, T. B., and C. N. Clayton. 1972. Role and survival of *Monilinia fructicola* in blighted peach branches. Phytopathology 62:1369-73.

72. Tate, K. G. 1973. Nitidulid beetles as vectors of *Monilinia fructicola* (Wint.) Honey in California stone fruits. Ph.D. dissertation, University of California, Davis, 53 pp.

73. Tate, K. G., J. M. Ogawa, B. T. Manji, and E. Bose. 1974. Survey for benomyl-tolerant isolates of *Monilinia fructicola* and *Monilinia laxa* in stone fruit orchards of California. Plant Dis. Rep. 58:663-65.

74. Terui, M., and Y. Harada. 1966. Apothecial production of *Monilinia fructicola* on artificial media. Trans. Mycol. Soc. Japan. 7:309-11.

75. Tilford, P. E. 1936. The relation of temperature to the effect of hydrogen and hydroxyl-ion concentration on *Sclerotinia fructicola* and *Fomes annosus* spore germination and growth. Ohio Agr. Exp. Sta. Bul. 567:1-27.

76. Wade, G. C. 1956. Investigations on brown rot of apricots caused by *Sclerotinia fructicola* (Wint.) Rehm. I. The occurrence of latent infection in fruit. Australian J. Agric. Res. 7:504-15.

77. Weaver, L. O. 1943. Effect of temperature and relative humidity on occurrence of blossom blight of stone fruit. Phytopathology 33:15. (Abstr.).

78. Wilson, E. E. 1942. Experiments with aresenite sprays to eradicate *Sclerotinia laxa* in stone-fruit trees as a means of controlling the brown rot disease in blossoms. J. Agr. Research 64:561-94.

79. Wilson, E. E., and G. A. Baker. 1946. Some aspects of the aerial dissemination of spores, with special reference to conidia of *Sclerotinia laxa*. J. Agr. Research. 72:301-27.

80. Wilson, E. E. 1950. Sodium pentachlorophenate and other materials as eradicative fungicides against *Sclerotinia laxa*. Phytopathology 40:567-83.

81. Wilson, E. E. 1953. Apricot and almond brown rot. *In* Plant Diseases. U. S. Dept. Agr. Yearbook 1953:886-91.

82. Winter, G. 1883. Ueber einige Nordamerikanische Pilz. Hedwigia 22:26-72, 129-31.

83. Wormald, H. 1919. The brown rot disease of fruit with special reference to two biologic forms of *Monilia cinerea* I. Ann. Botany 33:361-404.

84. _____ 1920. The brown-rot disease of fruit trees with special references to the two biologic forms of *Monilia cinerea* II. Ann. Botany 34:143-71.

85. _____ 1921. On the occurrence in Britain of the ascigerous state of a brown rot fungus. Ann. Botany 35:125-34.

86. _____ 1928. Further studies of the brown-rot fungi. III. Nomenclature of the American brown-rot fungi. A review of literature and critical remarks. Trans. British Mycol. Soc. 13:194-204.

87. _____ 1954. The brown rot diseases of fruit trees. Ministry of Agric. and Fisheries (Engl.) Tech. Bul. No. 3. 113 pp.

88. Yates, W. E., J. M. Ogawa, and N. B. Akesson. 1974. Spray distribution in peach orchards from helicopter and ground application. Trans. ASAE 17(4):633-39, 644.

89. Zwygart, T. 1970. Studies on host parasite interactions in *Monilia* diseases of fruit trees. Phytopathol. Z. 68:97-130.

Ceratocystis (Mallet Wound) Canker of Almond and Prune
Ceratocystis fimbriata Ell. & Halst.

The disease of almonds (*Prunus amygdalus* Batsch.) called "mallet wound canker" has been known in California for about 40 years. This canker develops in areas of the branches struck by rubber-covered mallets during harvesting, and on other areas damaged by the mechanical harvesting equipment. Extensive damage by the disease is reported on almonds and prunes (*P. domestica* L.), and occasionally on peach (*P. persica* L. Batsch.) and apricot (*P. armeniaca* L.) (5). The cause of the disease was first reported in California in 1960 (3). Its increased importance was coincident with the mechanical harvesting of stone fruit crops and the degree of bark damage. In a survey in 1964, over 13,000 acres of bearing French prune trees in the Sacramento Valley were affected. In certain orchards, 100 percent of the trees were involved. On almonds the disease is not as extensive except on certain cultivars such as Mission and Nonpareil (4).

Symptoms. The cankers appear first as water-soaked and darkened areas which become sunken and amber-colored. Gum usually forms at the margins of cankers. Infected tissues on prune trees are found to be red while on almond, peach, and apricot the tissues are dark-brown (fig. 24A). The heartwood shows permeations of brownish-black stain that extend logitudinally 50 cm or more past the margins of the canker in the bark. Small cankers may develop under the intact bark tissues during periods of high temperatures (11). These cankers develop only in injured bark and expand throughout the year, but extend fastest during the summer months. Cankers eventually may girdle and kill infected limbs or trunks (fig. 24B). A limb 4 to 6 inches in diameter can be girdled in 3 to 4 years.

Causal organism. *Ceratocystis fimbriata* Ell. & Halst. causes the disease, although other *Ceratocystis, Graphium, Peptographium* and *Chalaropsis* species have been isolated from freshly-injured bark tissues. Carrot discs were tested as a selective medium for isolation by Parkinson (13), and later this medium was shown to be selective for *Ceratocystis fimbriata* by Moller and DeVay (11). Halstead first described the fungus in 1890 (7) on sweet potatoes and established the genus as *Ceratocystis*, although he mistook the perithecia for pycnidia. Elliott (6) in 1923 discovered the perithecia with evanescent asci and designated the fungus *Ceratostomella fimbriata* (Ell. & Halst.) Elliott. The fungus was later transferred to *Ophiostoma* H. and P. Sydow by Melin and Nannfeldt (9) in 1934, and to *Endoconidiophora* Munch by Davidson (2) in 1935. In 1950, Bakshi (1) revived the generic name *Ceratocystis*. This position was maintained by Hunt (8), who considered the other genera as synonyms. *Ceratostomella* was excluded because it contains only species with persistent asci.

Ceratocystis fimbriata is a diverse species consisting of numerous strains characterized by pathogenic specialization (and asexual stages), but with morphological characteristics of the perithecia and ascospores quite uniform. The perithecial dimensions on nine single isolates from different hosts ranged from 130 to 250 μm in diameter at the perithecial base, 250 to 900 μm in the neck length, with 10.8 μm neck width at the tip. The number of ostiolar hyphae ranged from 7 to 16 with a mean width of 2.2 μm (14). The ascospores are hat-shaped with the gelatinous brim tapering from 0.5 to 1.0 μm in width and their dimensions are 2 × 6 μm (14). Three types of asexual spore forms are produced. The dimensions of the cylindrical endoconidia are 2.4 in width × 17.4 μm in length; doliform endoconidia are 7.2 × 6.4 μm; the thick-walled conidia are 12.9 × 10.5 μm with conidiophore length means of 79.8 × 4.8 μm, 34.9 × 6.1 μm, and 33.8 × 4.9 μm, respectively. On malt-extract agar, the color of the hyphae of stone-fruit isolates range from brown to dark olive and perithecia are produced in clumps or in concentric rings in 6 to 12 days. Thiamine is required for perithecial production, vegetative growth being sparse in absence of this material. The optimum growth occurs between 24 and 27 °C. The flask-shaped (tapered) endoconidiophore which gave rise to cylindrical endoconidia are hyaline to subhyaline and septate, and may arise singly or in clusters from both aerial and sub-surface hyphae; the truncate endoconidia are in chains up to 20 spores long.

The endoconidiophores which produce the doliform endoconidia are shorter and wider at the tip. The spores are first hyaline in color and later subhyaline to light brown; they arise singly, but tend to aggregate around perithecia.

The shape of the thick-walled conidia varies from oval to subglobose with smooth to rough walls. They are formed singly, or in short chains on simple or branched conidiophores, and are pale brown to olive brown in color. They germinate in 48 hr at 25 °C.

The various strains of *C. fimbriata* are cross-fertile.

Disease development. The primary inoculum source comes from the fungus sporulating on old diseased bark. The spores contaminate insects or are ingested and excreted by them. Vectors of particular importance are the nitidulid beetles, *Carpophilus freemani*, and a drosophilid fly, *Chymomyza procnemoides*, and to a lesser degree, *C. hempiterus*, *Litargus balteatus*, *Euzophera semifuneralis*, *Scolytus rugulosus*, *Drosphilia melanogaster*, and a species of *Tarsonemus*. The pathogen could be detected on *C. freemani* up to 8 days after it stopped feeding on the fungus. Pupation of contaminated larvae resulted in emerging adults still retaining the fungus (12). The adult insects in old bark wounds are contaminated by the fungus even in the winter months.

Bark injury is prerequisite to infection because the fungus invades exposed cambium tissue. Injuries are susceptible to infection for about 10 days but are resistant after 14 days on Mission almond. They are most susceptible in orchards with recent irrigation. Once infection is established, mature perithecia have been found in bark tissue 4 to 5 days after the initial bark injury. Infection usually does not occur from December through April, at which time the established canker expands very slowly (4). However, in summer when temperatures are higher the canker margins may expand 2 to 3 inches a month. The cankers are perennial and continue their activity year after year. Among the stone fruits, apricot trees are the most susceptible to the fungus, followed by Texas, Ne Plus, and Nonpareil almonds. French and Robe d'Sergeant prunes are next in order of susceptibility, followed by cling peach varieties. Cherries are resistant, no Ceratocystis cankers having been found in cherry orchards.

The fungus can be isolated only from the margins of the cankers and seldom invades deeper than the xylem tissue of the previous year's growth (5). The fungus initially colonizes injured bark and exposed cambium, then invades uninjured bark tissues (except cork) and young xylem. The dark stain permeates the heartwood but the fungus seldom penetrates further than the xylem of the previous year (5).

Control. Bark injuries, especially those involving crushing or loosening of bark, should be prevented. If they do occur, the rough portions should be shaved to promote callus formation. In large cankers, the infected bark and about 1/4 to 1/2 inch layer of the woody tissue underneath should be removed to at least 1 inch beyond the visible margins of the canker. Surgery should be done during winter and dressing should be applied immediately after to keep out insects. Orchards should not be irrigated near harvest time because of increased insect activity.

72

The development of trunk shakers which do not injure the bark has greatly lessened the incidence of new infections.

References

1. Bakshi, B. K. 1950. Fungi associated with ambrosia beetles in Great Britain. Brit. Mycol. Soc. Trans. 33:111-20.
2. Davidson, R. W. 1935. Fungi causing stain in logs and lumber in the southern states, including five new species. J. Agr. Res. 50:789-807.
3. DeVay, J. E., H. English, F. L. Lukezic, and H. J. O'Reilly. 1960. Mallet wound canker of almond trees. Calif. Agr. 14(8):8-9.
4. DeVay, J. E., F. L. Lukezic, W. H. English, *et al.* 1965. Controlling Ceratocystis canker of stone fruit trees. Calif. Agr. 19(10):2-4.
5. _____ 1968. Ceratocystis canker of deciduous fruit trees. Phytopathology 58:949-54.
6. Elliott, J. A. 1923. The ascigerous stage of the sweet potato black rot fungus. Phytopathology 13:56. (Abstr.).
7. Halstead, B. D. 1890. Some fungous diseases of the sweet potato. The black rot. New Jersey Agr. Exp. Sta. Bul. 76:7-14.
8. Hunt, J. 1956. Taxonomy of the genus *Ceratocystis.* Lloydia 19:1-58.
9. Melin, E., and J. A. Nannfeldt. 1934. Researches into the blueing of ground wood pulp. Svenska Skogsvardsforen. Tidskr. 32:397-616.
10. Moller, W. J., and J. E. DeVay. 1968. Insect transmission of Ceratocystis fimbriata in deciduous fruit orchards. Phytopathology 58:1499-1508.
11. _____ 1968. Carrot as a species-selective isolation medium for *Ceratocystis fimbriata.* Phytopathology 58:123-24.
12. Moller, W. J., J. E. DeVay, and P. A. Backman. 1969. Effect of some ecological factors on Ceratocystis canker on stone fruits. Phytopathology 59:938-42.
13. Parkinson, B. W. 1964. Studies on the etiology of Ceratocystis canker of stone fruits. M. S. Thesis, Univ. of California, Davis. 32 pp.
14. Webster, R. K., and E. E. Butler. 1967. A morphological and biological concept of the species *Ceratocystis fimbriata.* Can. J. Bot. 45:1457-68.

Coryneum Blight of Stone Fruit
Coryneum beijerinckii Oud. =
Stigmina carpophila (Lev.) Ellis

This disease, known as "California peach blight," "peach blight," "shot hole," "Coryneum blight," and "corynosis," is particularly prevalent in the Pacific Coast states, but occurs to some extent in other western states and occasionally in midwestern and eastern states. It is also known in Canada, Australia, Africa, Asia, New Zealand, Europe, and South America.

The disease was first described in 1843 (10) on peaches near Paris, France, and by 1864 was in England (3). Between 1882-1889 it destroyed the Maori cultivar of peaches in New Zealand. In the U.S. it was first reported in Michigan in 1894 and later in California in 1900 (16). Severe outbreaks of *Coryneum* were experienced in California following the years of economic depression in the 1930's.

Coryneum blight is a major disease of peaches, nectarines, apricots, and almonds in California, but is rarely found on other stone fruit trees. In the northwestern U. S. and British Columbia, however, it sometimes does much damage to cherries. Other plants attacked are prune, plum, cherry laurel *(Prunus laurocerasus),* and some species of native American cherry.

Symptoms. The lesions on twigs first appear as purplish spots 2 to 3 mm in diameter (fig. 25A). As these enlarge, the centers become brown and dead. Examination of the necrotic areas with a hand lens will show small tufts of spores. The scales of affected buds are dark-brown-to-black and sometimes covered with a gummy exudate which gives them a varnished appearance. Leaf and fruit lesions are at first small purplish areas which expand to spots 3 to 10 mm in diameter. On leaves the lesions frequently are surrounded by a narrow zone, light-green-to-yellow in color (fig. 25B). Fruit lesions later become rough and corky (fig. 25C). The symptoms vary on the four kinds of stone fruits. On peaches and nectarines, principal symptoms are twig and bud blighting. In apricot, bud blighting, fruit and leaf spotting are the principal symptoms, while twig lesions rarely occur. On almonds, the principal symptoms are leaf spotting and blossom and fruit infection; some twig infection occurs but is not serious (21). Defoliation following leaf infection is much more common on apricots and almonds than on peaches and nectarines.

Causal organism. Mycologists differ as to whether the fungus belongs to Melanconiales or Moniliales. It does not form an acervulus in the true sense of the term, but on twigs does produce a slight stromatic cushion from which the conidiophores arise (21). Largely as a result of this feature the fungus was named *Coryneum beijerinckii* Oud in the U.S. European workers classified it with the Moniliales as *Clasterosporium carpophilum* (Lev.) Ader. (1, 17) and later changed it to *Stigmina carpophila* (Lev.) Ellis. Jauch (8) suggested the combination *Coryneum carpophilum.* The spores offer a reliable means for identifying the fungus. They are elongate-ovoid, light greenish-yellow, 4- to 6-celled with characteristic restrictions at the septations including hyaline end-cells (21). Vuillemin (19) claims the fungus produces a perfect stage, *Ascospora beijerinckii* on dead leaves, but this has not been noted by others. A great range in size is found among conidia in nature (23 to 62 × 12 to 18 μm) (15).

Disease development. The pathogen survives from one season to the next on lesions on twigs and blighted buds. Conidia are produced on twigs and in blighted buds, the later source being particularly important in apricot, nectarine, and peach. In peach, holdover is probably largely in blighted buds and twig lesions. Conidia are present inside blighted buds the year-round, and may be produced for at least 18 months after buds are blighted. Under favorable conditions crops of conidia can be produced in 6 hours; in spring they are produced on old twig lesions, on infected blossoms and leaves. The fungus rarely sporulates on fruit lesions. When kept dry, conidia remain viable for several months (17, 21). They are not easily detached from the conidiophores by moving air, but are readily detached by water and so are largely disseminated by rain. In the germination process all cells do not germinate at one time, thus providing a mechanism for extended viability of spores during heavy rain. Spores can germinate immediately after formation and germination has been observed in a 1-hour period. In 15 to 20 hours, and at 15 to 27 °C, all of the spores may germinate.

The fungus is easily cultured, but the most rapid growth is on a basal agar medium in which beta-maltose supplies the carbon, L-asparagine provides the nitrogen, the pH is 5.4 to 5.8, and the culture is incubated at 15 °C (20).

Direct penetration of leaves by germ tubes from the conidia has been observed (1, 17). The conidia germinate equally well on both surfaces, but the underside of leaves are more prone to infection than the upper side (12). In all probability, the fungus is capable of penetrating the twig, fruit, and blossoms in the same manner. In California, twig and bud infection of peach and apricot occurs during the rainy season at anytime from autumn until spring. Lesions on twigs and buds develop during winter and spring, and blossoms and young leaves are infected when they emerge in the spring. Incubation period of the disease is from 5 to 14 days depending on tempeature and the type of tissue infected; it apparently is longer in twigs than in leaves and flowers.

Samuels (17) found the fungus to be inter- as well as intracellular in leaves. Host cells adjacent to the

mycelia die. "Shot-holing" of *Prunus* leaves is due to an abscission layer which forms around the infected area (17).

The spores germinate over a relatively wide range of temperature and as low as 2 to 4 °C, so California winters do not limit germination. Moisture, however, is a factor in disease production: at least 24 hours of continuous moisture is necessary for twig infection, the incubation period being 7 to 11 days. This is probably the reason twig infection is not usually initiated during the first autumnal rains, which commonly are of short duration. Leaf infection, however, may be initiated during such rains.

Soil conditions have little or no influence on infections, but an extremely low soil fertility might influence the tree's susceptibility by producing less growth.

Cultivar susceptibility. Most cultivars of peach in California are susceptible to infection. Clingstone cultivars such as Gaume, Palora, and Phillips Cling appear to be more susceptible than others; freestone types grown in California are less affected. In Oregon, New Improved Elberta peach and common cultivars of apricots are very susceptible. Among almonds, the Ne Plus Ultra, Drake, Peerless, and Nonpareil are probably the most susceptible.

Control. Common cultural practices, such as furrow-irrigation, cultivation, and soil fertilization, have no apparent influence on Coryneum blight, but recent use of sprinkler-irrigation has increased the incidence of Coryneum blight.

In the past, Bordeaux mixture and the fixed copper material have been the standard fungicide for control of the disease. However, these materials often cause leaf injury if applied soon after leaves emerge. Symptoms of such injury—leaf spots, chlorosis of leaf blade, and eventual leaf fall—are very similar to those produced by *C. beijerinckii*.

In California the organic fungicides ziram, ferbam, dichlone, and captan, have proved as effective as copper fungicides and are not toxic to foliage. Zineb and nabam with zinc, iron, and manganese salts are less effective against the pathogen (5, 6, 13).

While the principal damage to peach and nectarine from Coryneum blight is the killing of twigs and buds (fruit and leaf infection being much less important), the principal damage to apricot is caused by fruit and leaf infection. In addition, bud infection in apricot sometimes causes some crop loss. Almonds suffer very little loss of twigs or buds, but may be damaged by defoliation following severe leaf infection. Fruit infections occur primarily on the upper surface and may restrict the normal enlargement of the affected side, especially on almond hulls (13). Fruit infection is of no consequence in almond unless overhead sprinkler irrigation is practiced (2).

Timing of protective spray applications must be varied to meet such differences in the effects of the disease. For peach and apricot, for example, an autumn application after leaf fall but before winter rains begin is necessary to protect against twig and/or bud infection. No other application is usually necessary for peaches, but a spring application at full bloom to petal-fall stage of bloom may be necessary to prevent severe fruit and leaf infection in apricot. For almonds where protection of leaves is of prime importance, a single ziram spray applied at the end of the blossoming period (petal-fall stage) has given control throughout the remainder of the season. A dormant spray at bud swell with sodium pentachlorophenoxide has also significantly reduced the disease.

Spray applications with concentrate sprays of ziram using 20 gallons per acre were as effective as high-volume spray application of 400 gallons per acre. Helicopter spray applications gave excellent disease control provided spray droplet size was reduced from 450 μ to 320 μ and forward speed reduced to about 25 mph (12). Fixed-wing aircraft gave little spray deposit on undersurface of leaves and afforded poor control (14).

Almond hulls are used for cattle feed, so chemical residues which persist on the hulls at harvest should not exceed the legal limits.

References

1. Aderhold, R. 1902. Ueber *Clasterosporium carpophilum* (Lev.) Ader. un Beziehungen dessel ben zum Gummiflusee des Steinobstes. Arb. Biol. Reichst. a Forstw. 2:515-59.
2. Aldrich, T., W. J. Moller, and H. Schulbach. 1974. Shot hole disease control in almonds—by injecting fungicides into overhead sprinklers. California Agriculture 28(10):11.
3. Berkeley, M. J. 1864. (Report of peach blight in England). Note in Gard. Chron. 24:938.
4. Boucher, W. A. 1901. Peach fungus *(Clasterosporium amygdalearum)*. New Zeal. Dept. Agr. 9th Rept. p. 348-52.
5. English, H. 1958. Fall application of ziram and ferbam effectively control peach leaf curl in California. Plant Dis. Rep. 42:384-87.
6. English, H., and J. R. Davis. 1962. Efficacy of fall applications of copper and organic fungicides for the control of Coryneum blight of peach in California. Plant Dis. Rep. 46:688-91.
7. Ghanea, M. A., and P. Assadi. 1970. Shot-hole of stone fruits in Iran: *Stigmina carpophila* (Lev.) Ellis = *Coryneum beijerinckii*. Oud. Iranian J. Plant Pathol. 7:39-63.
8. Jauch, C. 1940. A spotting of stone fruits in Argentina. *Coryneum carpophilum* (Lev.) Nov. comb. Rev. argen. agron. 7:1-26.
9. Kilgore, W. W., W. E. Yates, and J. M. Ogawa. 1964. Evaluation of concentrate and dilute ground air-carrier and aircraft spray coverages. Hilgardia 35:527-36.
10. Leveille, J. H. 1843. Observations sur quelques Champignons de la floce des environs de Paris. Ann. Sci. Bot. 19:215.
11. Luepschen, N. S., et al. 1968. Coryneum blight infection and control studies. Colo. State University Exp. Sta. Progress Report. 68-2.
12. Ogawa, J. M., W. E. Yates, and W. W. Kilgore. 1964. Susceptibility of almond leaf to Coryneum blight, and evaluation of helicopter spray applications for disease control. Hilgardia 35:537-43.
13. Ogawa, J. M., H. English, W. E. Yates, and H. J. O'Reilly. 1959. Chemical control of Coryneum blight. Almond Facts 23:4.
14. O'Reilly, H. J. 1957. Relative efficiency of airplane and ground application of sprays in controlling almond shot hole disease. Phytopathology 47:530. (Abstr.).
15. Parker, C. S. 1925. Coryneum blight of stone fruits. Howard University Rev. (Washington, D. C.) 2:3-40.
16. Pierce, N. B. 1900. Peach leaf curl. U.S. Dept. Agr. Div. Veg. Physiol. and Path. Bul. 20:1-204 (see p. 179).
17. Samuel, G. 1927. On the shot-hole disease caused by *Clasterosporium carpophilum* and on the "shot-hole" effect. Ann. Bot. 41:374-404.
18. Smith, R. E. 1907. California peach blight. Cal. Univ. Agr. Exp. Sta. Bul. No. 191:73-100 (out of print).
19. Vuillemin, Paul. 1888. L'*Ascospora beijerinckii* et la maladie des cerisiers. J. botanique (France) 2:255-59.
20. Williams, R. E., and A. W. Helton. 1971. An optimum environment for culturing of *Coryneum carpophilum*. Phytopathology 61:829-30.
21. Wilson, E. E. 1937. The shot-hole disease of stone-fruit trees. Cal. Univ. Agr. Exp. Stn. Bul. 608:3-40 (out of print).

Cytospora and Rhodosticta Cankers of Stone Fruit
Cystospora leucostoma Sacc.
Rhodosticta quercina Carter

This disease, commonly known as "cytospora canker," has also been called "perennial canker" and "peach canker." It occurs throughout the U.S. and southeastern Canada (14, 27, 38) and has been reported from Japan (32) and England (42).

The disease affects peaches in the U.S. where it was found in New York as early as 1900 by Steward, Rolfs, and Hall (31). It also occurs on plums, prunes (7), cherry, and apricot. It has been found on apple in New Mexico (20), the Pacific Northwest (4), and in Illinois (30).

Cytospora canker occurs throughout the central valley of California on *Prunus domestica* plums such as President, French, and Imperial prune. It does not affect cultivars of *Prunus salicina,* nor is it a serious problem on peaches (26) in California.

Symptoms: Twigs, spurs, and large branches are attacked (fig. 26A). The canker affects primarily the cortical tissue, causing it to collapse and sometimes exude gum. Terminal margins are zonate, indicating the perennial nature of the disease. Black pycnidia break through the surface of the affected bark (fig. 26B).

Causal organism. Earlier investigators of the disease identified the causal organisms as *Cytospora leucostoma* Sacc. (*Valsa leucostoma* Fr.), *Cytospora cincta* Sacc., *Valsa persoonii* Nit., and *Cytospora rubescens.* Though Hildebrand (14) considered *C. cincta* more aggressive than *C. leucostoma* on peaches in New York, Treshow and Scholes (33) and Treshow, Richards, and Scholes (34) in Utah identified the principal species on peach as *C. rubescens;* Lukezic, DeVay and English (25, 26) identified two species on plums in California as *C. rubescens* and *C. leucostoma,* but their reported serological relationships are not clear (23).

More recently Kern (19) split the genus *Valsa,* placing *V. leucostoma* in the genus *Leucostoma* as *L. persoonii* (Nits.) V. Hohn on the basis that the ascostroma is surrounded by a black conceptacle. Asci are clavate, and the eight ascospores are 8 to 14 × 1.5 to 3 μm, hyaline and allantoid. The conidial stroma is similar to but considerably smaller than the ascostroma. Conidia are allantoid, hyaline, 4 to 6.5 × 0.5 to 1.5 μm and are released from the stroma as thin dark-red threads.

Kern (19) placed *Cytospora cincta* in the genus *Leucostoma* but did not mention *C. rubescens.* According to Willison (40) the ascostroma of *C. cincta* has loose texture and is delimited from the host cells by a thin black zone. The ascospores are 14 to 18 × 4 to 7 μm. Pycnospores range from 5-10 μ × 1-2 μm. The perithecial stromata are intermingled with the pycnidia.

Another organism associated with severe cankers on President plum in California is *Rhodosticta quercina* Carter (26). Colonies of this fungus on potato-dextrose agar grow slowly and are characterized by an entire margin, orange pycnidia, and zonate color that is dark orange in the center and white at the margins with an orange pigment diffusing through the medium.

Mycelial growth in culture of *L. persoonii* is stimulated by the combination of thiamine and biotin. The response to myo-inositol is variable. Choline is also stimulatory to most isolates. Response to mycelial growth in culture was decreased as pH was increased from pH 4 to pH 8. *R. quercina* was not able to grow in media prepared with deionized water supplemented with myo-inositol, but on basic agar medium or PDA supplemented with myo-inositol growth was stimulated (26). Myo-inositol was utilized as a carbon source by *L. persoonii* but not by *R. quercina* (26).

Optimum temperature for growth in culture of *C. leucostoma* was 36 °C (Min. 6 °C and max. 39 °C) while with *C. cincta* the optimum was 24 °C (Min. 0C and max. 36 °C) (1).

Disease development. Cytospora canker can be confused with bacterial canker caused by *Pseudomonas syringae.* Cytospora is active in spring and summer, whereas bacterial canker is most active in winter and early spring (26). Moreover, bacterial canker commonly attacks cultivars of *Prunus salicina* and *Cytospora* canker does not. Typical symptoms of *Cytospora* canker are gumming followed by necrosis of cortical tissues and depression of bark surface. Upon cutting of the canker margin, zonation of the diseased tissue is apparent (26).

Availability of the inoculum, infection sites, and predisposition of the tree are all highly important in disease development of *Cytospora.* The inoculum was found on dead and cankered branches throughout the year (21). Conidia of *C. leucostoma* are dispersed by wind-blown rain, whereas ascospores are released during or after rains. The pycnidia generally form within 4 to 6 weeks after a cankered branch dies, while the ascostromata do not form until 2 or 3 years later. With each rain as many as 430 × 10⁶ conidia are released, and ascospores release up to 1.4 × 10⁶ per collection from a single tree (1). Pruning sites and other mechanical injuries are frequent infection courts. Infections of blossom and fruit peduncles and dead buds have been reported (14, 29). In California, pruning cuts and leaf scars are not important infection courts but sunburned areas are major infection sites (1).

Infection is not necessarily followed by canker development. Sunburn areas may serve as infection sites on prune but do not necessarily predispose trees to canker development. On French prunes, *C. leucostoma* cankers develop rapidly on weakened trees during the summer but not on healthy vigorously growing mature or young trees (1, 29). The failure to develop cankers appears limited by a healing reaction. Weakening of limbs beyond the point of infection (as expressed by wilting and defoliation) is attributable to plugging of xylem vessels by gum (6). Trees subjected to moisture stresses and freezing damages, as well as trees deficient in potassium, are more susceptible to canker development (7, 8, 18, 29). However, it is reported that young vigorously growing President plum trees have been as severely infected with *L. persoonii* and *R. quercina* as were older trees (3). *R. quercina* is not a problem on such plum cultivars as Beauty and Duarte. Its mechanism of resistance is not clearly understood, although myoinositol has been implicated (20).

Investigators in Idaho report induced resistance below the infection point when multiple inoculations of *C. cincta* were made on branches of prune and peach (2, 11). Systemic resistance was also associated with localized Prunus ringspot virus infections (12). No explanation of the mechanisms of resistance is available. Susceptibility of host tissues to the fungus has been related to warm temperatures followed by freezing damage (7, 18, 29). Canker size also can vary with infection by different fungus isolates. A range in mean canker length from 2.0 to 7.0 cm has been reported for *C. leucostoma* (1).

R. quercina cankers are similar to those caused by *L. persoonii* except that infected tissues are reddish orange, and erumpent stromata emerging from the bark are light red to dark orange with an irregular outer surface and not crustose. No layer of callus is formed by the trees, as is sometimes formed around cankers caused by *L. persoonii*. On President plum, *R. quercina* is equal in pathogenicity to *L. persoonii* but on Duarte plum it is nonpathogenic.

Control. Little if any effective chemical control has been developed for this disease. Cultural methods such as removal of the affected parts from the trees and paintings of the cuts with shellac (21) are advisable. Delayed pruning is suggested in Colorado (21) and should be effective in other areas. In addition, maintaining the trees in good vigor will suppress canker extension in infected areas, and any aid in preventing sunburn of branches will reduce infection sites. No major variations in resistance has been found in peach cultivars (22). The use of induced resistance is not confirmed or suggested at this time (12).

References

1. Bertrand, P. F. 1974. Cytospora canker of French prune. Ph.D. dissertation. Department of Plant Pathology, University of California, Davis. 113 pp.
2. Braun, J. W., and A. W. Helton. 1971. Induced resistance to *Cytospora* in Prunus persica. Phytopathology 61:685-87.
3. Chiarappa, L. 1960. Distribution and mode of spread of *Cytospora* canker in an orchard of the president plum variety in California. Plant Dis. Rep. 44:612-16.
4. Fisher, D. F., and F. L. Reeves. 1931. A Cytospora canker of apple trees. J. Agr. Research 43:431-38.
5. Gairola, G., and D. Powell. 1970. Cytospora peach canker in Illinois. Plant Dis. Rep. 54:832-35.
6. Hampson, M. C., and W. A. Sinclair. 1973. Xylem dysfunction in peach caused by *Cytospora leucostoma*. Phytopathology 63:676-81.
7. Helton, A. W. 1961. Low temperature injury as a contributing factor in *Cytospora* invasion of plum trees. Plant Dis. Rep. 45:591-97.
8. _____ 1962. Effect of simulated freeze-cracking on invasion of dry-ice-injured stems of Stanley prune trees by naturally disseminated *Cytospora* inoculum. Plant. Dis. Rep. 46:45-47.
9. _____ 1962. Relative efficiency of three methods of inoculating tree stems with *Cytospora* fungi. Phytopathology 52:1266-68.
10. _____ 1970. Effect of culture age on virulence of artificial *Cytospora* infections on Prunus domestica. Phytopathology 60:1694.
11. Helton, A. W., and J. W. Braun. 1970. Relationship of number of *Cytospora* infections on *Prunus domestica* to rate of expansion of individual cankers. Phytopathology 60:1700-01.
12. Helton, A. W., and J. J. Hubert. 1968. Inducing systemic resistance to *Cytospora* invasion in *Pruns domestica* with localized Prunus ringspot virus infections. Phytopathology 58:1423-24.
13. Helton, A. W., and D. E. Konicek. 1961. Effect of selected *Cytospora* isolates from stone fruits on certain stone fruit varieties. Phytopathology 51:152-57.
14. Hildebrand, E. M. 1947. Perennial peach canker and the canker complex in New York, with methods of control. Cornell Univ. Agr. Exp. Sta. Mem. 276:3-61.
14. Hubert, J. J., and A. W. Helton. 1967. A translocated resistance phenomenon in *Prunus domestica* induced by initial infection with *Cytospora cincta*. Phytopathology 57:1094-98.
16. James, W. C., and T. R. Davidson. 1971. Survey of peach canker in the Niagara peninsula during 1969 and 1970. Can. Plant Dis. Surv. 51(4):148-53.

17. Jones, A. C., and N. S. Leupschen. 1971. Seasonal development of Cytospora canker in peach in Colorado. Plant Dis. Rep. 55:314-317.

18. Kable, P. F., P. Fliegel, and K. G. Parker. 1967. Cytospora canker of sweet cherry in New York State: association with winter injury and pathogenicity to other species. Plant Dis. Rep. 51:155-57.

19. Kern, H. 1955. Taxonomic studies in the genus *Leucostoma*. Michigan Acad. Sci. Arts and Letters 40:9-22.

20. Leonian, L. H. 1921. Studies on the Valsa apple canker in New Mexico. Phytopathology 11:236-43.

21. Luepschen, N. S., and K. G. Rohrbach. 1969. Cytospora canker of peach trees: Spore availability and wound susceptibility. Plant Dis. Rep. 53:869-72.

22. Luepschen, N. S., A. C. Jones, K. G. Rohrbach, and L. E. Dickens. 1970. Peach varietal susceptibility to Cytospora canker. Colorado State Univ. Exp. Sta. PR 70-5. 2 pp.

23. Lukezic, F. L., and J. E. DeVay. 1965. Serological relationships between pathogenic and non-pathogenic isolates of *Leucostoma persoonii* and *Rhodosticta quercina*. Mycologia 57(3):442-47.

24. _____ 1964. Effect of myo-inositol in host tissues on the parasitism of *Prunus domestica* var. President by *Rhodosticta quercina*. Phytopathology 54:697-700.

25. Lukezic, F. L., J. E. DeVay, and H. English. 1960. Occurrence of Cytospora canker in stone fruit trees in California. Phytopathology 50:84. (Abstr.).

26. _____ 1965. Comparative physiology and pathogenicity of *Leucostoma persoonii* and *Rhodosticta quercina*. Phytopathology 55:511-18.

27. McCubbin, W. A. 1918. Peach canker. Canadian Dept. Agr. Bul. 37:1-20.

28. Rohrbach, K. G., and N. S. Luepschen. 1968. Environmental and nutritional factors affecting pycnospore germination of *Cytospora leucostoma*. Phytopathology 58:1134-36.

29. Rolfs, F. M. 1910. Winter killing of twigs, cankers, and sun scald of peach trees. Missouri State Exp. Sta. Bul. 17:1-101.

30. Stevens, F. L. 1919. An apple canker due to *Cytospora*. Illinois Agr. Exp. Sta. Bul. 217: 367-79.

31. Stewart, F. C., F. M. Rolfs, and F. H. Hall. 1900. A fruit disease survey of western New York in 1900. New York Agr. Exp. Sta. Bul. 191.

32. Togashi, K. 1931. Studies on the pathology of peach canker. Imperial Coll. Agr. and Forestry, Morioka, Japan Bul. 16:1-178.

33. Treshow, M., and J. F. Scholes. 1958. The taxonomy of some species of *Cytospora* found in Utah. Utah Acad. Proc. 35:49-51.

34. Treshow, M., B. L. Richards, and J. F. Scholes. 1959. The relation of temperature to patho-genicity of *Cytospora rubescens*. Phytopathology 49:114. (Abstr.).

35. Tsakadze, T. A. 1959. The effect of *Cytospora leucostoma* toxin on the plant cell. Bull. Cent. Bot. Gdn., Moscow. 1959:75-77.

36. Walton, R. C., and D. C. Babcock. 1916. The parasitism of *Valsa leucostoma*. Phytopathology 6:112-13.

37. Wensley, R. N. 1964. Occurrence and pathogenicity of *Valsa* (*Cytospora*) species and other fungi associated with peach canker in southern Ontario. Can. J. Bot. 42:841-57.

38. Willison, R. S. 1933. Peach canker investigation. I. Some notes on incidence, contributing factors and control measures. Scientific Agr. 14:32-46.

39. _____ 1935. Innoculation studies in peach canker. Sci. Agr. 15:435.

40. _____ 1936. Peach canker investigation. II. Infection studies. J. Canadian Research 14:27-44.

41. _____ 1937. Peach canker investigations. III. Further notes on incidence, contributing factors, and related phenomena. J. Agr. Research 15:324-39.

42. Wormald, H. 1912. The Cytospora disease of cherry. J. Southeastern Agr. Coll. (Wye, Kent.) 12:367-80.

43. Wysong, D. S., and L. S. Dickens. 1962. Variation in virulence of *Valsa leucostoma*. Plant Dis. Rep. 46:274-76.

Eutypa Dieback of Apricot
Eutypa armeniacae Hansf. & Carter

This disease, primarily one of apricot trees and also called "gummosis," "dieback," and Eutypa canker," is known to occur in Australia, New Zealand, South Africa, Spain, Switzerland, France, and California (2, 6, 9, 12, 14, 15). The disease was first reported in Tasmania by Dowson in 1931 (16) and in Australia by Harris in 1932 (20). However, Adam, Grace, and Flentje (2) believe that it has been present much longer in South Australia as well as in Victoria and New South Wales.

These authors report that while the disease varies greatly from district to district, it commonly affects from 23 to 68 percent of the trees in many older orchards. Its destructiveness is due to the fact that infection progressively involves larger and larger branches.

Symptoms. Diagnosis of this disease is covered by Adam, Grace and Flentje (2), English (17), and most recently by Carter (7). The symptom first noted is death of leaves on certain branches in the tree in early summer; the symptom is most apparent in summer after the fruit is harvested. During this time leaves on a branch may suddenly wilt and dry out, although they remain attached to the affected branch throughout the following winter season. The bark of such branches is dead, the wood is discolored light to dark brown, and the entire limb is dry, brittle, and breaks easily when bent. Examination of the affected branch reveals a canker adjacent to a pruning wound or other injuries which have exposed the xylem. The bark in this area is usually depressed and darkened, and at times longitudinal cracks develop. The internal wood is light or dark brown and has a definite margin with the adjacent healthy wood (fig. 27A). Although gum may ooze profusely from cracks in the bark, this is not a regular feature of the disease.

The disease occurs mostly in mature trees. Leaves on branches which are infected but not girdled by the canker may be larger than normal, but are abnormally cupped and marked by chlorotic patches or a slight silvering effect with burned or scorched margins. The latter symptom is said to resemble the symptoms of silver-leaf disease caused by *Stereum purpurem*. The fruit on such branches ripen earlier and leaves fall earlier than those on uninfected branches.

Causal organism. The causal organism occasionally produces pycnidia of the *Cytosporina* type. Carter in 1955 (3) showed that the fungus produces a perithecial stage, and he named this stage *Eutypa armeniacae* Hansf. & Carter. The perithecial stage was found in California in 1966 (24).

Pycnidia are single or closely aggregate, partly immersed or sitting almost wholly exposed on a black irregularly pulvinate stroma which may be up to 2 mm in diameter. Exposed pycnidia possess an apical round pore; immersed pycnidia have a short neck protruding to the surface of the bark. Pycnidia may be separate or more or less confluent, or sometimes compound with irregular locules partially divided by folds of the walls. Conidiophores are hyaline, simple, straight or slightly bent, 8 to 15 μm in length × 1 μm in width. Hyaline, bent, to arcuate, filiform pydniciospores, 18 to 25 × 1 μm are borne on ends of conidiophores. Pycnidiospores are extruded in cirri or as droplets from the pycnidia. So far, the pycnidiospores have not been germinated, and thus their function is in doubt.

Branches on which perithecia develop have been dead for 2 to 5 years, are largely decorticated, and look as if they had been partially burned by fire (fig. 27B). Perithecia, produced in the black stromatic layer, are globose bodies with fleshy-membraneous walls and are 450 μm in diameter. The asci, which attenuate into a stipe, are cylindric-clavate and measure 4 to 30 μm. The eight one-celled ascospores are 1 to 2 seriate, overlapping and allantoid. At maturity the ascospores are pale yellowish-brown, slightly bent with rounded ends, and are 7 to 11 μm long by 1.5 to 2 μm wide.

All eight ascospores are discharged at one time and disseminated intact. Germination occurs at relative humidities over 90 percent (4).

When cut tangentially the immersed perithecia within a stroma reveal the locules. When wet, the asci appear as a gelatinous, olivaceous-grey mass in the locules of the perithecia. Ascospores readily stain with aniline blue in lactophenol (7).

Potato dextrose or Czapek-Dox agars are best suited for isolation of the fungus. Culture from infected living wood can be obtained from margins of the canker, the white mycelia becoming apparent in 2 to 3 days when incubated at 15 to 25 °C. Cultures from perithecia are easily obtained by washing the stromata, immersing them in water for 1 to 1½ hours, and draining the excess water. They are then attached to the lids of sterile Petri dishes containing the culture medium for 10 minutes to allow for discharge of the ascospores onto the medium. The cultures are incubated at 15 to 25 °C. Ascospores germinate in 12 to 24 hours (7).

Price (29) was able to use serological methods to identify isolates from diseased apricots from Switzerland and South Africa. Cell-wall free extracts were used in the tests. Fluorescent antibody staining techniques gave less reliable results than the gel diffusion assay.

Other hosts. In addition to apricot, Carter (3) found the fungus to be saprophytic on European grape, almond, apple, tamarisk, peach, nectarine, and prune. The fungus also causes a canker disease of *Ceanothus* is Australia (21) and California (26) as well as western choke-cherry (*P. demissa*) in California (18).

Disease development. As no one has succeeded in germinating the pycnidiospores, and as the perithecial stage is rare in some areas, identity of the source, the fungus, the inoculum and its method of dissemination are unclear in those areas. Carter (5) found the perithecial stage to be abundant in the high-rainfall areas (greater than 20 inches) of Australia, but rare in the low-rainfall areas (less than 13 inches). A similar finding was reported by Ramos (30) in California.

In Australia, apricot branches were readily infected when 100 or more ascospores were placed in wounds in the winter (11). Under Australian conditions, wound susceptibility during dormancy declines rapidly in the first 2 weeks after pruning (10). Under California conditions, Ramos (30) showed, pruning wounds made on mature trees on September 21 remained susceptible to the fungus for at least 42 days, while wounds made on March 15 became resistant within 14 days. Young trees proved more susceptible at temperatures optimum for tree growth (20 °C) than under dormant conditions (3 °C). High humidity around the inoculation sites hastened development of resistance. Post-inoculation temperatures between 7 to 19 °C had no effect on the degree of infection, but canker size was proportional to the temperature. On Modesto apricot the size of pruning wounds was proportional to the degree of infection, but heartwood of large pruning wounds was not susceptible to infection. Four to 6 months of incubation was required for symptom development when inoculations were made with mycelia, and longer when inoculations were made with ascospores. Patterson apricot developed fewer cankers than did Modesto. On Tilton apricot the California isolate was more virulent than was the Australian isolate (30).

Ramos (30) provided evidence for long-distance dispersal of airborne ascospores from the areas of high rainfall such as Suisun and Hayward (greater than 20 inches) to the interior valley apricot districts of Tracy, Patterson, and Los Banos —a distance of about 50 miles. Correlation of ascospore release with rain and long-distance dissemination with prevailing winds was established. Limited numbers of perithecia were found in areas with mean annual rainfall of 13 to 15 inches (San Jose, Hollister, and Brentwood). No ascospore dispersal occurred during dry summer months, small numbers were dispersed in winter and spring, and the greatest numbers were dispersed in the fall.

Control. The following measures have been suggested by English *et al.* (18) to combat the disease: 1) All dying or abandoned apricot trees in the vicinity of commercial apricot orchards should be removed and burned; nearby dead or weakened grapevines should also be removed. 2) After the rainy season, infected limbs on the orchard trees should be removed and burned, otherwise fresh pruning cuts made in the fall and winter would provide entry points for the fungus; pruning tools should be sterilized with 5 percent formalin solution. 3) Large pruning wounds should be sealed with a grafting wax or oil base paint. 4) Use a modified system of pruning to reduce cuts on the main leaders to a minimum; this method leaves a portion of the lateral branches and permits removal of infected portions without sacrificing the leaders. Application of benzimidazole sprays in winter after pruning provided some protection while a high level (2.4 percent) of fungicide hand-painted onto large wounds provided better control and appeared commercially feasible (27).

Biological control studies using *Fusarium lateritium* spore suspensions containing 10^4 macroconidia per ml applied to pruning cuts protected against *E. armeniacae*. *F. lateritium* is restricted to a zone of sapwood 2 cm from the pruned surface (8, 13). Furthermore, *F. lateritium* tolerated water suspensions containing 400 ppm benomyl or thiabendazole. Studies on the practical use of *Fusarium* in combination with a fungicide are being made.

References

1. Adam, D. B. 1938. A progress report on a gummosis (dieback) disease in South Australian apricot trees. J. Dept. Agr. S. Australia 42:14-29.
2. Adam, D. B., J. Grace, and N. T. Flentje. 1952. The "gummosis" or "dieback" disease of apricots. J. Dept. Agr. S. Australia 55:450-55.
3. Carter, M. V. 1955. Apricot gummosis—a new development. J. Dept. Agr. S. Australia 59:178-84.
4. _____ 1957. *Eutypa armeniacae* Hansf. & Carter, sp. nov., an airborne vascular pathogen of *Prunus armeniaca* L. in Southern Australia. Australian J. Botany 5:21-35.
5. _____ 1957. Vines aid spread of apricot "gummosis." J. Dept. Agric. S. Austr. 60:482-83.
6. _____ 1960. Further studies on *Eutypa armeniacae* Hansf. & Carter. Australia J. Agr. Sci. 2:498-504.
7. _____ 1968. Diagnosis of canker disease of apricot trees caused by *Eutypa armeniacae* Hansf. and Carter. Tech. Communications International Soc. Hort. Sci. 11(III):389-90.
8. _____ 1971. Biological control of *Eutypa armeniacae*. Aust. J. Exp. Agric. and Animal Husb. 11:687-92.
9. Carter, M. V., and A. Bolay. 1972. *Eutypa armeniacae* die back of apricot is prevalent in Switzerland. Phytopath. Z. 75:187-89.
10. Carter, M. V., and W. J. Moller. 1970. Duration of susceptibility of apricot pruning wounds to infection by *Eutypa armeniacae*. Aust. J. Agric. Res. 21:915-20.
11. _____ 1971. The quantity of inoculum required to infect apricot and other *Prunus* species with *Eutypa armeniacae*. Aust. J. Exp. Agric. Anim. Husb. 11:684-86.
12. _____ 1974. *Eutypa armeniacae* canker of apricot in Spain. Plant Dis. Rep. 58:442-43.
13. Carter, M. V., and T. V. Price. 1974. Biological control of *Eutypa armeniacae*. II. Studies of the interaction between *E. armeniacae* and *Fusarium lateritium*, and their relative sensitivities to benzimidazole chemicals. Aust. J. Agric. Res. 25:105-19.
14. Carter, M. V., G. S. Morvan, and C. Castelain.

13. Carter, M. V., G. S. Morvan, and C. Castelain. 1964. An extension of the known distribution of *Eutypa armeniacae*. Nature 202:1134-35.
15. Dingley, J. M. 1960. Eutypa canker of apricots. Orchardist of New Zealand 33:78-79.
16. Dowson, W. J. 1931. The die-back of apricots. Preliminary note. Tasmanian J. Agr. H.S. 2:165.
17. English, W. H. 1960. A new apricot fungus disease found in Santa Clara County orchards. Sunsweet Standard 43:5, 13-14.
18. English, H., and J. R. Davis. 1965. Apricot dieback fungus found on western chokecherry. Plant Dis. Rep. 49:178.
19. English, H., H. J. O'Reilly, L. B. McNelly, J. E. DeVay and A. D. Rizzi. 1963. Cytosporina dieback of apricot. Calif. Agr. 2-4.
20. Harris, J. B. 1932. Dieback of apricot trees in the Varossa district. J. Dept. Agr. S. Australia 35:1394.
21. Moller, W. J. 1964. Apricot disease found on garden shrub. S. Australian J. Agr. 67:251.
22. Moller, W. J., and M. V. Carter. 1965. Production and dispersal of ascospores in *Eutypa armeniacae*. Aust. J. Biol. Sci. 18:67-80.
23. _____ 1970. Field evaluation of benomyl for control of limb dieback (gummosis) in apricots. Australian J. of Exper. Agr. and Anim. Husb. 10:488-89.
24. Moller, W. J., H. English, and J. R. Davis. 1966. The perithecial stage of *Eutypa armeniacae* in California. Plant Dis. Rep. 50:53.
25. Moller, W. J., H. English, and J. R. Davis. 1968. *Eutypa armeniacae* on grape in California. Plant Dis. Rep. 52:751.
26. Moller, W. J., D. E. Ramos, and W. R. Hildreth. 1971. Apricot pathogen associated with Ceanothus limb dieback in California. Plant Dis. Rep. 55:1006-1008.
27. Moller, W. J., D. E. Ramos, and R. R. Sanborn. 1977. Eutypa dieback in California apricot orchards: Chemical control studies. Plant Dis. Rep. 61:600-4.
28. Ogawa, J. M., B. T. Manji, and E. Bose. 1968. Efficacy of fungicide 1991 in reducing fruit rot of stone fruit. Plant Dis. Rep. 52:722-26.
29. Price, T. V. 1973. Serological identification of *Eutypa armeniacae*. Australian J. Biol. Sci. 26:389-94.
30. Ramos, D. E. 1974. Epidemiology of Eutypa *(Cytosporina)* dieback of apricot. Ph.D. dissertation, Department of Plant Pathology, University of California, Davis. 64 pp.
31. Samuel, G. 1933. "Gummosis" or "Dieback" in apricot trees. J. Dept. Agr. S. Australia 36:979-80.
32. Smith, L. C. 1953. Apricot gummosis investigations—progress report, 1951-53. J. Dept. Agr. S. Australia 57:64-65.

Damping-Off of Peach Seedlings
Pythium species

Peach seedlings grown for rootstocks frequently die when grown in untreated soil (fig. 28). Such damping-off may occur before the seedling emerges from the soil, in which case the cotyledons and embryo of the seeds undergo a soft-watery rot. In other cases the primary root of the emerging plant is rotted. Such conditions differ from the failure of seeds to grow because of poor viability (1), or because of undeveloped or aborted embryos (5). Gardner and Marth (2) found great variations in germination among seeds from various peach cultivars.

Cause. Halliwell and Johnson (3) reported that an unidentified species of *Penicillium* caused seed rot and seedling tip necrosis of peach. Mircetich and Fogle (4) reported that *Pythium debaryanum, P. irregulare, P. mamillatum, P. paroecandrum,* and *P. ultimum* caused damping-off of peach seedlings.

Control. The solution to damping-off has been to grow seedlings in soil that has been fumigated with methyl bromide to kill the causal fungus or fungi. To reduce contamination, seeds were dipped in chlorine solution before planting.

References

1. Cochran, L. C., W. C. Cooper, and E. C. Blodgett. 1961. Seeds for rootstocks of fruit and nut trees. *In* Seeds, The Yearbook of Agriculture. p. 233-39.
2. Gardner, F. E. and P. C. Marth. 1937. Germination of seedling vigor of peach varieties for understock. Amer. Soc. Hort. Soc. Proc. 35:409-414.
3. Halliwell, R. S. and J. D. Johnson. 1964. Seed rot and seedling tip necrosis of peach caused by a species of *Penicillium*. Plant Dis. Rep. 48:136-38.
4. Mircetich, S. M. and H. W. Fogle. 1969. Role of *Pythium* in damping-off of peach. Phytopathology 59:356-58.
5. Theobald, W. L. and L. F. Hough. 1960. The relationship between stage of peach embryo development and seedling growth and survival. Amer Soc. Proc. 75:163-70.

Dothiorella Canker of Almond
Botryosphaeria dothidea
(Moug. ex. Fr.) Ces. and de Not.

A canker of the trunk and scaffold branches of almond *(Prunus amygdalus)* was reported by English, Davis, and DeVay (1) in 1965. This disease was first noted in 1959 as occurring in Tehama and Stanislaus counties of California. It was found again in San Joaquin County in 1960, in Merced County in

1961, and in Yolo County in 1963. Occurrence since that time has been sporadic (2).

Symptoms. The disease is restricted primarily to Nonpareil, and occurs most frequently in more vigorous trees. Narrow bandlike or irregular-shaped cankers may extend around the trunk or scaffold branches (fig. 29). They differ from other cankers in that their greatest dimension is transverse to the long axis of the branch or trunk. They appear to originate in growth cracks, usually become noticeable in summer, and are accompanied by copious gum formation.

The bark of the branch including the cambium is killed and these areas become noticeably sunken because of the subsequent desiccation. Where a girdling canker extends to the wood, the portion of the branch or trunk above the canker dies. Although complete girdling of the trunk is relatively uncommon, half or more of its circumference may be involved. Scaffold branches are frequently killed.

Cankers are active during the growing season in which they first appear, but they usually do not become active again in subsequent seasons. Because of this feature and the fact that it occurs infrequently, the disease is of relatively minor importance.

Cause. One or both of two fungi may be associated with canker development of almond. These are the *Dothiorella* stage of *Botryosphaeria dothidea* (Moug. ex Fr.) Ces. and de Not and *Hendersonula toruloidea* Nattrass. The latter is the cause of a branch wilt of English walnut in California, and is also pathogenic to peach and apricot trees in California (4). It has been associated with dieback symptoms of plum, apricot, and apple trees in Egypt (3).

Isolations from almond cankers occurring in different parts of the Sacramento and San Joaquin valleys indicated that *B. dothidea* was much more common than *H. toruloidea*. Moreover, *B. dothidea* was the only fungus found at the margins of "apparently active" cankers. English, Davis, and Devay (2) therefore concluded that this fungus was ". . . largely responsible for this canker condition, and that *H. toruloidea* was a common secondary invader." Nevertheless, either fungus was ". . . able to induce canker formation when mycelial inoculum was placed in cortical wounds on the cambium, or on xylem exposed by pruning" (2).

Susceptible cultivars of almonds. Nonpareil was found to be more susceptible than either Mission or Ne Plus Ultra. Natural infection in Davey and Drake almonds was observed only once.

References

1. English, H., J. R. Davis, and J. E. DeVay. 1966. Dothiorella canker, a new disease of almond trees in California. Phytopathology 56:146. (Abstr.).
2. _____ 1975. Relationship of *Botryosphaeria dothidea* and *Hendersonula toruloidea* to a canker disease of almond. Phytopathology 65:114-22.
3. Nattrass, R. M. 1933. A new species of *Hendersonula (H. toruloidea)* on deciduous trees in Egypt. Trans. Brit Mycol. Soc. 18:189-98.
4. Wilson, E. E. 1947. The branch wilt of Persian walnut trees and its cause. Hilgardia 17:413-36.

Hull Rot of Almond
Rhizopus species; *Monilinia fructicola* (Wint.) Honey; *Monilinia laxa* (Ader. & Ruhl). Honey

Hull rot of almond has occurred sporadically in the Sacramento and San Joaquin valleys for many years. In some years it causes considerable loss of the current crop and some reduction of new shoots. Diseased fruit which remains on the trees harbors the navel orange worm in wintertime (1).

Symptoms. There are three macroscopic symptoms of the disease: (a) In late summer, after almond hulls have begun to dehisce (separate at the suture), light brown spots appear on the hulls usually along the suture. These later coalesce and the entire hull becomes wrinkled and shrunken. Mycelia, black conidia, and conidiophores of the fungus frequently develop on the inner surface of the separating hull (fig. 30A). Mycelia are found on the inner surface of the hull. (b) Leaves on twigs nearest affected fruit curl and later dry up but remain attached to the twig. Where rotted fruit occurs on a terminal shoot, leaves along the side of the shoot on which the fruit is attached may curl and dry up; some of these leaves may, before drying up, develop necrotic streaks along one side of the midvein. (c) Soon after leaves wither, the supporting twig (spur or terminal shoots) becomes discolored and dies.

Causal organism. Both *Monilinia laxa* and *M. fructicola* occasionally are found to produce hull and twig symptoms (fig. 30B). Mycelia of *Rhizopus* spp. are found on the inner hull of the fruit. Isolates of this fungus readily produce both the hull rot and shoot blight. The species involved are, according to keys of Zycha (5) and Kockova-Kratochvilova (2), *R. stolonifer* (Ehr. ex Fr.) Lind., *R. circinans* u. Tilgh. and *R. arrhizus* Fischer (3).

Although mycelia of the fungus may occur in fruit stems, they are not present in twigs or leaves. Twig and leaf symptoms are caused by a toxin (fumaric acid) produced by the fungi (4). C^{14}-labeled fumaric acid tests show that fumaric acid is present in large

Fig. 1. Blast of pear. **A.** Blasted and healthy blossoms in cluster **B.** Blighted twig showing papery bark condition. **C.** Necrotic spotting on immature fruit. (Courtesy of P. Bertrand.)

Fig. 2. Fireblight of pear. **A.** Blighted shoots on young tree. **B.** Blighted blossom cluster showing bacterial ooze.

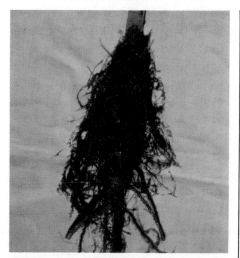

Fig. 3. Hairy root of apple showing excessive root formation.

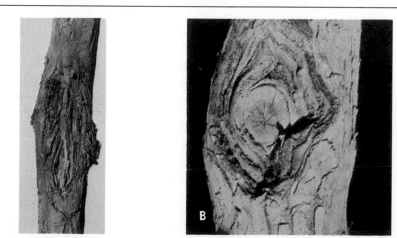

Fig. 4. **A.** Anthracnose canker of apple. **B.** Perennial canker of apple. (Both photos courtesy of Mid-Columbia Exp. Sta., Hood River, Oregon.)

Fig. 5. Typical white, wefty, aerial mycelial growth of *Dematophora* in soil around rotted roots. (Courtesy of R. D. Raabe.)

Fig. 6. European canker of apple. **A.** Zonate annual cankers extending from initial leaf scar infections. **B.** Red-colored perithecia. **C.** Calyx-end infections.

Fig. 7. Phytopthora crown and root rot of young nursery stock shown with few roots in disease area (right) compared to normal root development (left). (Courtesy of S. M. Mircetich.)

Fig. 8. Powdery mildew of apple. **A.** Terminal leaves with mildew on left and healthy terminal with fruit on right. **B.** Blossom cluster with all floral parts infected.

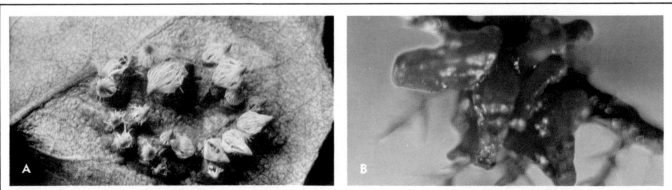

Fig. 9. Trellis rust of pear. **A.** Aecial stage on leaf. (Courtesy of California State Department of Food and Agriculture). **B.** Wet telial horns on juniper. (Courtesy of Z. Punja.)

84

Fig. 10. Scab of apple. **A.** Black scabby irregular lesions on fruit. (Courtesy of M. Szkolnik.) **B.** Black irregular lesion on under-surface of leaf.

Fig. 11. Scab symptoms on pear leaves, peduncle, fruit and stem.

Fig. 12. Apple measles expressed as numerous irregular necrotic lesions on cut surface.

Fig. 13. Bitter pit of apple with numerous circular dark brown pits.

Fig. 14. Black-end of pear fruit. (Courtesy of K. Ryugo.)

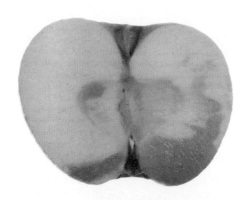

Fig. 15. Water-core symptoms expressed as water-soaked areas of apple flesh.

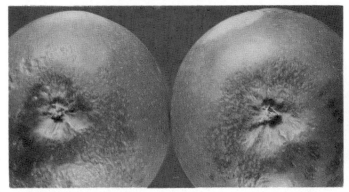

Fig. 16. Scald of apple shown as large brown, irregularly shaped patches on stylar-end of fruit. (Courtesy of California State Department of Food and Agriculture.)

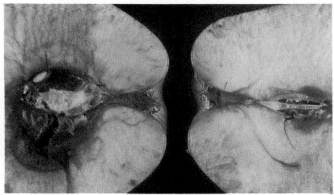

Fig. 17. *Alternaria* developing in fruit core. (Courtesy of California State Department of Food and Agriculture.)

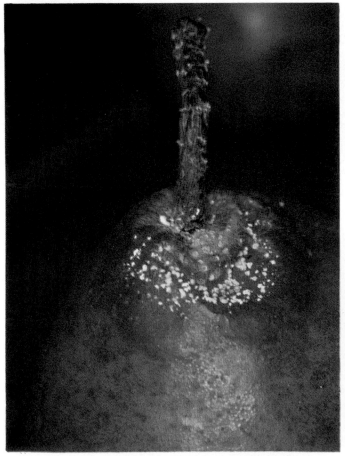

Fig. 18. Blue mold sporulating on stem-end of fruit.

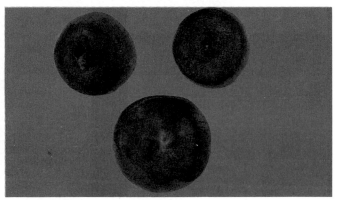

Fig. 19. Fruit showing nondescript lesions of *Phomopsis*. (Courtesy of N. F. Sommer.)

Fig. 20. Cluster of prune blossoms blasted by bacterial infections.

Fig. 21. Progression of leaf scorch of almond. **A.** Initial symptoms are marginal scorching of leaves on terminal shoots. **B.** Scorching of whole leaves except for the green at midrib. **C.** Diseased wood detected by immersion in acidified methanol to show distinct reddish-purple streaks as in three samples on left. (Courtesy of S. M. Mircetich.)

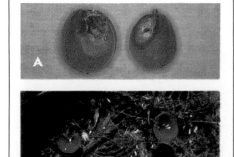

Fig. 22. Green fruit rot. **A.** Infection of fruit from *Botrytis*-infected blossom part. **B.** Light-brown small apothecia of *Whetzelinia* (below peach pit with two large apothecia of *Monilinia fructicola*).

Fig. 23. Brown rot of stone fruits. **A.** Blossom and twig blight on apricot (*Monilinia laxa*). **B.** Sporodochia of *M. laxa* showing masses of spores. **C.** Peach fruit decaying from infection by *Monilinia fructicola*.

Fig. 24. Ceratocystis canker. **A.** Dark-brown infected tissue of an apricot branch. **B.** Scaffold of almond tree dying from infection originating in shaker injury.

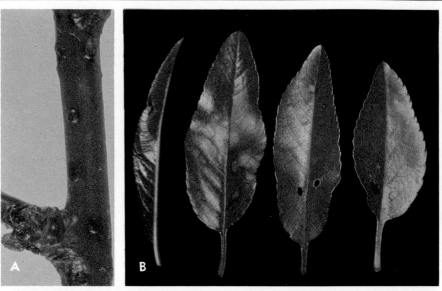

Fig. 25. Coryneum blight. **A.** Circular purplish-colored spots with white centers on twig. **B.** Necrotic lesions on young leaves and shot-holing on older leaves. **C.** Dormant bud blight and brown circular lesions on upper surface of apricot fruit.

Fig. 26. Cytospora canker. **A.** Spore tendrils on peach scaffold. **B.** Black pycnidia with white ostiole, found beneath surface of infected bark.

Fig. 27. Eutypa dieback of apricot. **A.** Light-brown internal wood with definite margin adjacent to healthy wood. **B.** Perithecia developing on black stromatic layer on wood.

Fig. 28. Nursery bed showing apricot seedlings killed by *Pythium.*

Fig. 29. Narrow, band-like, irregular-shaped cankers formed around trunk of Nonpareil almond infected by *Dothiorella.* (Courtesy of W. H. English.)

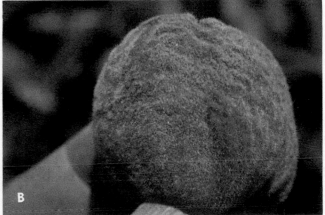

Fig. 30. Hull rot of almond. **A.** *Rhizopus*-infected hull (sporulating under the inner surface of split hull) with shoot dieback. **B.** *Monilinia* infection and sporulation on hull.

Fig. 31. Leaf blight of almond. **A.** Sudden death of leaves caused by infection at base of leaf petiole. **B.** Remains of leaves during fall, winter, and spring with infections moving into stem and bud.

Fig. 32. Leaf curl symptoms on sweet cherry.

Fig. 34. Leaf spot fungus infections on sour cherry showing yellow leaves with pycnidia.

Fig. 35. Large bladder-like diseased fruit with plum pocket diseases.

Fig. 33. Leaf curl of peach. **A.** Curling of first formed leaves with new healthy growth. **B.** Fruit infection on Red Haven peach.

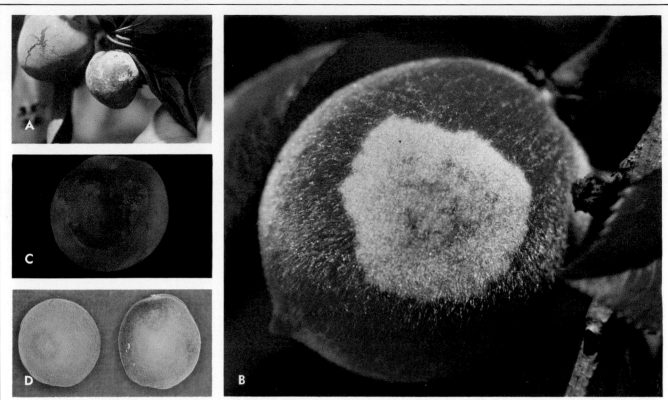

Fig. 36. Powdery mildew. **A.** *Sphaerotheca pannosa* on Kelsey plum which later turns brown and rough in texture. **B.** Typical-mildew on peach fruit caused by *S. pannosa.* **C.** Brown russeting symptoms developing from infection by *Podosphaera leucotricha.* **D.** *S. pannosa* developing on apricot fruit before pit-hardening stage.

Fig. 37. Rust of prune. **A.** Distinct yellow lesions on top surface. **B.** Advanced stages of disease showing upward curling and abundant uredial and telial spores on undersurface.

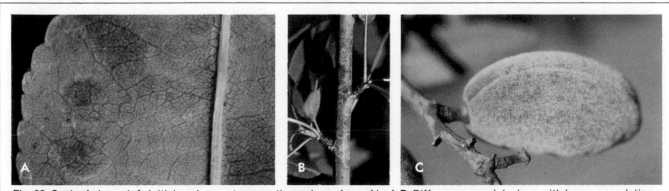

Fig. 38. Scab of almond. **A.** Initial scab symptoms on the undersurface of leaf. **B.** Diffuse grey scab lesions with heavy sporulation at the margins on shoots. **C.** Superficial grey scab on upper surface of fruit.

Fig. 39. Corky growth of Jordanolo almond kernel.

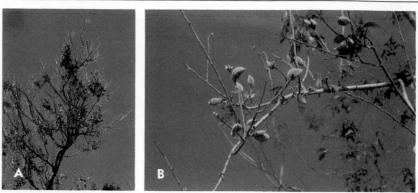

Fig. 40. Noninfectious bud failure of almond. **A.** Branch having many dead and few live shoots. **B.** Irregular growth of branch.

Fig. 41. Russet scab of prune. **A.** Lack of epidermal wax on developing fruit. **B.** Symptoms at harvest and after drying.

Fig. 42. Postharvest fruit decay. **A.** Molds on fresh sweet cherries are predominately *Rhizopus stolonifer, Monilinia fructicola,* and *Botrytis cinerea.* **B.** On apricot fruit: *Rhizopus* spp., *Monilinia laxa, Aspergillus* spp., and *Alternaria alternata.* **C.** On peach fruit: *R. stolonifer* and *M. fructicola.* **D.** On dried prune: *Aspergillus* spp.

Fig. 43. Bacterial canker. **A.** Canker extending from scaffold into trunk of plum. **B.** Infection of dormant apricot buds in winter. **C.** Black depressed lesions on fruit and peduncle of sweet cherry. **D.** Shot–holing of leaf on apricot. **E.** Infection of apricot fruit after freeze injury of epidermis.

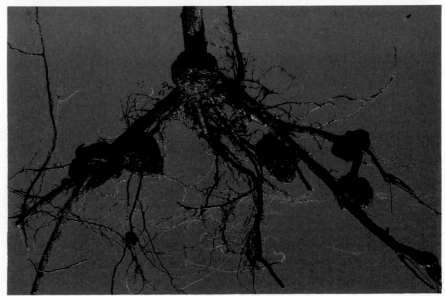

Fig. 44. Crown and root galls on young almond nursery stock.

Fig. 45. Armillaria root rot. **A.** Typical white mycelial plaque found under infected bark. **B.** Rhizomorphs on surface of roots. **C.** *Armillaria* sporophore (mushroom) at base of diseased peach tree. **D.** Sporophore showing annulus and typical honey coloration.

Fig. 46. Phytophthora crown and root rot. **A.** Orchard dying from *Phytophthora* infections. **B.** Fruit infected during sprinkler irrigation with stagnant water from lake. **C.** Crown rot symptoms at point below the soil line.

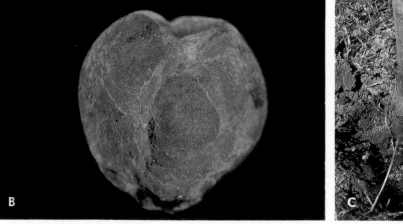

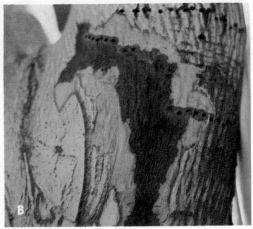

Fig. 49. Bark canker of walnut. **A.** Black stain and ooze on surface of bark. **B.** Irregular shallow brown necrotic lesions. (Courtesy of Z. Punja.)

Fig. 47. Silver leaf. **A.** Peach branch with upward rolled silvery leaves instead of deep-green coloration. **B.** Sporophore of *Stereum purpureum.*

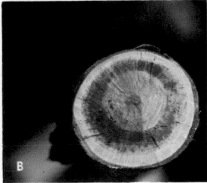

Fig. 48. Verticillium wilt. **A.** One-sided wilting of almond tree. **B.** Darkening of xylem tissue in branch.

Fig. 50. Blight of walnut. **A.** Suspected holdover canker on twig. **B.** Catkin infection showing bacterial ooze. (Courtesy of D. J. Ravetto.) **C.** Stylar-end infection of nut.

Fig. 51. Crown gall formation at base of mature Paradox hybrid rootstock.

Fig. 54. White to pale-yellow downy spots on underside of English walnut leaves.

Fig. 52. Phloem canker extending throughout bark and staining the wood.

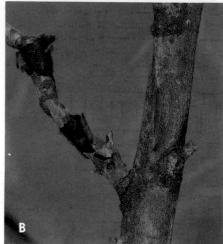

Fig. 53. Branch wilt of walnut. **A.** Branch killed from girdling of the stem. **B.** Uplifting of the branch periderm showing masses of black spores.

Fig. 55. Black line of walnut **A.** Decline in vigor of tree having water sprouts on black walnut rootstock. **B.** Distinct necrosis at graft union.

Fig. 56. Olive knot. **A.** Defoliation and killing of twigs and branches was caused by formation of galls or knots. **B.** Galls formed at leaf scars.

Fig. 58. Olive tree scaffold killed by Verticillium wilt.

Fig. 57. Cycloconium leaf spot. Infections first show as olivaceous green circular lesions, and are later expressed as green lesions and yellow leaves.

Fig. 59. Small spherical-shaped fruit called "shotberry."

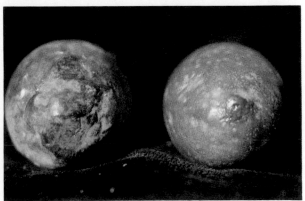

Fig. 60. Soft nose of olive fruit expressed as early red pigmentation of the fruit stylar-end, which later becomes black with necrosis of tissue.

97

Fig. 61. Endosepsis of fig. Two healthy on top row and two diseased on lower row.

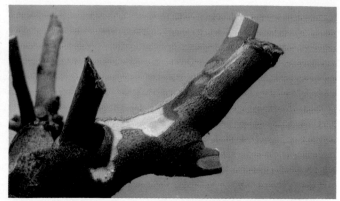

Fig. 62. Fig phomopsis canker symptoms extending from pruning-wound infections.

Fig. 63. Smut of fig expressed in the split fruit at the right. Fruit on left is healthy.

Fig. 64. Souring in fig fruit results in exudate dripping from the eye. (Courtesy of E. Smith.)

Fig. 65. Alternaria rot on fig fruit is expressed as water-soaked and sunken brown lesions.

Fig. 66. Fruit rots of pomegranate. **A.** *Aspergillus niger* infection in cracked fruit. **B.** *Botrytis* and *Penicillium* infection in cracked fruit.

amounts in rotted hulls, is transported via the xylem vessels up the twig, and accumulates in the leaves before leaf and twig symptoms appear. During symptom development the toxin disappears and the radioactive carbon is then found in the malic, citric, and tartaric acid components of the leaves and twigs.

Disease development. Inoculation of fruit apparently occurs shortly after the hull separates along the suture and the fungus spores gain entrance to the moist inner hull tissue. *Rhizopus* is unable to infect through the outer surface of the hull. Consequently, the disease develops during late summer before the fruit is to be harvested and is favored by rain showers, though these are not required.

All almond varieties may be affected but the disease occurs most commonly in Nonpareil and Jordanolo. Although hulls of Texas and NePlus Ultra may be rotted, little blighting of the supporting twigs occur (1).

Hull rot occurs in almond-growing districts of the Sacramento and San Joaquin valleys.

Control. No control method has been developed for the disease caused by *Rhizopus* spp. Hull rot caused by *Monilinia laxa* can possibly be controlled by the use of a dormant eradicant-type fungicide, but no control measure has been developed for hull rot caused by *Monilinia fructicola*.

References

1. Browne, L. T., J. M. Ogawa, and B. Gashaira. 1977. Search continues for control of almond hull rot. California Agriculture 31:16-17.
2. Kockova-Kratochvilova, A. and V. Palkoska. 1958. A taxonomic study of the genus Rhizopus Ehrenberg 1820. Preslia 30:150-64.
3. Mirocha, C. J., and E. E. Wilson. 1961. Hull rot disease of almond. Phytopathology 51:843-47.
4. Mirocha, C. J., J. E. DeVay, and E. E. Wilson. 1961. Role of fumaric acid in the hull rot disease of almond. Phytopathology 51:851-60.
5. Zycha, H. 1935. Mucorineae in Kryptogamenflora der Mark Brandenburg Vol. 6a, Leipzig. Gerhrudes Borntraeger. 264 pp.

Leaf Blight of Almond
Hendersonia rubi West.

Leaf blight first became known in 1950 when it developed in a few orchards in the Sacramento Valley near Chico, Butte County, California. It later appeared in the northern part of the San Joaquin Valley. Eighty-six percent of the state's almond orchards are located in these two areas. The disease was recently reported in Australia (2).

Although leaf blight seldom destroys more than 15 to 20 percent of the leaves, repeated attacks eventually weaken the tree. An immediate reduction in productivity follows the loss of flower buds killed by the extension of the causal fungus from the leaf petiole into the supporting twig.

Symptoms and signs. Leaf blight (fig. 31A) is characterized by sudden dying of leaves. Beginning in June, one or more leaves of spurs or shoots wither, turn brown, and dry out; other leaves then die throughout the summer. Though a few affected leaves fall, most do not; fragments of the petioles of such leaves remain on the tree until spring (fig. 31B).

No signs of the causal fungus are present on affected leaves in summer. In winter, however, the lower end of the persisting diseased petiole turns light tan and shortly afterwards small, dark fruiting bodies of the fungus develop on this area.

In late fall, buds in the axils of affected leaves are killed by growth of the fungus from the petiole into the twig. In spring, flowers are killed in the same manner as they emerge from the winter buds.

Susceptibility of almond cultivars. Almond cultivars vary considerably in susceptibility. Drake, NePlus Ultra, and Peerless are highly susceptible; Nonpareil, Texas (Mission), and IXL are moderately susceptible.

Causal organism. Only the imperfect stage of the causal fungus is known to occur on almond. This stage has been identified as *Hendersonia rubi* West. According to Zeller (5, 6), the ascigerous stage of *Hendersonia rubi* developed on canes of affected raspberries in Oregon; he identified it as *Ascospora rubi* (West) Zeller. This conidial stage has been assigned to the genus *Coryneum* because the conidial fruiting bodies vary from acervuli to pycnidia. Archer (1) showed that acervulus-like fruiting bodies are more common than pycnidia on raspberry stems.

In culture, the fungus colony consists of abundant brown subsurface mycelia and dirty gray aerial hyphae. Conidia are produced in separate sporodochium-like structures, which at first are arranged in concentric rings but which later become so numerous as to form a continuous layer. In some isolates pycnidia may be quite abundant, on others comparatively few. The conidia, borne on the ends of slender tapering conidiophores, are elliptical in shape but with the basal end more pointed than the apical end. Most of them are four-celled; the lower cell is subhyaline while the other cells are light brown in color. The wall of the conidium is slightly constructed where the septum joins it.

On the host, the acervulus-like type of fruiting body varies from 115 to 165 μ in diameter. In the early stages this structure may be uncovered, or it may possess a covering of loosely-connected hyphal elements so fragile that it is seldom found to be intact after the conidia mature.

The pycnidia are ovoid in shape, with a peridium of relatively thick-walled pseudoparenchymatous cells and an ostiole. They range in diameter from 95 to 115 μm. The conidia produced in pycnidia are identical with those produced in acervuli and are more uniform in size and in number of cells than those from culture. They range from 11.9 to 117 μm in length and from 6.1 to 7.5 μm in breadth. See Saccardo (4) for measurements of conidia of *Hendersonia rubi*.

Disease development. The cycle of the pathogen pertaining to development of the disease is completed on the tree. The fungus survives from one year to the next in affected petioles that remain on twigs throughout the winter. It is quiescent in these parts during summer, but after rains begin in winter it produces conidia in fruiting bodies that develop over the basal part of the petiole. Nothing is known about how and when the conidia are disseminated. They are probably washed about by rains in winter, but it is unlikely that they are freely disseminated by air currents. Conidia produced in acervuli occasionally may be picked up and distributed by air, but those in pycnidia probably seldom are. In some manner, however, they succeed in reaching leaf petioles which they infect. Once inside the petiole, the fungus interferes with water conduction and the leaf withers. The pathogen grows from the petiole into the twig and kills the bud in late autumn and winter. Enlargement of the twig lesion is resumed in the spring, at which time flowers are killed as they emerge from the winter buds.

Control. Leaf blight has been controlled by spraying the trees with either a protective fungicide or an eradicative fungicide. Captan, 2 lb; ziram, 2 lb; or dichone, ¾ lb in 100 gallons of water have been effective protective fungicides if the spray is applied at petal-fall stage. Eradicative treatment consists of spraying trees in early spring before the winter buds begin to open with a preparation containing 4 lb of sodium pentachlorophenoxide in each 100 gallons of water (3).

References

1. Archer, W. A. 1956. Morphological characters of some Sphaeropsidales in culture. Annales Mycologia 24:46-51.
2. Moller, W. J. 1972. *Hendersonia rubi* and *Rhizopus stolonifer,* two newly recorded fungal pathogens of almond in South Australia. Search 3(3):86-87.
3. Ogawa, J. M., E. E. Wilson, and Harley English. 1959. The leaf blight of almond and its control. Hilgardia 28:239-54.
4. Saccardo, P.A. 1884. Sylloge Fungorum 3:4241.
5. Zeller, S. M. 1925. *Coryneum ruborum* Oud., and its ascigerous stage. Mycologia 17:33-41.
6. _____ 1927. A correction. Mycologia 19:150-51.

Leaf Curl of Cherry
Taphrina cerasi (Fkl.) Sadeb.

Cherry leaf curl, also known as "witches-broom," occurs worldwide, having been reported from Europe, Australia, New Zealand, South Africa, Japan and North America. In Oregon it occurs every year, but in California it occurred only in Napa County in 1929 (2), in Berkeley in 1935 (2) and in San Joaquin County in 1970. The disease is not of great economic importance.

Symptoms. Symptoms on leaves resemble the typical leaf curl found on peaches and nectarines with curling, slightly thickened leaves, and reddish coloration (Fig. 32). On branches, large broom-like tufts develop and are distinguishable at blossom time because they have few flowers and develop a full flush of leaves earlier than healthy branches. These branches bear no fruit. The disease incidences in California in 1929 and 1970 showed only leaf symptoms.

Cause and disease development. *Taphrina cerasi* (Fkl.) Sadeb. attacks cultivated cherries (*Prunus avium* and *P. cerasus*). In California it has been observed only on the former. Ascospores are produced on leaves which attack the buds and stimulates excessive branching (witches'-broom). The asci are hypophyllous, rarely amphigenous, clavate, rounded at the apex and provided with a stalk cell. There are eight ascospores per ascus. These are round, ovate, or elliptic, and often bud in the ascus. Dimensions of the clavate asci are 17 to 53 × 5 to 15 μm; of stalk cells 5 to 26 um in length × 4 to 12 μm in width; and of ascospores 3.5 to 9 long × 3 to 6 μm broad (2). Once infected, the branch produced witches'-broom each year and the leaves on these branches are diseased; this indicates that the fungus is perennial within the shoot (1).

Control. Copper or sulfur has been recommended to prevent leaf infections (3). When witches'-broom occurs these should be pruned at least 12 inches below the point of normal branching (1).

References

1. MacSwan, I. C., and P. A. Koepsell. 1974. Oregon Plant Disease Control Handbook. OSU Bookstores, Inc., P. O. Box 489. Corvallis, Oregon 97330. 187 pp.

2. Mix, A. J., 1949. A monograph of the genus *Taphrina*. University of Kansas Science Bul. 33(1). 167 pp.

3. Smith, R. E. 1941. Diseases of fruits and nuts. Calif. Agr. Ext. Cir. 120. P. 54 (out of print).

Leaf Curl of Nectarine and Peach
Taphrina deformans (Berk.) Tulasne

Peach leaf curl, described as early as 1821 in England, is now practically coextensive with peach and nectarine culture (13). In addition to these hosts the disease has been reported on almonds in Europe and New Zealand and on apricots in New Zealand (6), but leaf curl has not been reported from either host in the western U.S.

In spite of control measures the loss of peach fruit in the U.S. in 1929 was 254,000 bushels (30), in 1922, 145,000 bushels (12), and 840,000 bushels in 1924 (33). Losses are negligible today with proper control.

Symptoms. In spring, reddish areas appear on the developing leaves (fig. 33A). These areas progressively become thick and puckered causing the leaf to curl dorsally and soon fall. Shoots are also frequently invaded; they become thickened and distorted and frequently die. Blossoms which are sometimes infected shrivel and fall. Though fruit infection is rare, fruit sometimes develop irregular somewhat elevated wrinkled lesions (fig. 33B).

Cause. The causal fungus has been called *Taphrina deformans* (Berk.) Tulasne; = *Exoascus deformans* (Berk.) Fuckel, and *Exoascus amygdali* Jaczewaki (28). Asci of the fungus are 17 to 25 μm in length × 7 to 13 μm in width and the ascospores are 3 to 7 μm long × 3 to 7 μm broad. Pierce (30) described the "vegetative" and "fruiting" hyphae of the fungus, the former being more thread-like and with longer cells than the latter. The fruiting hyphae are composed of irregular short cells, mostly located on leaves. The mycelia in infected shoots are largely vegetative.

Disease development. Survival of the fungus from one year to the next was first believed to be by means of perennial mycelia in twigs (32), but Pierce (30) recognized that such a concept did not explain the behavior of the disease in the orchard. Caporali (8) stated that hyphae rarely survive through January in the cortical tumors of branches. It is now believed that the fungus survives our hot dry summers as ascospores and when fall rains begin the ascospores germinate, giving rise to bud-conidia—which were seen by most earlier workers including Pierce (30) and which were studied by Caporali (8). As a result of the successive budding of the bud-conidia, the twigs and buds of the trees are covered by a film of spores (15).

Ascospores are capable of surviving several months of dry hot weather. Mix (24) showed that the sprout of bud conidia dried on the glass slides survived for 140 days at 30 °C and 315 days at lower temperatures. Fitzpatrick (15) found that sprout conidia in a dry condition survived 1½ years. Dissemination was only by water, with little evidence of lateral drift of spores from unsprayed trees to nearby sprayed trees (37).

Infection was observed by Fitzpatrick (15) to occur as follows: The spore fastens itself to the leaf surface by means of a short infection thread which grows out of the spore at a position usually occupied by the daughter bud. As the infection thread presses against the leaf cuticle, a thickening of the cuticle at this point takes place. The content of the spore passes into the thickened cuticle and the spore collapses. Infection may occur through either surface of the leaf. Martin (21) claims to have found stomatal penetration but Fitzpatrick did not. Nuclear conditions of the penetrating hyphae (dicaryon) and the various forms of cells formed from budding ascospores (both uninucleate and binucleate) are reported by Caporali (8).

Some controversy still exists as to the exact time of initial infection of the leaf, although Fitzpatrick (15) showed by means of spray application that most if not all infection occurs after leaves are fully emerged from the bud. Repeated infection of young leaves by spores may occur if climatic conditions such as those found in the coastal areas with recurrent fog prevail. However, there is a certain type of leaf infection which, because of its occurrence during dry weather, is possibly due to the growth of the fungus mycelia from infected shoots up through the leaf petiole into the base of the leaf. In 1949, a considerable amount of infection occurred in leaves developed during an unusually dry spell—in these the shoots had been infected earlier. As the shoot elongated, symptoms (enlargement and distortion of the stem) appeared on the new tissue. In addition the stems and bases of the leaves which arose from the new portion of the shoot developed symptoms. These features, together with the fact that the weather was unfavorable for infection by spores, suggested that the fungus grew from the previously infected shoot into the petiole and thence into the leaf.

Fitzpatrick (15) stated that in eastern Canada summer infection rarely occurs. This he considered to be evidence that the current crop of ascospores does not take part in the infection during the summer in which they are produced.

The incubation period for leaf-curl symptoms in the field is about 2 weeks after leaves emerge from the buds. Fitzpatrick (15) found that at a mean temperature of 44 F the time between inoculation and the first recognizable symptoms was 14 days.

Symptoms on leaves do not develop until the slender hyphae move downward between the epidermal cells and reach the palisade or parenchyma cells, depending on which surface infection occurs. The host cells fail to differentiate, begin to enlarge, lose their chlorophyll, and often accumulate a red pigment in large vacuoles. Thus, only host cells in direct contact with the mycelia are affected and a single infection produces a sharply delineated and isolated area. Later surfaces of swollen leaves appear white due to production of asci and ascospores.

Yarwood (38) studied the diurnal cycle of ascus maturation on ornamental peaches in April and May. Binucleate ascogenous cells occurred between the epidermal cells and cuticle, and the ascogenous cells underwent nuclear fusion and elongation between 5 and 9 p.m. Septa were formed by midnight and three successive nuclear divisions were completed by 5 a.m. By 8 a.m. ascospores were delimited and discharge began in the afternoon, reaching the maximum by 6 p.m.

Caporali (8), used a medium rich in glucosides, organic and inorganic nitrogen compounds, and mineral salts, to complete the life cycle of the fungus in culture. Dicaryotic mycelial threads and ascogenous cells with mature ascospores which develop in culture were similar to those observed on naturally infected peach leaves.

Periods of cool, wet weather at the leaf-emergent stage favors leaf curl development. The optimum temperature for growth of the fungus in culture is about 20°C, the minimum is about 8.9°C, and the maximum is between 26°C and 30.5°C (21). It is probable also that cool weather prolongs the period of leaf susceptibility by checking leaf growth.

Control. Control of leaf curl is dependent on chemicals because no commercially accepted peach cultivars have high resistance, and sanitation and cultural practices have proved ineffective. Many chemicals, including standard fungicides, effectively control the disease if applied at the proper time. In the eastern U.S. fungicides have been usually applied in early spring before the leaf buds begin to open. In California, leaf curl and *Coryneum* blight have been controlled by a single spray applied after leaf fall in autumn. Copper fungicides have been commonly used because of their long-lasting residual quality. English (14) showed that late-fall dimethyldithiocarbamate applications on peaches in California provided better control than did nabam plus coordinated salts, coppers, captan or dichlone, although all provided significant disease control. Difolatan (captafol) was superior to any chemicals tested in high-rainfall regions (20), but it was not registered for use in California.

References

1. Anonymous. 1922. Losses due to peach leaf curl in 1921. Plant Dis. Rep. Sup. 24:510.

2. _____ 1923. Losses due to peach leaf curl in 1922. Plant Dis. Rep. Sup. 30:484-85.

3. _____ 1924. Varietal susceptibility to peach leaf curl in 1924. Plant Dis. Rep. Sup. 33:96-97.

4. _____ 1925. Losses due to peach leaf curl in 1924. Plant Dis. Rep. Sup. 43:404-05.

5. Atkinson, G. F. 1894. Leaf curl and plum pocket. Cornell Agr. Exp. Sta. Bul. 73.

6. Atkinson, J. B. 1971. In Diseases of Tree Fruits in New Zealand. A. R. Sherrer, Wellington, New Zealand. 406 pp.

7. Brefeld, O. 1891. Die Formen der Ascomyceten und ihre Kultur in Nahrlosungen. Untersuchungen aus dem Gesammtgebeite der Mykologie 9: 119-49. Munster.

8. Caporali, L. 1965. Le comportement du *Taphrina deformans* (Berk.) Tul. in vitro. Revue de Cytologie et de Biologie Vegetales Tome XXVIII: 301-413.

9. _____ 1964. Nouvelles observations sur la biologie du *Taphrina deformans* (Berk.) Tul. Extrait des Annales de L'institut National Agronomique Tome II.

10. Cation, D. 1935. One spray controls peach leaf curl. Mich. Agr. Exp. Sta. Quart. Bul. 18(2): 86-88.

11. Dangeard, P. A. 1895. La production sexuelle des Ascomycetes. Le Botaniste 4:21-58.

12. Duggar, B. M. 1899. Peach leaf curl. Cornell Agr. Exp. Sta. Bul. 164:371-88.

13. Eftimiu, P. 1927. Contribution a l'etude cytologique des Exoacsees. Le Botaniste 18:1-154.

14. English, H. 1958. Fall applications of ziram and ferbam effectively control peach leaf curl in California. Plant Dis. Rep. 42:384-86.

15. Fitzpatrick, R. E. 1934. The life history and parasitism of *Taphrina deformans*. Sci. Agr. 14(16): 305-26.

16. _____ 1935. Further studies on the parasitism of *Taphrina deformans*. Sci. Agr. 15:341-44.

17. Grady, E. E., and F. T. Wolf. 1959. The production of indole acetic acid by *Taphrina deformans* and *Dibotryon morbosum*. Physiol. Plant. 12:526-33.

18. Knowles, Etta. 1887. The curl of the peach leaves; a study of abnormal structure induced by *Exoascus deformans*. Bot. Gaz. 12:216-18.

19. Link, G. K. K., H. W. Wilcox, and V. Eggers. 1938. Growth tests with extracts of *Erwinia amylovora, Phytomonas rhizogenes, Taphrina cerasi, T. Deformans*, and *Ustilago zeae*. Phytopathology 28:15.

20. MacSwan, I. 1970. Diseases of stone fruits. 44th Annual Western Cooperative Spray Project, Port-

land, Oregon, January 14-16, 1970. p. 17. (Abstr.).

21. Martin, E. M. 1925. Cultural and morphological studies of some species of *Taphrina*. Phytopathology 15:67-76.

22. _____ 1927. Cytological studies on the Exoascaceae. *Taphrina johansonii* and *Taphrina deformans*. J. Elisha Mitchell Sci. Soc. 43:15-16.

23. _____ 1940. The morphology and cytology of *Taphrina deformans*. Amer. J. Bot. 27:743-51.

24. Mix, A. J. 1924. Biological and cultural studies of *Exoascus deformans*. Phytopathology 14:217-33.

25. _____ 1925. The weather and peach leaf curl in eastern Kansas in 1924. Phytopathology 15:244-45.

26. _____ 1929. Further studies on Exoascaceae. Phytopathology 19:90.

27. _____ 1935. Life history of *Taphrina deformans*. Phytopathology 25:41-66.

28. _____ 1949. A monograph of the genus *Taphrina*. Univ. of Kansas Science Bul. 33 (Part 1, No. 1):3-167.

29. _____ 1953. Differentiation of species of *Taphrina* in culture. Utilization of nitrogen compounds. Mycologia 45:649-70.

30. Pierce, N. B. 1900. Peach leaf curl: its nature and treatment. USDA Div. Veg. Path. and Physio. Bul. 20:1-204.

31. Roberts, C. and J. T. Barrett. 1944. Intercellular mycelium of *Taphrina deformans* in peach fruit. Phytopathology 34:977-79.

32. Sadebeck, R. 1893. Die parasitichen *Exoascen*. Hamburg.

33. Selby, A. D. 1898. Preliminary report upon diseases of the peach. Ohio Agr. Exp. Sta. Bul. 92:226-31.

34. _____ 1899. Variations in the amount of leaf curl of the peach *(Exoascus deformans)* in the light of weather conditions. Proc. Assoc. Prom. Agr. Sci. Ann. Meeting 20:98-104.

35. Sommer, N. F. 1961. Production by *Taphrina deformans* of substances stimulating cell elongation and division. Physiol. Plant. 14:460-69.

36. Wallace, E., and H. H. Wetzel. 1910. Peach leaf curl. Cornell Agr. Exp. Sta. Bul. 276.

37. Wilson, E. E. 1937. Control of peach leaf curl by autumn applications of various fungicides. Phytopathology 27:110-12.

38. Yarwood, C. E. 1941. Diurnal cycle of ascus maturation of *Taphrina deformans*. Amer. J. Bot. 28:355-57.

Leaf Spot of Cherry
Coccomyces hiemalis Hig.

This disease does not occur in the major sweet cherry-growing areas of California and sour cherries are not grown commercially in this state. The name "yellow leaf" and "shot-hole disease" has been used because the leaves turn yellow soon after symptoms develop (fig. 34) and the necrotic circular lesions often drop out.

This disease was first described in Finland in 1885 (5), in America by Peck from New York in 1878 (9), and in California by Smith in the coastal districts on sweet cherries (10). The organism was first described as *Cylindrosporium padi* in 1884 by Karsten (5), while in America the fungus name used was *Septoria cerasina* (Peck, 1878). The ascigerous stage was found by Arthur in 1887 but he did not name it (1) and Higgins in 1913 and 1914 described three species with *Coccomyces hiemalis* occuring commonly on *Prunus cerasus, P. avium, and P. pennsylvanicum* (3, 4). Other species are *C. prunophorae* on plum and *C. lutescens* on mahaleb cherry.

The economic importance resulting from this disease is extensive defoliation and debilitation of the tree resulting in reduction of fruit set and size and in the regions with severe cold temperatures, the lack of stored sugars in the wood cause freezing and death of trees.

The characteristic symptoms on the leaves are numerous, minute purple spots on the upper leaf surface which enlarge and become necrotic. The center of the spots may fall out causing a shot-hole effect. Affected leaves turn yellow and fall off early in the season but frequently the area around the infected spots remain green giving the leaf a mottle appearance. Infections may also occur on the petioles, fruit, and pedicels.

Infections occur through the stomata and an intercellular septate mycelium (stroma) is formed between the epidermis and mesophyll tissue. Ascervuli are formed on the stroma and the hyaline, elongated, curved or flexuous conidia break through the lower epidermis as a creamy mass which is seen as a whitish speck. The conidia are 45 to 60 by 2.4 µm with one to two septa. In spring apothecia arise from the same stroma in fallen leaves, and produce ascospores (30 to 50 in length by 3.5 to 4.5 µm in width) which are forcibly ejected when leaves are thoroughly soaked. Initial infections of unfolding leaves are from ascospores and conidia are responsible for much of the secondary infections during rains.

Control. Resistant varieties are not available for either the sweet or sour cherries.

Eradicant dinitro sprays applied on leaves on the orchard floor have been reported to reduce initial inoculum. Three protective sprays have been recommended starting from the petal-fall stage of bloom with such fungicides as captan, dodine, ferbam, and dichlone in Oregon (8). Bordeaux mixture or lime sulfur applied soon after fruit set was suggested control by Smith (10).

References

1. Arthur, J. C. 1887. Report of the botanist. N. Y. (Geneva) Agr. Exp. Sta. Rept., 5:259-96.
2. _____ 1888. Report of the botanist. N.Y. (Geneva) Agr. Exp. Sta. Rept. 6:343-71.
3. Higgins, B. B. 1913. The perfect stage of *Cylindrosporium* on *Prunus avium*. Science, N. S., 37:637-38.
4. _____ 1914. Contribution to the life history and physiology of Cylindrosporium on stone fruits. Am. J. Bot. 1:145-73.
5. Karsten, P. A. 1885. Symbolae ad mycoligiam Fennicam, XVI, Medel. Soc. Fauna et Flora Fennica, 11:148-61.
6. Keitt, G. W. 1918. Inoculation experiments with species of *Coccomyces* from stone fruits. J. Agr. Res., 13:539-69.
7. Keitt, G. W., E. G. Blodgett, E. E. Wilson, and R. O. Magie. 1937. The epidemiology and control of cherry leaf spot. Wis. Agr. Exp. Sta. Research Bul. 132.
8. MacSwan, E. C. and P. A. Koepsell. 1974. Oregon Plant Disease Control Handbook. Oregon State University Bookstores, Inc., Corvallis, Oregon 97330, 187 pp.
9. Peck, C. H. 1878. Report of the botanist. N.Y.
10. Smith, R. E. 1941. Diseases of fruits and nuts. Calif. Agr. Ext. Ser. Circ. 120, 168 pp (out of print).

Phytophthora Crown and Root Rot of Stone Fruit
Phytophthora sp.

Phytophthora crown and root rot can cause severe tree losses in years of heavy rainfall, but because of constant changes in fruit culture and the introduction of new rootstocks this disease is always a threat. In 1975, 15 to 25 percent of the mature cherry trees in San Joaquin County were killed by crown rot. Whole plantings of young and mature almond and peach trees have been killed. Least affected have been prunes.

To prevent infection of the crown, the trees are planted on soil ridges with the upper roots near the soil level. This keeps rain and irrigation water from accumulating around the crowns. Heavy clay soils should be provided with good drainage. Proper choice of rootstocks is important, but in making such choices other disease problems must also be thoroughly considered.

Details of this disease are discussed in section III of this publication.

Plum Pocket
Taphrina pruni Tul.

"Plum pocket," "bladder plum," "mock plums," or "fools" are names given to a disease that attacks plum species. The disease occurs to some extent in California on the American species of plums, but is not often found on *Prunus domestica* (European plum) or *Prunus salicina* (Oriental plum) (4), the more common species grown in California. Apparently the European species of *Taphrina, T. pruni* Tulasne (3) does not occur commonly in the state.

The causal organism. *Taphrina pruni* Tul., described as *Exoascus communis* by Sadebeck in 1898 and later transferred to the genus *Taphrina,* is believed to be the correct designation for species such as *E. longipes* Atk. and *E. mirabalis* Atk. (3). The fungus produces asci without ascocarps in the subcuticular layer of the fruit. The asci are club-shaped 17 to 53 μm long by 5 to 17 μm broad. The roundish ascospores commonly bud even while in the ascus, thereby increasing the propagules of the fungus in a way similar to that of *T. deformans.*

Symptoms. As the name implies the most distinctive phase of the disease occurs on the fruit of the plum (fig. 35). Infected plum fruits are enlarged bladder-like objects lacking pits and with a leathery flesh. The surface of the fruit is covered by a whitish coating, and the asci of the fungus projects above the subcuticular layer.

Disease development. The exact cycle of this disease has not been studied in detail, but apparently infection is initiated in spring soon after the plum blossoms begin to open. Infection is apparently produced by the bud conidia, which persist on the tree surfaces from one growing season to the next in a manner similar to that of *T. deformans.*

Control. When necessary, a spray should be applied in spring before blossom buds begin to open. Bordeaux mixture or other equally persistent fungicides have been used.

References

1. Atkinson, G. J. 1894. Leaf curl and plum pockets. *Exoascus pruni* Fckl. Cornell Univ. Agr. Exp. Sta. Bul. 73:329-30.
2. Galloway, B. J. 1889. Plum pocket. U. S. Agr. Comm. Rept. 1888:366-69.
3. Mix, A. J. 1949. A monograph of the genus *Taphrina*. Kansas Univ. Sci. Bul. 33:3-167.

4. Smith, Ralph E. 1941. Diseases of fruit and nuts. California Agr. Exp. Sta. Extension Service Circ. 120:1-168 (out of print).

5. Swingle, D. B., and H. E. Morris. 1918. Plum pocket and leaf gall of American plums. Montana Agr. Exp. Sta. Bul. 123:167-88.

Powdery Mildew of Stone Fruit
Sphaerotheca pannosa (Wallr. ex Fr.) Lev.
Podosphaera tridactyla (Wallr.) deBary
Podosphaera oxycanthae (DC.) deBary
Podosphaera leucotricha (E. & E.) Salm.

The climate typical in areas suited for stone fruit production favors the attack and survival of powdery mildew fungi (29, 30). On orchard trees the primary destructive effects are on the fruit. In the absence of control measures, powdery mildew can spoil fruit of apricots, cherry, nectarine, peach, and plum. Fruit infection on almond has never been reported, and it was observed on French prune fruit for the first time in California in 1973. Susceptibility of fruit to powdery mildew varies greatly among cultivars. In peach, nonglandular Peak and Paloro are most susceptible, while glandular cultivars such as Walton, Johnson, Halford, and Stuart (15) are more resistant. In cherry, Black Tartarian, Bing, and Chapman are most susceptible. Interplanting of cultivars for pollination increases the chance of losses. Early plum fruit infection results from exposure to other hosts of mildew such as roses growing nearby. Kelsey, Gaviota, and Wickson plums are the most susceptible cultivars. On the Beauty plum, mildew infections do not reduce its market quality because the plum does not show any marked symptoms upon brushing during postharvest treatments with fungicides. In apricot, Blenheim is more susceptible than Tilton but both can be severely affected.

Foliage infections by powdery mildews are of primary concern in nursery plantings, especially cherry. On other stone fruits, damage from infection on leaves in nursery or orchard has not been fully assessed. The inoculum source of mildew on leaves for fruit infections is fully realized. Crop loss from killing of buds appear to be minor, as is that from shoot blight.

Symptoms. Leaves, buds, green shoots and fruits are commonly attacked, but flower infection is rare. As with apple, the inner transplant scales in buds are also susceptible (25). Infection of plant parts is largely determined by the species of the pathogen and the maturity of the tissue. Young leaves are more susceptible than are older leaves in spring and summer; this is also true for shoots and fruit. The first evidence of infection is a cobweb-like growth on the surface. Soon the fungus starts to sporulate, producing masses of powdery spores (fig. 36A). At this time very little chlorosis of leaves occurs, but soon after chlorosis and necrosis may occur on infected parts. If leaves are covered with the fungus they tend to curl upward and dehisce, but if infection is localized they tend to remain on the tree. Infected shoots are commonly stunted and infected lateral buds may be destroyed. On twigs, mildew appears as a white felt-like growth even in winter. On leaves or shoots, cleistothecia (*Podosphaera* only) first appear as yellow then brown, then reddish brown and finally black, spherical bodies. Cleistothecia of *Podosphaera oxycanthae* and *P. tridactyla* are common, but those of *Sphaerotheca pannosa* have never been found on fruit trees and only occasionally on rose in California. Young fruit are susceptible and show typical mildew growth with slight deformation of the fruit which is either a depression or a slight enlargement (fig. 36B). After the pit-hardening stage of maturity, peach and plum fruit become resistant and develop necrosis of the epidermis. The scabby condition remains visible on nectarine, peach, apricot, and plum fruit even at maturity. Occasionally, on apricot and peach fruit the infected area remains green, but on Beauty plum fruit infected areas show no such effect. On sweet cherries, infected areas on fruit are most noticeable near harvest time as mycelia on fruit surfaces develop a web-like growth.

The causal organism. Identification of powdery mildews species on stone fruit is difficult because more than one species can occur on a single host. Furthermore, cleistothecia are difficult to find. Zaracovitis (33) placed the mildews into three groups based on rate of germination and appressorial formation *in vitro* at 21 ± 1°C in a saturated atmosphere and in the dark: (a) germination greater than 70 percent with appressorial formation in 5 hours *(Uncinula necator),* (b) germination and formation of distinct appressoria in 10 hours *(Erysiphe graminis),* and (c) germination less than 30 percent in 5 hours. Greater than 70 percent germination requires more than 10 hours (all species of *Podosphaera* and *Sphaerotheca*). The conidia of group c germinate by producing straight, rather long, germ tubes without well-differentiated appressoria. Powdery mildew fungi attacking stone fruits belong to group c.

Blumer (3) has classified the mildews on the basis of conidial and cleistothecial characteristics and has divided *P. oxycanthae* into species such as *P. tridactyla* on apricot and almond and *P. clandestina* on cherry. On samples collected in California, appendage location of *Podosphaera* on cherries and plums differ from that on apricots and does not fit into other categories described by Blumer. Thus, the binomial *P. oxycanthae* is retained for mildew on cherries and the foliage mildew of plum.

Hosts and mildew species reported on the various crops are as follows:

Host	Pathogen
Almond (*Prunus amygdalus* Batsch.)	*Podosphaera tridactyla* (Wallr.) de Bary (23) *Sphaerotheca pannosa* (Wallr. ex Fr) Lev. (18)
Apricot (*P. armeniaca* L.)	*S. pannosa* (Wallr. ex Fr.) Lev. (18) *P. tridactyla* (Wallr.) de Bary (31)
Cherry (*P. avium* L.)	*P. oxycanthae* (DC.) de Bary (8)
Plum (*P. salicina* Lindl.)	*S. pannosa* (Wallr. ex Fr.) Lev. (16) *P. oxycanthae* (DC.) de Bary (16)
Prune (*P. domestica* L.)	Unidentified—California 1973
Peach (*P. persica* (L.) Batsch.	*S. pannosa* (Wallr. ex Fr.) Lev. (32) *P. oxycanthae* (DC.) de Bary (11) *P. leucotricha* (E. & E.) Salm (13)

Synonyms. According to Blumer, *P. tridactyla* (Wallr) de Bary is the same as *P. clandestina* (Wallr. ex Fr.) Lev. var. *tridactyla* (Wallr.) W. B. Cooke; *P. oxycanthae* (DC.) de Bary var. *tridactyla* (Wallr.) Salm.; and *P. oxycanthae* (DC.) de Bary. *S. pannosa* (Wallr. ex Fr.) Lev. is the same as *S. persicae* Woronich.) Erikss. and *Oidium leucoconium* Desm.

Podosphaera tridactyla (Wallr.) de Bary as described in the C.M.I. descriptions of pathogenic fungi and bacteria (No. 187) (5) is as follows:

Mycelium is amphigenous, usually disappearing at maturity. Cleistothecia are scattered or loosely aggregated, globose to subglobose, dark brown, 70 to 110 μm in diameter, cells of the polygonal peridium are up to 15 μm wide. Appendages 2 to 8, 1 to 8 times the diameter of the cleistothecium, usually unequal in length, springing in a cluster from the apex of the cleistothecium, more or less erect, upper half hyaline, lower half brown, broader at base, apex 3 to 6 times dicotomously branched, primary branches usually more or less elongated and sometimes slightly recurved, ultimate branches rounded, swollen and more or less knob-shaped. Ascus one per cleistothecium, globose to subglobose, 60 to 80 × 60 to 70 μm, with no distinct stipe. Ascospores 8, ovate to ellipsoidal, 18 to 30 × 12 to 15 μm. Conidia few, formed apically in chains on septate conidiophores, hyaline, ellipsoidal, 22 to 45 × 14 to 20 μm with fibrosin granules.

Podosphaera oxycanthae (DC.) de Bary is similar to *P. tridactyla* (Wallr.) de Bary except in the placement of the appendages on the cleistothecium. Cleistothecia on cherry leaves from Wisconsin, and on cherry and plum leaves from California, were similar but differed from those on apricot. On cherry and plum leaves, appendages were located randomly on the upper portion of the cleistothecium, not radially as noted by Blumer (3) for *P. clandestina* on Crataegus.

Sphaerotheca pannosa (Wallr. ex Fr.) Lev. described by C.M.I., descriptions of pathogenic fungi and bacteria No. 189 (5), is as follows:

Mycelia persistent, on stem, thorns, calyz, fruit, as felt-like patches are first white, then grey to buff, and composed of densely interwoven hyphae. Cleistothecia rare, those developing are embedded in mycelial felt, and are most frequent on stems, and especially around thorns, they are globose to pyriform, 80 to 120 μm diameter. Peridial cells are obscure, 10 μm wide. Appendages few, narrow, hyaline to slight brown, septate, shorter than the diameter of cleistothecia. Ascus one per ascocarp, broadly oblong, subglobose to globose, 60 to 75 × 80 to 100 μm. Ascospores eight, oval, hyaline, 20 to 30 × 12 to 17 μm. Conidia, in chains on long conidiophores, are ellipsoidal, hyaline, 30 to 35 × 14 to 20 μm.

Disease development. Because of variations in the life cycle of the pathogens on the various stone fruit cultivars, each is discussed separately.

On plum, as on apricot, *S. pannosa* is important on the young green fruit (16, 24) while foliage infection in the late summer is caused by *Podosphaera* (16). *S. pannosa* does not overwinter on the plum trees. There are no signs of the fungus on any part of the foliage or the shoots during the spring months. Infection, especially on the interior fruit clusters, occurs shorly after the flowering period. The frequency of infection in these areas is probably related to the persistence of moisture or high humidity. Mycelial growth appears in 6 days and sporulation occurs in 14 days. Spores from the 14-day-old lesions are capable of producing the disease. Mildew spreads very quickly on the fruit surface and causes chlorotic areas, which later turn into scabby lesions with no sign of fungus. The fruit at this stage is resistant to new infection. The primary sources of inoculum for apricot are rose bushes (31). The fungus was found to overwinter in the buds of rose; about 50 percent of the new growth shows infection of the terminal buds. Cleistothecia were absent on the rose and on the plum fruit.

Podosphaera lesions appear on leaves in late summer after fruit harvest. By November, cleistothecia production is heavy.

The *S. pannosa* spores are disseminated by wind as indicated by a gradient of infection outward from the spore source.

Though Keil and Wilson (11) reported *P. oxycanthae* on peach seedlings in the eastern U.S. only *S. pannosa* has been reported from the western U.S. The fungus *S. pannosa* overwinters as mycelia in the inner transplant scales of the buds (28). Leaves are infected as they emerge from the bud; symptoms became apparent about a month before the blooming period. Secondary infection of young developing leaves occurs throughout the season; symptoms become apparent about a month before the blooming period. Fruit are susceptible during the early stages of growth to about the beginning of the pit hardening stage of fruit growth. According to Weinhold (25) neither foliage nor fruit infection appeared to be influenced by environmental conditions found in the orchard. According to Yarwood (32) optimum temperature for germination of conidia of *S. pannosa* is 21 to 37°C, with slight germination at 4°C and no germination at 37°C. The optimum temperature for *P. leucotricha* is 16°C. Increase in moisture to saturation increased the percent germination, and presence of free moisture appears to be the primary requirement for germination (12, 17, 26). Presence of sugars and amino acids in the water does not favor germination. The significance of susceptibility of only the terminal leaves is explained as morphological barriers induced by increased thickness of the cuticle from 3.0 to 3.6 µm (14, 25). Apparently, infection of leaves at night or in early morning is most likely to occur because moisture then is highest and osmotic pressure of leaves lowest. This explains why mildew is more severe during overcast weather than during bright sunny days. However, this does not agree with studies by Childs (4) indicating that spore release of *S. pannosa* is high from 10 a.m. to 4 p.m.

Another condition affecting only the fruit, and first reported by Blodgett (2) was rusty spots on Elberta peaches (Fig. 36C). He found spots on young fruit in Idaho that resembled those left by drops of rusty water settled into hairs on fruit surfaces. Fruit collected by workers in Colorado showed the same condition. In 1956 Sprague (20) was unable to detect any fungus associated with such areas. In 1960, however, Daines and coworkers (6) in New Jersey discovered mycelia in such lesions and found the condition developed on peaches near the vicinity of mildew-infected apple trees. They suggested the rusty spots resembled old lesions produced by the common peach mildew fungus *(S. pannosa)* but differed in being more bare, by causing more host cell necrosis, and by a sparsity of fungus hyphae and sporulation on Rio Oso Gem, Goldeneast and Summer Queen. In 1972, Manji (13) in California reported outbreaks of rusty spot on Rio Oso Gem interplanted among Jonathan apple trees severely infected with mildew. Inoculation tests with both *S. pannosa* and mildew spores from Jonathan developed symptoms of typical peach mildew with the former and typical rusty spot with the latter. Considering that *P. oxycanthae* does not readily infect apples (11), it is reasonable to conclude that the mildew from apple was *P. leucotricha*. However, it is possible that *P. oxycanthae* may produce the rusty-spot condition.

Mildew on foliage of cherry *(Prunus avium)* was reported by Galloway in 1889 (9) and mentioned by Steward in 1915 (22), but it was not until 1947 that infection of the fruit was reported (3). The pathogen *P. oxycanthae* attacks young shoots and leaves as they emerge in the spring. The source of inoculum is not known but could be from mycelia in dormant buds or the overwintering cleistothecia. Secondary infection occurs throughout the growing period and by the time of fruit harvest numerous black cleistothecia form, especially on the undersurface of the leaves. Fruit infection is not common, but can be severe in certain orchards especially after a period of cool overcast weather or intermittent rains. Fruit infection does not continue to spread in storage.

P. tridactyla (Wallr.) de Bary was reported on almond seedlings for the first time in California by Weigle in 1955 (23). Sprague (19) in 1954 gave the first report of powdery mildew on almonds in the U.S.; he said the fungus appeared to be *Sphaerotheca pannosa* (Wallr. ex Fr.) Lev. In 1938, De Nardo (7) reported *S. pannosa* in Malta and in 1940 Gianai (10) reported *Phyllactinia salmonii* Blummer in India. Powdery mildew on almonds is rare in California where most of the commercial production of the U.S. is located. Powdery mildew infection has been found on the tip leaves of young shoots of seedling almonds late in the fall months.

On apricots, *Sphaerotheca pannosa* (Wallr. ex Fr.) Lev. is responsible for leaf and fruit infections (18) in spring (fig. 36D), and *Podosphaera tridactyla* (Wallr.) de Bary attacks leaves (32) in summer and fall. The *S. pannosa* inoculum for infection comes from mildewed *Rosa banksiae* (31) and Dorothy Perkins roses. In one instance (25) the only inoculum source found was a heavily infected Palora peach tree. Secondary infection on leaves and fruit is minimal because sporulation on primary lesions on these leaves and fruit is sparse. Cleistothecia of *S. pannosa* have not been found on apricot, rose or on peach in California. Thus the only primary inoculum source appears to be mycelia overwintering in leaves and dormant buds of roses. The spread of mildew from peaches to apricots has not been established. Mildew infections seen after the harvest season occur initially on the upper surface of leaves located in the inner part of the leaf canopy. Infected leaves are not distorted nor do they fall off the tree readily. Abundant cleistothecial production occurs in fall and early winter. Infection of stem or buds has not been observed. The source of inoculum for infection is not thought to be infected buds because new shoots in spring do not develop mildew, as do apple and peach shoots.

Control. Mildew control on stone fruits has been based largely on the use of fungicides and the eradication of other host-sources of inoculum. Fungicides have been used as protectants and no eradicant types which kill the mildew after infection have been developed. On peaches Ogawa and Charles (15) obtained excellent disease control with three applications, the first before any signs of mildew developed (March 24), the second at the time of dehiscence of the floral tube (April 7), and the third when first infections were visible and expanding (April 28). According to data by Weinhold (25), the third spray may probably be too late for protection because by this time the fruit may have become resistant to infection. Either liquid-lime sulfur, a mixture of lime-sulfur and wettable sulfur, or Karathane 50 can significantly reduce shoot infections and increase the amount of marketable fruit. Actidione, however, caused injury to leaves and induced dropping of green fruits. New classes or formulations of fungicides which are especially effective on *Sphaerotheca pannosa* on roses have not been tested sufficiently. Fungicides of this type are semicarbazone and derivatives of cycloheximide, actidione, folpet, benomyl, and triforine. Studies comparing performance of such compounds in controlling *Podosphaera* on stone fruit have not been made. Karathane, benomyl, and sulfurs have been recommended for apple mildew control.

Removal of rose plantings near orchards of apricots and plums reduce mildew infections on the fruit of these crops. Roses such as *Rosa banksiae* and Dorothy Perkins, which are very susceptible to mildew, are of greatest concern although other cultivars provide an inoculum source. Cultural practices which favor vigorous shoot growth also favor mildew infection.

References

1. Bailey, L. H. 1949. Manual of cultivated plants. The Macmillan Co., New York. 1116 pp.
2. Blodgett, E. C. 1941. Rusty spot of peach. Plant Dis. Rep. 25:27-78.
3. Blumer, S. 1933. Die Erysiphaceen Mittleuropas. 483 pp. Fretz A. G. Zurich.
4. Childs, J. F. L. 1940. Diurnal cycles of spore maturation in certain powdery mildews. Phytopathology 30:65-73.
5. Commonwealth Mycological Institute. Descriptions of pathogenic fungi and bacteria. No. 187 and 189. Ferry Lane, Kew, Surrey, England.
6. Daines, R. H., C. M. Haenseler, E. Brennan, and I. Leone. 1960. Rusty spot of peach and its control in New Jersey. Plant Dis. Rep. 44:20-22.
7. DeNardo, A. 1938. Report on plant pathology. Report on the Department of Agriculture of Malta, 1936-1937. Pp. 60-63.
8. English, W. H. 1947. Powdery mildew of cherry fruit in Washington. Phytopathology 47:421-24.
9. Galloway, B. T. 1889. The powdery mildew of cherry. U.S. Agr. Comm. Rept. 1888:352.
10. Gianai, M. A. 1940. A species of *Phyllactinia* occurring on almond *(Prunus amygdalus)*. Indian J. Agr. Sci. 10:96-97.
11. Keil, H. L., and R. A. Wilson. 1961. Powdery mildew on peach. Plant Dis. Rep. 45:10-11.
12. Longree, K. 1939. The effect of temperature and relative humidity on the powdery mildew of roses. Cornell Univ. Agr. Exp. Sta. Mem. 223:1-43.
13. Manji, B. T. 1972. Apple powdery mildew on peach. Phytopathology 62:776. (Abstr.)
14. Mence, M. J., and A. C. Hildebrandt. 1966. Resistance of powdery mildew on rose. Ann. Appl. Biol. 58:309-20.
15. Ogawa, J. M., and F. M. Charles. 1956. Powdery mildew on peach trees. California Agriculture 10(1):7 & 16.
16. Ogawa, J. M., D. H. Hall, and P. A. Koepsell. 1967. Spread of pathogens within crops as affected by life cycle and environment. Symposia Soc. Gen. Micro. Airborne Microbes. 1967.
17. Rogers, M. N. 1959. Some effects of moisture and host plant susceptibility on the development of powdery mildews of roses, caused by *Sphaerotheca pannosa* var. *rosae*. N.Y. (Cornell) Agr. Exp. Sta. Mem. 363. 37 pp.
18. Smith, R. E. 1941. Diseases of fruits and nuts. CAES Cir. 120.
19. Sprague, R. 1954. Powdery mildew on almonds. Plant Dis. Rep. 38:695.
20. Sprague, R., and P. Figaro. 1956. Rusty spot, powdery mildew, and healthy skin of peach fruit compared histologically. Phytopathology 46:640. (Abstr.).
21. Steward, V. B. 1915. Some important leaf diseases of nursery stock. N. Y. (Cornell) Agr. Exp. Sta. Bul. 258:171-268.
22. _____ 1915. Some important leaf diseases of nursery stock: powdery mildew of cherry. Cornell Univ. Agr. Expt. Sta. Bul. 358:192-94.
23. Weigle, C. G. 1956. Powdery mildew *(Podosphaera tridactyla)* on almond. Plant Dis. Rep. 40:584.
24. Weigle, C. G., and A. M. French. 1956. Laboratory diagnosis. Bul. Calif. Dept. Agr. 45:186.

25. Weinhold, A. R. 1961. The orchard development of peach powdery mildew. Phytopathology 51:478-81.

26. _____ 1961. Temperature and moisture requirements for germination of conidia of *Sphaerotheca pannosa* from peach. Phytopathology 51:699-703.

27. Weinhold, A. R., and H. English. 1964. Significance of morphological barriers and osmotic pressure in resistance of mature peach leaves to powdery mildew. Phytopathology 54:1409-14.

28. Yarwood, C. E. 1939. Powdery mildews of peach and rose. Phytopathology 29:282-84.

29. _____ 1950. Dry weather fungi. California Agriculture 4(10):7-12.

30. _____ 1957. Powdery mildews. Bot. Rev. 23:235-301.

31. _____ 1952. Apricot powdery mildew from rose and peach. Bul. Calif. Dept. Agr. 41:19.

32. Yarwood, C. E., S. Sidky, M. Cohen, and V. Santilli. 1954. Temperature relations of powdery mildews. Hilgardia 22:603-22.

33. Zaracovitis, C. 1965. Attempts to identify powdery mildew fungi by conidial characters. Trans. Brit. Mycol. Soc. 48:553-58.

Replant Problem of Stone Fruits
Cause—Unknown

In many parts of the world the replanting of peach or apple on land on which the same type of trees has been grown results in poor growth and sometimes death of the newly planted trees. In the U.S. this has been called the "replant problem." Savory (29), in England, who has reviewed the literature extensively, prefers the name "specific replant disease." The following tree fruits are severely affected by specific replant diseases: Apple, cherry, peach, and citrus. Less severely affected are plum and pear (29).

The characteristic which makes the replant problem specific is that, as Koch (18) in Ontario stated, apricots and sour cherries grow normally after peach while peaches do not; peaches grow well after apple or plum; apples grow well after cherries but not after apples. In California, Proebsting and Gilmore (27) stated that sweet cherry and Myrobalan plum grow well on old peach soils. So do almond and apricot, unless they are on peach root.

Symptoms. Above-ground indications of the replant disease are abnormal growth of the tree, short internodes, and small leaves. Koch (18) reported the presence of interveinal chlorosis. None of these symptoms are specific, inasmuch as trees may exhibit the same symptoms when growing in a soil low in fertility.

The root systems of affected trees are small and even the living roots are short and dark-colored. Many of the rootlets are rotted, according to Koch (18).

Causes. The following are considered possible contributing causes of the replant problem.

Nutrient deficiency. The deficiency of certain nutrients in old orchard soils has been considered as a possible cause of the replant problem. However Proebsting and Gilmore (27) obtained no improvement in replanted peach trees by adding large amounts of N, P, K, Mn, Zn or Cu. Proebsting (26) later confirmed the lack of response to these elements. Havis, Morris, Manning and Demmon (12) obtained no response to N, P, K, dolomitic limestone or trace elements in old peach soil. Fastabend (7) reported a lack of response of apple trees in old apple soil to addition of Cu, B, and other elements. Hewetson (13), however, obtained a response of replanted peach trees from 23:21:27, NPK fertilizer in solutions—but little response was obtained from adding 10:10:10 NPK fertilizer plus Al, B, Cu, Co, Fe, Mg, Mn, and Mo.

Nutrient imbalance. Savory (29) after reviewing the literature on the subject concluded that "...it would seem most unlikely that a nutrient deficiency or imbalance can be the primary cause of specific replant diseases."

Spray residues, soil compaction. Savory (29) also stated that there is no conclusive proof that spray residues, or soil compaction due to use of heavy equipment in the orchard, are factors in the development of specific replant diseases.

Fungi. Savage (28) in Georgia, suggested that *Clitocybe tabescens* was the cause of the replant problem. Peterson (24), however, placed pieces of peach wood infected by that fungus under newly planted peach trees and found that in 4 years the fungus had not affected the roots to any great extent. Hine (14) attributed the poor growth of replanted peach trees to *Pythium ultimum*, *Fusarium* sp. and *Rhizoctonia* sp. Mircetich (20) found no relationship between peach tree decline and the occurrence of *Pythium ultimum*, *P. irregulare*, and *P. vexans* in peach tree roots or orchard soil.

It is difficult therefore to find clear-cut evidence that any one fungus is responsible for a specific replant disease. It is evident that weakly pathogenic fungi occur in old fruit soils and these fungi may attack the roots of poorly-growing fruit trees.

Nematodes: Chitwood (4) in Maryland and Johanson (17) in Connecticut believed that nematodes were possible factors in the peach replant problem in their states. Chitwood, Specht, and Havis (5) later advanced the theory that nematodes such as *Meloidogyne javanica* and *M. incognita* affected the growth of the plants by influencing its chemical composition. Colgran (6) believed that the poor growth of replanted apple trees in Australia was due to the attack of *Pratylenchus coffeae*. Hoestra (16) found the replant problem in Holland occurred in old apple soils with a low population of nematodes. Likewise no evidence was obtained by Proebsting (26) and Proebsting and Gilmore (27) that attacks of nematodes were responsible for the peach replant problem in California.

Although one must conclude that while the evidence concerning the role of nematodes in the specific replant disease is not conclusive, it must be admitted that nematodes do affect the growth of orchard trees.

Viruses. Savory (29) cited examples of apple plants that had made poor growth in an old orchard site but which recovered their vigor and made good growth when transferred to fresh soil. This he believed does not support the assumption that a soil-borne virus is involved in specific replant diseases. He also cited unpublished results of an experiment in which grafting of scions from stunted apple replants onto healthy rootstocks did not reduce the vigor of the resultant plant. This he interpreted as evidence that a graft-transmissible virus is not involved in the replant problem.

Toxins: McCalla (19), among others, noted that decomposing crop residues in soil can produce injury to plants growing therein. Apparently, there is no specificity involved here as in the replant problem. Nevertheless, experiments reported by Proebsting and Gilmore (27), Proebsting (26), and Havis and Gilkeson (11) indicated that decomposing peach roots contain a material or materials toxic to young peach trees. Likewise, Fastabend (7) and Börner (2) reported that apple root residues are toxic to young apple trees when added to the soil in which the young apple trees are growing. According to Börner (2) five phenolic compounds that occured in soils to which the apple-root residues were added produce marked retardation of young apple trees. These are phlorizin, phloretin, phloroglucinol, *p*-hydroxy-hydrocinnamic acid, and *p*-hydroxybenzoic acid. Only phlorizin is a normal constituent of apple bark. It is thought, therefore, that the other materials are breakdown products of phlorizin.

Havis and Gilkeson (11) and Proebsting (26) reported, however, that the addition of peach roots to soil did not always result in toxicity to peach trees growing therein. Proebsting (26) explained the exceptions as indicating that the formation of a toxic substance from peach roots occurred only when a certain group of soil microorganisms decompose the roots. Later, work by Patrick (21) and by Wensley (32) tended to substantiate this theory. Patrick (21) found that decomposition products of amygdalin, as well as materials produced in the decomposition of peach roots, were toxic to rootlets of growing peach trees. Hine (15) however did not believe that the breakdown of amygdalin to HCN contributes to the replant problem.

Gilmore (8, 9) in pot experiments found that peach root bark somewhat reduced growth of peach seedlings, and that peach root wood (previously found fairly harmless) greatly stunted peach seedlings. Repetition of the experiment using root bark of peach, apricot, cherry, myrobalan plum, and almond and the addition of ammonium nitrate to all treatments, resulted in slightly better growth than the controls. In a repetition of the same experiment without the addition of nitrogen, all peach seedlings grew well except those receiving peach root wood. Upon the addition of nitrogen, the latter plants began to grow but never regained normal vigor. There is evidence that there is a toxic effect from root residues in the soil when ample nitrogen is not available to the plants growing therein. Upshall and Ruhnke (30) reported that the growth of pear, Mazzard and Mahaleb cherries, and myrobalan plum on old peach land was poor, except where ample nitrogen was present.

Discussion. In light of the foregoing one must agree with Savory (29) who stated that "...no really satisfactory cause of specific replant diseases has yet been demonstrated." Patrick, Toussoun and Koch (22) also agreed with this conclusion, and stated that many questions concerning this complex problem remain to be answered. One possible cause not yet investigated is that of the action of bacteria, Bowen and Rovira (3) and others have shown that bacteria are capable of inhibiting root growth and causing root discoloration of a number of plant types.

Control. Growing for several years a crop or crops not affected by the specific replant disease offers a method of control that has been partially successful according to Savory (29), unless specific (such as control of nematodes) can be corrected.

References

1. Blake, M. A. 1947. The growing of peach after peach was an old world problem in 1768. New Jersey State Hort. Soc. News 28:1910.

2. Börner, H. 1959-60. The apple replant problem. I. The excretion of phlorizin from apple root residues. Contrib. Boyce Thompson Inst. 20:39-56.

3. Bowen, G. D., and A. D. Rovira. 1961. The effect of microorganisms on plant growth. I. The development of roots and root hairs in sand culture. Plant and Soil 15:166-68.

4. Chitwood, B. G. 1949. Ring nematode (Criconematinae) a possible factor in decline and replanting problems of peach orchards. Proc. Helminthol. Soc. Wash., D. C. 16:6-7.

5. Chitwood, B. G., A. W. Specht, and L. Havis. 1952. Root knot nematodes. III. Effects of *Meloidogyne incognita* and *M. javanica* on some peach rootstocks. Plant and Soil 4(1):77-95.

6. Colbran, R. C. 1953. Problems in tree replacement. I. The root lesion nematode *Pratylenchus coffeae* Zimmerman as a factor in the growth of replanted trees in apple orchards. Australian J. Agric. Res. 4:384-89.

7. Fastabend, H. 1955. Uber die Ursachen der Bodemudigkeit in Obstbaumschulen Landwirtschaft —Angewandte Wissenschaft. Sonderheft Gartenbau 4, Landwirtschaftsverlag, Hiltrup/Mainster.

8. Gilmore, A. E. 1959. Growth of replanted peach seedlings in pots. Proc. American Soc. Hort. Sci. 80:204-06.

9. _____ 1963. Pot experiments related to the peach replant problem. Hilgardia 34:63-78.

10. Grümmer, G. 1961. The role of toxic substances in the interrelationships between higher plants. *In* Society for Experimental Biol. Symposia 15:219-228.

11. Havis, L., and A. L. Gildeson. 1947. Toxicity of peach roots. Proc. Am. Soc. Hort. Sci. 50:206.

12. Havis, L., H. F. Morris, R. Manning, and J. E. Demmon. 1958. Responses of replanted peach trees to soil treatments in field tests in Texas. Proc. American Soc. Hort. Sci. 71:67-76.

13. Hewetson, F. N. 1953. Re-establishing the peach orchard: the influence of various nutrient solutions and fertilizers on the growth and development of one-year peach trees. Proc. American Hort. Sci. 69:122-125.

14. Hine, R. B. 1961. The role of fungi in the peach replant problem. Plant Dis. Reptr. 45:462-65.

15. _____ 1961. The role of amygdalin breakdown in the peach replant problem. Phytopathology 51:10-13.

16. Hoekstra, H. 1961. The role of nematodes in the orchard replant problem. Reprint Paper 6th Inst. Nematology Symposium. Gent, Belgium. 1961 No. 77.

17. Johanson, F. D. 1950. A preliminary report on the incidence of two types of plant parasitic nematodes on peaches in Connecticut. Storrs Agr. Exp. Sta. Bul. No. 10.

18. Koch, L. W. 1955. The peach replant problem in Ontario. Can. J. Agr. 33:450-60.

19. McCalla, J. M., and F. A. Haskins. 1964. Phytotoxic substances from soil microorganisms and crop residues. Bot. Rev. 28:181-207.

20. Mircetich, S. M. 1971. The role of *Pythium* in feeder roots of diseased and symptomless peach trees and in orchard soils in peach tree decline Phytopathology 61:357-60.

21. Patrick, Z. A. 1955. The peach replant problem in Ontario. II. Toxic substances from microbial decomposition of products of peach root residue. Can. J. Agr. 33:461-86.

22. Patrick, Z. A., T. A. Toussoun, and L. W. Koch. 1964. Effect of crop-residue decomposition products on plant roots. Annu. Rev. Phytopathol. 2:267-92.

23. Patrick, Z. A., T. A. Toussoun, and W. C. Snyder. 1963. Phytotoxic substances in arable soils associated with decomposition of plant residues. Phytopathology 53:152-61.

24. Petersen, D. H. 1961. The pathogenic relationship of *Clitocybe tabescens* to peach trees. Phytopathology 51:819-23.

25. Prince, V. E., L. Havis, and L. E. Scott. 1955. Effect of soil treatment in a greenhouse study of the peach replant problem. Proc. American Soc. Hort. Sci. 65:139-48.

26. Proebsting, E. L. 1950. A case history of a "peach replant" situation. Proc. Amer. Soc. Hort. Sci. 56:46-48.

27. Proebsting, E. L., and A. E. Gilmore. 1941. The relation of peach root toxicity to re-establishing of peach orchards. Proc. Amer. Soc. Hort. Sci. 38:21-25.

28. Savage, E. F. 1953. Root rot of peaches. American Fruit Gr. 73:16, 42-43.

29. Savory, B. M. 1966. Specific replant diseases. Research Review No. 1. Commonwealth Bur-Hort. and Plantation Crops. East Malling, Kent, England. 64 p.

30. Upshall, W. H., and G. N. Ruhnke. 1935. Growth of fruit tree stocks as influenced by a previous crop of peach trees. Sci. Agr. 16:16-20.

31. Ward, G. M., and A. B. Durkee. 1956. The peach replant problem in Ontario. III. Amygdalin content of peach tree tissues. Can. J. Bot. 34:419-22.

32. Wensley, R. N. 1953. Preliminary microbiological investigations of the peach replanting problem. Can. Phytopath. Soc. Proc. 21:19. (Abstr.)

33. _____ 1956. The peach replant problem. IV. Fungi associated with replant failure and their importance in fumigated and nonfumigated soil. Can. J. Bot. 34:967-82.

Rust of Stone Fruit
Tranzschelia discolor Fuckel
Tranzschelia pruni-spinosae
var. *discolor* (Fuckel) Dunegan

The rust disease considered here affects peach, nectarine, apricot, plum, prune, almond and cherry. It is widely distributed geographically, and while it occurs more or less sporadically it may be a serious disease in certain years. In the coastal areas of California, for example, it commonly causes heavy defoliation of plum and prune. In the Sacramento and San Joaquin valleys it appears suddenly and at infrequent intervals in clingstone varieties of peach. Major outbreaks occured in many Sacramento Valley orchards in 1925, 1926, 1927 and 1942.

Symptoms. On peach fruit, circular spots 2 to 3 mm in diameter develop and become green and sunken when the fruit ripens. On peach leaves, bright yellow somewhat angular spots appear on the under surfaces. On peach twigs, lens-shaped cracks 5 to 10 mm long develop in the bark; the center of the cracks are filled with a rusty-brown powdery mass of uredospores. Lesions on the leaves are abundant and visible, but those on twigs are few and inconspicuous. Even in years of severe leaf and fruit infection, only about 1 to 2 percent of the twigs develop lesions.

On apricot, similar lesions occur on the fruit and leaves whereas on plums, prunes (fig. 37A, 37B) and almond only leaf infection has been noted.

The causal organism. The name of the causal fungus has undergone several changes. An early designation by Persoon was *Puccinia pruni-spinosae*. Arthur (2) maintained that the name should be *Tranzschelia punctata* in recognition of the work of W. A. Tranzschel (15) on heteroecism of the fungus. Later, Dunegan (7) made a careful study of the rust in the central U.S. and found what he considered to be two forms of *T. pruni-spinosae*. He called the one occurring on wild species of *Prunus, T. pruni-spinosae typica,* and that occuring on cultivated species of *Prunus* he called *T. pruni-spinosae discolor*. The latter form was later raised to specific rank as *T. discolor* by American workers. Those in other countries continue to call the fungus *T. pruni-spinosae*.

W. A. Tranzschel (15) produced infection on almond and the wild *Prunus* species, *P. spinosa* and *P. divaricata,* with aeciospores from *Anemone divaricala*. Arthur (2) later listed *Hepatica* and *Thalictrum* as other alternate hosts of the fungus. Though *T. discolor (T. pruni-spinosae)* is macrocyclic under certain conditions, and the passage from one host to another is probably necessary to its survival in colder climates, the aecial stage produced on *Anemone, Hepatica* and *Thalictrum* is apparently not necessary to its survival in warmer regions such as those on the Pacific Coast. Though the aecial stage has been found on *Anemone coronaria* in California, it is comparatively rare and the alternate host apparently plays no part in severe outbreaks of rust on peaches in the Sacramento Valley. Goldsworthy and Smith (10) found no aecial stage of the fungus in the Sacramento Valley during the 1925 and 1927 outbreaks, *Thalictrum* being the only possible alternate host occurring there. In addition they found no teliospores on peach in that locality.

Scott and Stout (14) reported teliospore production on prune leaves collected in 1931 from the Consumnes River district in Sacramento County. Teliospores are found to some extent on peach, and abundantly on prune and *P. domestica* plum foliage. Even so, the aecial host probably plays no important part in the life cycle of the fungus in these localities. Primary infection in the spring could be initiated by uredospores overwintered on the twigs or foliage, which in these localities frequently remains on the tree until spring. Cunningham (6) in New Zealand and Perlberger (12) in Palestine also discounted the importance of the aecial stage.

Identity of rust species on different hosts. Dunegan (7) reported that teliospores produced on cultivated peaches in the eastern states differ morphologically from those produced on indigenous *Prunus*. The so-called discolor type occurring on peach and other cultivated hosts are associated with the aecial stage on *Anemone coronaria*, whereas the typica type occurring on indigenous hosts are associated with the aecial stage on native species of *Hepatica* and *Anemone*. Scott and Stout (14) produced infection of peaches, apricot, almond and prunes with aeciospores from *A. coronaria*, but failed to obtain infection on any of 7 varieties of cherries.

Disease development. On peaches in the Sacramento Valley, the fungus undergoes a period of inactivity during summer and passes this period on infected leaves and twig lesions. A second period of inactivity probably occurs in mid-winter. During this time the fungus survives in twig lesions, some of which developed the previous season and others of which are initiated in autumn but do not break through the bark until spring. Barrett (3) noted that in the moderate climate of southern California the fungus passed the winter on leaves which stay on the tree. The fungus is widespread and most important on prunes in California. Alternate hosts play only minor roles in the life cycle of the fungus in this country.

112

Uredospores are the predominant if not the only inoculum for infection in the Sacramento Valley. They retain their viability for 4 to 6 weeks; they are spread about to a limited extent by wind but probably to a much greater extent by water.

The infection and disease development cycle is believed (10) to be as follows: In spring, infection occurs through the under surfaces of the leaves. There may be a series of leaf infections, depending upon the weather. Apparently, fruit is not susceptible to infection until of considerable size. Fruit lesions seldom appear until late May or early June. During most of the summer and throughout early fall, the disease is quiescent. Sometime during the fall or early winter twig infection occurs. Little activity of the fungus is evident in mid-winter. In the spring, however, initial infection (leaf infection) is started by uredospores produced on twig lesions.

The incubation period in twigs is not known; that in leaves is not known with certainty but is apparently 7 to 8 days.

Rains apparently are necessary to maintain moisture conditions favorable to leaf infection. Uredospores germinated only at 100 percent relative humidity. The optimum temperature for germination was between 13° and 25°C, the minimum 10°C or lower and the maximum about 38°C.

Control. An application of a fungicide in mid-October can prevent twig infection. An application of fungicides in early summer prevented leaf and fruit infection (18). On prunes, wettable sulfur applied before signs of rust pustules provided control of leaf infections during the summer.

References

1. Arthur, J. C. 1906. Cultures of Uridineae in 1905. J. Mycol. 12:11-27.
2. _____ 1929. The plant rusts (Uredinales). John Wiley & Sons, N. Y. 446 pp.
3. Barrett, J. T. 1915. Observations on prune rust, *Puccinia pruni-spinosae* Pers. in southern California. Phytopathology 5:293. (Abstr.)
4. Blumer, S. 1960. Studies on the morphology and biology of *Tranzschelia pruni-spinosae* and *Tranzschelia discolor* (trans. title). Phytopath. Z. 38: 355-85.
5. Carter, M. V., W. J. Moller, and S. M. Pady. 1970. Factors affecting uredospore production and dispersal in *Tranzschelia discolor*. Australian J. Agric. Research 21:906-14.
6. Cunningham, G. H. 1925. Fungous diseases of fruit trees in New Zealand. Brett Painting Co., Auckland, N.Z. 382 pp.
7. Dunegan, J. C. 1936. The occurrence in the United States of two types of teliospores of *Tranzschelia pruni-spinosae*. Phytopathology 26:91. (Abstrs.)
8. Duruz, W. P. 1928. Further notes regarding peach rust control. Proc. Amer. Hort. Sci. 25:333-37.
9. Duruz, W. P., and M. Goldsworthy. 1928. Spraying for peach rust. (A progress report). Proc. Amer. Soc. Hort. Sci. 24:168-71.
10. Goldsworthy, M. C., and R. E. Smith. 1931. Studies on a rust of clingstone peach in California. Phytopathology 21:133-68.
11. Jafar, H. 1958. Studies on the biology of peach rust *(Tranzschelia pruni-spinosae)* in New England. N. Z. J. agric. Res. 1:642-651.
12. Perlberger, J. 1943. The rust disease of stone fruit trees in Palestine. Rehovath Agr. Exp. Sta. Bul. 34:1-7. (Hebrew with English summary).
13. Pierce, N. B. 1894. Prune rust. J. Mycol. 7:354-63.
14. Scott, C. E., and G. L. Stout. 1931. *Tranzschelia punctata* on cultivated Anemone in the Santa Clara Valley. Calif. Dept. Agr. Mo. Bul. 20(10-11):1-7.
15. Tranzschel, W. A. 1905. Bietraege zur biologie dur Uredineen. Trav. Mus. Bot. Acad. Imp. Sci., St. Petersbourg 2:67-69.
16. Tranzschell, V. 1935. The cherry rust, *Aeucotelium cerasi* (Bereng) N. gen. N. Comb (*Puccinia cerasi* Cast.) and its aecial stage. Riv. Pat. Veg. 25(5-6):177-83 (trans. title).
17. Ward, J. R. 1955. Diseases of peaches and nectarines. Tasmanian J. Agri. 26:52-58.
18. Wilson, E. E., and C. E. Scott. 1943. Prevention of three peach diseases by ferric dimethyl-dithiocarbamate. Phytopathology 33:962-63.

Scab of Almond
Fusicladium carpophilum (Thum.) Oudem.

In 1924, Smith (4) reported almond scab which she attributed to the fungus *Cladosporium carpophilum* Thum., which was new to California. Since then the disease has been reported from many parts in the state, usually appearing in brief outbreaks and seldom causing great damage. Between 1953 and 1957, however, it became an important disease in the northern part of the Sacramento Valley and has become more prevalent with the change of irrigation from furrow to sprinklers (3).

Symptoms. Symptoms on almond leaves, fruit, and twigs are similar to those produced by the scab disease of peach (figs. 38A, 38B, 38C). On leaves the first visible evidence of infection is many small, indistinct, somewhat circular greenish-yellow blotches on the under surfaces. The lesions later enlarge, some reaching 10 mm or more in diameter, turning yellowish-brown and later dark brown. On petioles and midribs they are of the same color but are more elongate. Severe infection causes leaves to fall. Leaves with few lesions remain on the tree until autumn, the tissue beneath the lesions becoming necrotic. Premature dropping of the leaves is the most serious phase of the disease.

On shoots the lesions are indistinct water-soaked spots at first. Later, the spots becomes brown as a result of spore formation by the causal fungus. In fall and early winter the lesions develop dark centers surrounded by a lighter periphery.

On fruit, indistinct, circular, olivaceous spots develop and coalesce into large irregular greyish-black blotches. Though lesions may occur on any part of the fruit they are usually much more common on the upper-most side.

Causal organism. The causal fungus is similar morphologically to the peach scab pathogen which has been known for many years as *Cladosporium carpophilum* Thum. (2). More recently Hughes (1) proposed that the name *C. carpophilum* be changed to *Fusicladium carpophilum* (Thum.) Oudem. Oudem.

Varietal susceptibility. Though all the California almond varieties are susceptible to scab, NePlus Ultra and Drake are most severely infected.

Disease development. The causal fungus overwinters as mycelium in twig lesions. In spring it resumes growth at the margins of the lesions, where it produces conidia. Twig lesions develop in early spring (March), while leaf and fruit lesions usually do not appear until June.

Control. Spraying the trees 5 weeks after petal fall materially reduced leaf and fruit infection. Sprays applied for Coryneum blight at the petal-fall stage has given added protection. Fungicides reported effective against scab are ziram, captan, wettable sulfur, and dichlone.

References

1. Hughes, S. J. 1953. Some foliicolous Hyphomycetes. Can J. Bot. 31(5):560-76.
2. Keitt, G. W. 1917. Peach scab. U.S.D.A. Bul. 395:1-66.
3. Ogawa, Joseph M., Carl W. Nichols, and Harley English. 1955. Almond scab. Calif. Dept. Agr. Bul. 44(2):59-62.
4. Smith, E. H. 1924. Some diseases new to California. Phytopathology 14:125. (Abstr.).

Silver Leaf of Stone Fruit
Stereum purpureum (Pers. ex Fr.) Fr.

This disease, caused by the fungus *Stereum purpurem,* is important in Europe and New Zealand but is of minor importance in California, probably because of California's relatively dry climate. Only one apricot orchard in Contra Costa County and one peach orchard in Butte County have been reported to have the disease in the last few years. In both orchards, only a small area was infected and the disease did not spread to other orchards.

Details of this disease are covered in section III of this publication.

Verticillium Wilt of Stone Fruit
Verticillium dahliae Kleb.

Verticilium wilt on stone fruits is caused by the fungus *Verticillium dahliae* Kleb. which was also named *V. albo-atrum* in early literature. There are two strains of *V. dahliae* on cotton but the strain on stone fruits has not been positively identified. Because of the diversification of agriculture in California and the wide host range of the pathogen, the disease is important especially on young plantings of stone fruit and on mature trees grown in cool climates.

There are no preventive measures to be used before planting of young orchards. When newly planted trees are affected, an occasional tree is lost and some branches killed, but in most instances the trees recover. Interplants with susceptible hosts such as cotton, tomato, and strawberry should be avoided.

Details of this disease are discussed in section III of this publication. It is important that this disease not be confused with other diseases such as *Prunus* ring spot or crown rot which may give similar symptoms.

NONPARASITIC DISEASES OF STONE FRUIT

Cankers on Peach Seedlings Induced by Chilling
Cause—chilling

A condition developing in peach seedlings when the young plants were held at 3 to 7 °C, but not when they were held at 14 to 27 °C, was reported by Davis and English (2, 3). This condition, they concluded, was similar to "chilling injury" which develops in other plants exposed to temperatures slightly above freezing. Cankers similar to those on seedlings have occasionally been observed in the field on Red Haven, Lovell, and Halford peaches.

Although the lesions produced on young plants exposed to low temperatures resemble those produced by *Pseudomonas syringae,* the bacterial canker pathogen, they do not yield that organism. Furthermore, no other organism is associated with the cankers and attempts at graft-transmission of the disorder have failed (4).

Symptoms. Plants exposed to 6°C developed water-soaked areas, usually at the nodes of the stems. Necrosis of the affected portions follows along with gumming and a "sour-sap" smell. The lesions sometimes girdle the stem, killing the portions above it.

The root system of affected plants appears to be normal, and normal shoots later grow from the base of the plants below the lesions.

Factors affecting development of chilling injury. Davis and English (3) found that the condition developed when plants were exposed to temperatures of 3 to 7°C, which is well above freezing. It was, therefore, not brought on by temperatures that cause formation of ice in plant tissues. Nevertheless, as Belehradek (1) noted, the separation between chilling injury and freezing injury is not necessarily distinct.

The minimum time for production of chilling injury at 6°C is 25 to 30 days. A longer exposure to low temperature increases the extent of injury. Factors which cause early leaf drop during chilling result in fewer cankers. Increase in day-length or increase in nitrogen promotes the maintenance of green growth and thereby increases the plant's resistance to chilling injury. Chilling injury is reduced by treatment of leaves with gibberellic acid, which slows their aging, but is increased by treatment of leaves with peach seed leachate, which accelerates their aging. Lipe (5) reported the principle in peach seed leachate which accelerates leaf aging is dormin, or a material similar in its effects. Two applications of ziram or one application of decenylsuccinic acid, a treatment which Kuiper (4) recommended for freezing protection, did not lessen chilling injury in plants.

References

1. Belehradek, J. 1957. Physiological aspects of heat and cold. Ann. Rev. Physiol. 19:19-82.
2. Davis, J. R., and H. English. 1965. A canker condition of peach seedlings induced by chilling. Phytopathology 55:805-06.
3. _____ 1969. Factors involved in the development of peach seedling cankers induced by chilling. Phytopathology 59:305-13.
4. Kuiper, J. C. P. 1964. Inducing resistance to freezing and desiccation in plants by decenyl-succinic acid. Science 146:544-46.
5. Lipe, W. N. 1966. Physiological studies of peach seed dormancy with reference to growth substances. Ph.D. thesis. University of California, Davis. 112 p.

Corky Growth on Almond Kernel

This abnormality occurs sporadically in California and, except for one almond variety, Jordanolo, it is of minor importance.

Symptoms. A dry corky material, tan in color, is closely appressed to the surface of the kernel (fig. 39). A crack in the inner surface of the shell usually occurs in a position overlying the corky growth.

Cause and development. The exact cause of corky growth is not known but it is evidently related to the growth of the almond fruit. The almond fruit grows rapidly from the time it is formed until early May, and during this time the tissues of the hull and shell are soft and the endosperm is watery. After early May, growth of the hull and shell is less rapid. Under some conditions, the inner part of the shell hardens and ceases growth while the outer part of the shell continues to grow slowly. Probably it is owing to this that cracks develop in the inner part of the shell. It is during this period that the corky growth develops (1). The growth is produced by the extrusion of callus tissue from the cracks. This tissue becomes closely appressed to the surface of the kernel.

Contributing factors. Factors contributing to development of the disorder are those which favor rapid growth of fruit during the early stages of fruit development. Two of the more important factors are size of crop and root troubles which exert a girdling effect on the tree. Light crops, induced by frost or inadequate pollination, are also closely related to the incidence of corky growth. Jordanolo almond blossoms early when frosts are likely and when trees of other (pollinizing) varieties are not yet blossoming.

Experiments show that the removal of a strip of bark from around almond branches will increase both the size of the fruit and the amount of corky growth.

Control. The surest way to avoid corky growth is to not plant Jordanolo. Jordanolo also has another defect (noninfectious bud failure) which limit its value so it has not been recommended for new plantings. When Jordanolo trees occur in an almond orchard, the best procedures to prevent corky growth are protection of the trees against frost, provision for adequate pollinizers, and correction of adverse soil conditions affecting the root system of the trees.

Reference

1. Kester, D. E. 1957. Corky growth of kernels is recurring Jordanolo problem. Almond Facts 1957: 8-9. (Published by the California Almond Growers Exchange, Sacramento, California.)

Noninfectious Bud Failure of Almond
Cause—genetic

The disorder of almonds variously known as "bud failure", "crazy top", and "noninfectious bud failure" has for many years been seen occasionally in certain almond plantings and in certain almond cultivars. In the past 15 years, however, it has become quite general in the relatively new cultivar Jordanolo. Other cultivars developing the disorder are Nonpareil, Peerless, and Jubilee, the latter propagated from a seedling of unknown origin. Nonpareil and Peerless are old established cultivars, whereas Jordanolo resulted from a cross Nonpareil X Harriott, made by the U.S. Department of Agriculture and the University of California Agricultural Experiment Station. Because of its excellent fruiting habit and its large fruit Jordanolo became widely planted within a few years after its introduction, but the bud failure disorder subsequently became so extensive that it has been eliminated from plantings in recent years.

Symptoms. As the name implies the principal symptom of the disorder is the failure of buds to grow (fig. 40A). Failure is more prevalent in leaf buds than in flower buds, although the latter also fail to grow if leaf bud failure is prevalent.

The failure of buds to grow results in branches entirely or largely devoid of foliage. Practically all buds that do grow develop shoots instead of both spurs and shoots. Not infrequently the terminal bud on a shoot will fail while a lateral bud grows into a shoot. Repetitions of such an occurrence may result in the direction of growth being changed. This is the symptom which has been given the name of crazy top (fig. 40B).

A second symptom is the development of bands of rough-bark resulting from the necrosis of patches of outer bark of affected branches. As the branch develops the phellogen activity in the cortex beneath the necrotic areas causes the phelloderm to crack, thereby producing a band of rough bark around the branch.

Such cortical necrosis is common in Peerless, quite infrequent in Nonpareil, but occurs commonly in seedlings of Nonpareil and Jordanolo (Nonpareil X Harriott). Few leaf buds remain viable on areas of cortical necrosis, although an occasional flower bud may open and set fruit there.

Cause. Experiments to test the transmissibility of bud failure have been negative, even though the experiments were extended for several years (4, 10, 11). Moreover, observations in orchards where the grower had grafted over bud-failure-affected trees with scions from nonaffected orchards showed that the scions grew normally for 8 to 10 years, whereas branches growing from the original tree developed the bud failure condition. It was therefore concluded that the disorder is not caused by a transmissible entity such as a virus, and it was named "noninfectious bud failure."

The disorder is apparently a genetic type defect which develops in both scion and seedlings (9) of bud-failure-affected trees. Because Jordanolo is a seedling resulting from pollinating flowers of Nonpareil with pollen from Harriott, and because the disorder is known to occur in Nonpareil, it is apparent how the Jordanolo inherited the disorder. Although the original (S) Jordanolo tree was not available for observation, trees vegetatively propagated from the mother tree were observed. These S1 trees showed an occasional tree with a few branches exhibiting bud-failure symptoms. Trees (S2) propagated from S1 trees exhibited much more extensive symptoms as did S3 trees. Apparently, the disorder is intensified by repeated vegetative propagation.

Many of the hybrids, Nonpareil X Peerless, developed extensive symptoms of bud-failure if both parents exhibited the disorder, but only occasionally did they have the disorder when neither parent exhibited it (9).

One series of studies (1) indicated that a gibberellin-like substance (probably absicisic acid) is involved in development of the disorder.

Development of the disorder. Exposure of the growing trees to high temperatures seems to induce bud failure (3). Successive propagation from one scion generation to another also intensifies the disorder.

Control. The only sure method of controlling noninfectious bud failure has been to avoid propagating cultivars prone to the disorder. In selecting Nonpareil and Peerless budwood for propagation it is important to avoid trees from orchards in which the disorder occurs.

References

1. Hellali, R., D. E. Kester, and R. Ryugo. 1971. Noninfectious bud failure in almonds. Observations on the vegetative growth patterns and concurrent changes in growth regulating substances. Horticultural Science 6(3) Sec. 2:33.

2. Kester, D. E. 1969. Noninfectious bud failure in almonds in California. I. The nature and origin. California Agriculture 23(2):12-14.

3. Kester, D. E. and R. Hellali. 1972. Variations in the distribution of noninfectious bud-failure (BF) in almonds as a function of temperature and growth. Horticultural Science 7(3):Sect. 2:18.

4. Kester, D. E. and E. E. Wilson. 1961. Bud-failure in almonds. California Agriculture 15(6):5-7.

5. Kester, D. E., A. D. Rizzi, H. E. Williams, and R. W. Jones. 1969. Noninfectious bud failure in almond varieties. II. Identification and control of bud failure in almond varieties. Calif. Agr. 23(12):14-16.

6. Stout, G. L., and E. E. Wilson. 1947. Studies of a bud failure condition in almond trees. Phytopathology 37:364. (Abstr.)

7. Wilson, E. E. 1950. Observations on the bud-failure disorder in Jordanolo, a new variety of almond. Phytopathology 40:970. (Abstr.)

8. _____ 1952. Development of bud failure in the Jordanolo variety of almond. Phytopathology 42:520. (Abstr.)

9. _____ 1954. Seed transmission tests of almond bud failure disorders. Phytopathology 44:510. (Abstr.)

10. Wilson, E. E., and R. D. Schein. 1956. The nature and development of noninfectious bud failure of almonds. Hilgardia 24:519-42.

11. Wilson, E. E., and G. L. Stout. 1944. A bud failure disorder in almond trees. California Dept. Agr. Bull. 33:60-64.

12. _____ 1951. Almond bud failure. U.S. Dept. Agr. Agricultural Handbook 10:205-07.

Russet Scab of Prune
Cause—unknown

Russetting or "russet" of prunes was first brought to the attention of entomologists in the early 1930's. Since then it has caused severe losses in years of heavy rains during blossom period. In 1967, estimated losses in California from russet scab and associated defects (including brown rot, limb bruises, green fruit rot, etc.) were $3 million. This included lowering of the quality of the dried fruit and the extra costs of sorting (1). Though heavy losses have occurred only four times in the last 25 years (1), some russet scab is present each year.

The original name given to this condition was "lacy scab" because of the netted pattern on the fresh fruit. Corbin, Lider and Roberts (1) named it "russet scab" to describe the appearance of the affected dried prunes.

Symptoms. The symptoms are first apparent during shuck fall stage of bloom (fig. 41A). Wax on the surface of the fruit is lacking and the affected area is shiny (2); such areas may or may not constitute a major defect (fig. 41B). Some entomologists attributed the condition to feeding of thrips on the surface of the fruit beneath the shuck, but others have thought microorganisms must be involved. However, the effect of low temperature cannot be disregarded because the symptoms appear typical of frost damage to apple and pear fruit.

In a 1963 trial, fungicides applied for brown rot blossom blight reduced the incidence of russet scab (2), and this suggested that *Botrytis cinerea* might be involved. Later studies, however, revealed no benefits on scab from the use of benzimidazole fungicide (benomyl) which provides excellent control of *B. cinerea*. Thus, the cause of russet scab still remains unknown.

In 1963, and again in 1967, russet scab on prune fruit followed rainfall during the bloom period (1). Artificial overhead sprinkling of trees during the shuck-fall period also increased the incidence of russet scab (2). Removal of the shuck during full bloom reduced the incidence of russetting (2).

Most striking is the reduction of russetting by fungicides applied during the blossoming period. Effective control was shown by a full bloom spray with captan, folcid, or dichlone. Sprays applied during early bloom provided some reduction in russet scab, while sprays applied at or after petal-fall provided no control.

References
1. Corbin, J. B., J. V. Lider, and K. O. Roberts. 1968. Controlling prune russet scab. California Agriculture 22(11):6-7.

2. Ogawa, J. M., I. C. MacSwan, and B. T. Manji. (unpublished data).

POSTHARVEST DISEASES OF STONE FRUIT

The problem of decay has been the limiting factor in marketing of fresh agricultural products, but through use of proper fungicides, packaging, refrigeration, and transportation our farm products are now consumed throughout the world and grocery stores can stock fresh produce year-round. In processing, quality crops can be hand- or mechanically-harvested, ripened under optimum temperature and humidity, and canned or frozen afterwards without fear of excessive decay. Yet with each advance in technology ranging from new cultivars to handling procedures, new methods for decay control must be adapted to further extend storage life of crops. Some organisms such as *Alternaria, Mucor,* and higher temperature *Rhizopus* species are yet to be controlled.

The diseases described below are discussed by crops and in order of seasonal maturity. Some information on preharvest conditions as well as specific cultural techniques is repeated from earlier pages. The relation of postharvest decay to preharvest disease and condition of the fruit at harvest and storage is emphasized.

Sweet Cherries

Losses from fruit decay during transit and storage have limited shipments of sweet cherries to markets in the eastern U. S. (fig. 42A). Losses between 1936-42 in New York City averaged 2.8 percent per car lot, with 72 percent of the product showing from trace to 4 percent decay, and 10.2 percent showing 5 to 9 percent (112).

Pathogens causing decay are *Monilinia fructicola* (Wint.) Honey, *Rhizopus stolonifer* (Fr.) Lind, *Botrytis cinerea* Pers. ex Fr., *Whetzelinia (Sclerotinia) sclerotiorum* (Lib.) Korf & Dumont, *Penicillium expansum* Lk. ex Thom. *P. italicum* Wehmer, *Alternaria alternata* (Fr.) Keissl (= *A. tenuis* Nees), *M. laxa* (Aderh. & Ruhl.) Honey, *Aspergillus niger* v. Teigh., *Cladosporium herbarum* Lk., *Erwinia amylovora* (Burr.) Winslow, *Pullularia* sp., and yeasts (10, 112). Postharvest decay pathogens may differ from year to year because of environmental conditions during winter, blossoming period of the trees, final stages of ripening of the fruit, as well as treatment after harvest (such as temperature and time in storage, chemicals used, and amount of bruising the cherries receive).

Warm weather in winter promotes formation of double fruit and spurs (two fruit joined together, with one undeveloped)—these are sites for *A. alternata* and *R. stolonifer* infection. *Alternaria* infection occurs in the field before harvest, while injuries to these types of fruit during picking and packing provide avenues for infection by *R. stolonifer*. Rains during the blossoming period favor infections of blossoms by *B. cinerea, M. laxa, M. fructicola* and *S. sclerotiorum,* and evidence points to incipient infections from *B. cinerea* and *Monilinia*. Rains just before harvest induce cracking of fruit, and such injuries are susceptible to fungus pathogens as well as to bacteria and yeasts (12, 13, 34).

Seasonal and varietal effects of fruit decay have been observed in California during the last 10 years. For the earliest harvested cultivar, Burlat, decay problems have been limited, probably because of lack of pathogens in the field at that time, and also because it is flown to market and quickly consumed. Additionally, floral tubes of Burlat dehisce and fall off before the parts senesce, thus reducing chances for infection from such pathogens as *Botrytis*. Chapman and Black Tartarians have soft flesh, are easily bruised, and rot develops quickly. In addition, demand for them is not as great as for Burlat or the later-harvested Bing. Napoleon cultivar is used for canning, and the fruit is placed in a bisulfite-brine immediately after harvest. In early harvested cultivars the pathogens are primarily *Botrytis* and *Monilinia*. During mid-season and in higher temperatures, *Rhizopus* becomes more noticeable, especially on ripe and overripe fruits. During mid- and late-harvest *Alternaria* begins to predominate, especially on fruit held for an extended period. *Penicillium,* bacteria, and yeasts become more important with extended storage periods.

Botrytis decay. *Botrytis* decay of fruit can be traced to the incidence of blossom blight in the field. Blossoms are especially susceptible at about full bloom to shuck-fall when the floral parts are senescing. Infection of a single blossom could result in a cluster rot through contact of diseased with healthy blossoms, or through infection from spores, masses of which are quickly produced in blighted blossoms. Green fruits are occasionally infected from contact with blighted blossoms or infected floral shucks. Mummified green fruit produce large numbers of spores. Some *Botrytis* infections are invisible at first but will rot the fruit as it ripens in the field or after it is harvested. One infected fruit in a cluster causes rot of other fruit in the cluster. Symptoms of *Botrytis* decay on ripening fruit are identified as a firm light tan-colored area with or without typical sporulation of the fungus. It can be mistaken for *Monilinia* infection if not observed closely to note the lack of distinctive clusters of spores of that fungus. Detailed description of *Botrytis* is given under the discussion of blossom blight and green fruit rot of stone fruits.

Botrytis is spread from one fruit to another by contact and by air-borne spores during harvest and packing operations. In the hand-sorting operation, some *Botrytis* infections of fruits can be seen as light-brown areas but without typical sporulation— incipient infections cannot be seen by the unaided eye. Spores of *Botrytis* germinate even at near-freezing temperatures with the optimum at 20 °C (100). On fruit with incipient infections, decay and sporulation can develop in storage at 4.4 °C. At 20 °C, decay symptoms develop within 24 hours and heavy sporulation develops in 48 hours.

Monilinia decay. Monilinia decay, is also produced by spores from mummies of green and ripe fruit as well as from blighted blossoms. Overwintering spore sources of *Monilinia* occur in mummies on the tree but more commonly are in other host plants such as peaches, apricots, and flowering quince. The first *Monilinia*-blighted blossoms produce spores in time for infection of other blossoms. Healthy blossoms in contact with infected blossoms frequently become infected (12. 13). Green fruit becomes infected and produces masses of spores which are readily dispersed by water and wind. During ripening, cluster rotting of fruit occurs through contact of healthy fruit with mummified fruit or with blighted blossoms. Presence of mummified fruit is probably the reason why most if not all fruit is contaminated before harvest; during harvest the chance of contamination is even greater. *Monilinia* can infect uninjured fruit surfaces but infects injured surfaces more readily. Decays develop at storage temperatures below 5 °C, the optimum being around 25 °C. Symptoms on fruit are similar to those produced by *Botrytis* except that *Monilinia* spores are in chains. The color of the sporulating surface varies from almost white to grey. The whole fruit can rot in 48 hours at room temperature. The decayed flesh is firm to the touch and does not separate easily from the healthy portion. Partially mummified fruit tissue will appear dark because of the presence of pseudosclerotia.

Rhizopus decay. Rhizopus decay is primarily a post-harvest problem of ripe fruit—green fruit is not attacked by this fungus. Initial infections usually occur on injured or bruised fruit. Impact injury can occur during harvest, sorting, sizing, packaging, storage, and transit. *Rhizopus* spores are practically omnipresent and are the main infection propagules. At storage temperatures below 4.4 °C, *Rhizopus* is not a problem, but at 27 °C (its optimum growth temperature) complete decay can occur in 24 hours. Aerial hyphae develop during this period and sporulation occurs within 30 hours. *Rhizopus* rot is serious primarily because the mycelia spread from diseased to healthy fruit, and because the fruit and container are soiled by juice released from decaying fruit.

The pathogen, *R. stolonifer* (Ehrenberg ex. Fr.) Lind., on artificial media such as potato-dextrose agar is a rapid-growing fungus having white, coarse mycelia; optimum temperature is 27 °C, maximum temperature is 32.2 °C, and minimum temperature is 10 °C (74). At high humidity, aerial hyphae are abundant; at low humidity they are few in numbers. During shedding of spores, sporangia are first white, then grey, and then black. They range from 150 to 350 μm in diameter; the columella are broad, hemispheric and about 70 to 90 μm in height and 70 to 250 μm wide. Sporangiospores are released by disintegration of the outer sporangial wall and are unequal, irregular, round or oval, angular, striated, and about 7 μm wide and 10 to 15 μm long. Sporangiospores germinate readily at 7.2 °C but not at 4.4 °C (48, 74). Zygotes are black, measure about 150 to 200 μm in diameter and are formed on suspensors. The fungus is heterothallic (115). Zygospore germination has seldomly been observed.

Development of *R. stolonifer* in fruit packages is identified by masses of white mycelia with long stolons extending to adjacent healthy fruit. Black sporangia occur abundantly near the edge of the containers because of greater oxygen levels at that place. In the presence of this fungus, macroscopic evaluation of other molds is difficult if not impossible. Decaying fruit on the orchard floor is covered with black sporangia but shows little indication of mycelia or sporangiophores. Fruit infection on the tree is rare.

Penicillium decay. Decay by *Penicillium italicum* and *P. expansum* is found more often on fruit which have been stored for extended periods or those which are soft or over-ripe. These fungi cause watery rot like that of *Rhizopus*. The best features for identification are the typical masses of bluish-green spores. Infection occurs most commonly on bruised, double or spurred fruit.

Alternaria decay. *Alternaria* decay develops commonly on brusied, double and spurred fruit as a dark, olive-green depressed area. It can be identified by the spores which are typically muriform and catenulate. Infection is more common on ripe or overripe fruit and fruit harvested during the latter part of the season. Other fruit rot pathogens are controlled by Botran and benomyl, but *Alternaria* remains uncontrolled and therefore is the most common pathogen found on cherries in the market.

Bacterial and yeast decay. Bacteria and yeasts, which can make fruit slimy and sticky, develop quickly on fruit infected by other organisms.

Control. Control of the fungal diseases begins in the orchard. Sprays are applied to control blossom infections by *Botrytis* and *Monilinia*. Benzimidazole compounds (61) which also prevent incipient infections of fruit by *Botrytis* are used. Fungicides such as captan, copper, and carbamates are effective against *Monilinia* but are less effective against *Botrytis*.

Spraying twice during the 3 weeks before harvest with either captan, wettable sulfur, or Botran (2, 6-dichloro-4-nitro-aniline), however, failed to reduce fruit infections. Infections through cracks caused by rains (34) are common; it is probably not worthwhile to combat such infections, because cracked fruits cannot be marketed. Preharvest Botran sprays provided excellent postharvest control of *Rhizopus*, and sprays of benomyl are effective against *Monilinia*, *Botrytis*, and *Penicillium* provided the fruit is not washed before packaging (60, 61). For fruit that is mechanically sorted for size, spraying with Botran plus benomyl or Botran plus captan during the stem cutting and sizing procedures provides control of all primary molds mentioned except *Alternaria*. Reduction of cherry decay by washing in water has been suggested (113), but unless protectant chemicals are used in the water the decay increases. Chlorine washes before or during stem cutting and sizing have given added control of molds, including *Alternaria*, and have also reduced bacteria and yeast populations. Some *Alternaria* control has been obtained with dehydroacetic acid (114).

One of the best means of reducing decay in packages is to prevent injury of fruit before packaging. Injured areas become pitted (sunken) and are sites for fungal infections. Removal of decaying fruit, doubles, and those mechanically damaged delay development of molds. Rapid cooling of fruit with flesh temperature of 32 °C or more is beneficial, but those picked with flesh temperatures below 27 °C reach equilibrium with ambient temperatures very quickly.

Packaging of sweet cherries to prevent pressure bruising remains one of the critical areas for study because injuries are avenues for infection from fungus pathogens (55).

Modifying the storage atmosphere with carbon dioxide levels up to 20 percent reduced mold development on untreated fruits (30, 34, 83, 111). Temperatures near freezing, provided the best decay control. The length of exposure to a carbon dioxide atmosphere required to kill germinated spores prevents commercial consideration (15, 16). In the Pacific Northwest, fruit is placed in polyliners (plastic bags) (35, 36, 73) to prevent moisture loss and to build up the carbon dioxide levels (thereby reducing the rate of ripening and consequently the amount of decay).

Apricots

Decays cause losses in fruit destined for fresh market and for canning, freezing, and drying. The principal apricot cultivars in California are Blenheim (Royal) for fresh market and drying and Tilton for canning. For extra early shipment Derby Royal and Perfection, with harvest beginning in mid-May, are grown in western Yolo and Solano counties. The canning season in the southern Sacramento and Santa Clara valleys ends in mid-July.

Fruit for the fresh market is usually hand-picked and placed in wooden boxes holding about 50 pounds. Some fruit for processing is mechanically harvested and placed in bins holding about 800 pounds. Fruit for drying is placed in 50-pound boxes and ripened at ambient temperatures.

The most common decay pathogens are *Monilinia laxa* and *Rhizopus stolonifer* (62, 67, 94). *M. fructicola* is common in apricot orchards located near peaches. *Alternaria alternata*, *Rhizopus arrhizus*, and *R. circinans* are also common but their role in decay has not been fully assessed (Fig. 42B). Other pathogens are *Botrytis cinerea* and *Penicillium expansum* on fruit which is held in cold storage for extended periods. *Gilbertella persicaria*, *Aspergillus* spp., *Mucor* spp., and *Cladosporium* sp., develop rapidly as fruit ripens.

Control programs for *Monilinia* have been directed at reducing the inoculum in the field by controlling blossom blight and fruit rot. *Monilinia* infection of green fruit (102) have not been found to occur in California.

Captan sprays during the last 3 weeks before harvest followed by a post-harvest wax treatment can cause superficial blemishes on the fruit epidermis (20). Preharvest sprays with materials such as benomyl and wettable sulfur, however, do not result in fruit blemishes following postharvest wax treatments.

Preharvest or postharvest Botran applications provide excellent control of *Rhizopus stolonifer* but not *R. arrhizus* (62)—thus, for example, it is important to store fruit at below 40 °F. When the combination treatment of benomyl (61) and Botran (54, 56, 94) is used, the pathogens still to be controlled are *R. arrhizus*, *G. persicaria*, *Aspergillus*, *Mucor*, and *Alternaria*. For *Alternaria* the most promising fungicide is Difolatan and chlorothalonil.

For postharvest application of wax-fungicide combinations, a special horse-hair brush is used to prevent fruit damage. The fruit is sized, then sorted and packed loosely. Some packers vibrate the boxes (tight-fill) to prevent fruit brusing during transit (51).

Polyethylene wrappers (9) are used in Italy but not in California.

Nectarines and Peaches

Of the annual shipment of 36 million bushels of fresh fruit to New York City between 1935 and 1942, over one million dollars worth annually was lost to decay (112). Thanks to chemical control measures fresh fruit is now shipped economically even to distant markets and sold there as late as a month after harvest. Freestone peaches for processing are harvested when mature and canned or frozen after being held for ripening at a temperature of 20 °C and humidity of >85 RH for 1 to 5 days (58); without chemical treatment, serious decay would result within 24 to 48 hours. Mechanically harvested ripe cling peaches are more prone to decay than is hand-harvested fruit (67), but because of processing fruit within 12 to 18 hours of picking decays are not a real threat.

Postharvest decay pathogens are primarily *Monilinia fructicola* and *Rhizopus stolonifer,* with some lots showing considerable *R. arrhizus* and *Gilbertella persicaria* (5, 38, 53, 56, 78, 86). Decay from *Penicillium* and *Botrytis* infection occurs only in fruit held for extended period. Infection from yeasts has been reported (14, 85) but is rare in fruit produced in the western states. In general, fruit decays are more prevalent during the latter part of the harvest season. This may be attributed to increases in fungal inoculum in the field and to moisture in the environment.

While fruit of all nectarine and peach cultivars is susceptible to fungal decay, such cultivars as Kirkman Gem peaches with suture cracks are more difficult to treat chemically and are thus more subject to decay. Those with serious *Monilinia* blossom blight are most likely to develop fruit decay. Infection of harvested fruit is most common at the stem end where the epidermis may be torn during harvest. Control of insects such as the Oriental fruit moth is essential in order to eliminate larval holes into which Nitidulid beetles contaminated with fungus spores can enter (53).

Monilinia fructicola is the most common decay pathogen on peaches and nectarines and causes both blossom blight and fruit rot. *M. laxa* is less common on peach in California (54) but more common on peach in Oregon. Neither species present a problem in peach-growing areas of the Yakima Valley in Washington (75).

One can expect almost all fruit in the orchard to be contaminated if fungus-infected mummified fruit develop during the growing season, and serious decay will result if harvested fruit is held at room tempera-

ture. Fruit held below 4.4 °C develops decays more slowly. In packed products, decay starts most readily if the fruit touches each other or if placed in a plastic pack with stem-end down. In plastic packs, decay begins most commonly at the stem end where the highest humidity occurs.

Injured fruits contaminated by spores of *M. fructicola* may develop visible decay within 24 hours at 22.2 °C, and sporulation of the fungus will occur in 30 hours (fig. 42C). The decaying tissue is at first light-brown but later turns grey to black. The rotted tissue, which is firm and difficult to separate from the healthy tissue, extends into the mesocarp in a conical pattern. *Monilinia* is identified by presence of lemon-shaped spores, and differentiation of the species is by mycelial growth characteristics on potato-dextrose agar medium.

Rhizopus stolonifer spreads quickly from fruit to fruit (fig. 42C) causing the tissue to turn mushy and leaky in the boxes (5). Affected portions can easily be separated from the healthy tissue. Infection initially occurs only on injured fruit surfaces, hence it is rarely found in fruit on the tree although abundant on fallen fruit. Such fruit is commonly affected with *Rhizopus* species and *Gilbertella persicaria* (46).

At low humidity *Rhizopus* produces abundant spores on short aerial hyphae. In fruit packages, where humidity is high mycelia are abundant but spores are sparse. Though one cannot distinguish *R. stolonifer* from *R. arrhizus* in the field, they can be differentiated by incubating cultures at 36 °C, where *R. stolonifer* will not grow but *R. arrhizus* will. *Rhizopus* sporangiospores are first white, then black, and finally grey when the sporangial walls are broken. With *Gilbertella*, droplets of shiny black spore suspensions form on the sporangia. When dry these appear as black masses clinging to the split sporangium (14).

Rhizopus and *Gilbertella* are widely distributed in California orchards (17, 65). Neither organism will attack green immature fruit, but partially ripened slightly yellow fruit are highly susceptible. Spores of *Rhizopus* are ubiquitous and can remain alive under extreme conditions of desiccation and high temperatures.

Gilbertella persicaria (Eddy) Hesseltine is distinguished from *Rhizopus* by several hyaline appendages at both ends of the sporangiospores. Sporangia are often borne in a circinate fashion and split into two equal halves. The fungus is heterothallic (17). The temperature range for sporangiospore germination, mycelial growth in culture, and fruit rot is 4 to

39 °C, the optimum being 30 to 33 °C. Characteristic growth and sporulation occur on peaches, nectarines, plums, apricots and on other crops such as strawberries, tomatoes and sweet potatoes. Maximum decay of peaches occurs at 30 to 33 °C with little or none developing at 18 and 39 °C (56).

Gilbertella growing on a synthetic medium containing 2,6-dichloro-4-nitroaniline gave rise to a variant which could tolerate a high concentration of that chemical. On mycelial-inoculated peach fruit, a spray of 1,000 ppm of 2,6-dichloro-4-nitroaniline suppressed a non-variant but not the variant. The variant remains stable during successive transfers in agar culture and on peach fruit (66).

Rhizopus arrhizus, Fischer is differentiated from *R. stolonifer* by its ability to grow at temperatures of 36 to 40 °C and by its smaller spores (5 to 7 μm). On decayed fruit, the mycelial mass develops less sporangia and less turf. When *R. oryzae* is present it can be identified by its spore dimensions of 7 to 9 microns and stouter stolons (115). One of the best identifying tests for *Rhizopus arrhizus* is that it will grow in a medium containing 4 ppm of 2,6-dichloro-4-nitroaniline, while *R. stolonifer* will not (65). Thus far only one isolate of *R. stolonifer* tolerant to 2,6-dichloro-4-nitroaniline has been found in orchards; one isolate of *R. arrhizus* sensitive to that chemical has been reported (103).

Control. Postharvest treatments depend on whether fruit is for fresh market or for processing. For fresh market the main goal is to extend the decay-free life of the mature fruit; for processing the aim is to ripen the fruit without decay.

In the 1950's, sulfur (28, 84, 87, 89) and captan dusts were widely used as pre- and postharvest protectants against fungus pathogens. Also used, but with limited success, were cold-water sprays containing 100 to 125 ppm chlorine (45, 101). Dipping fruit in 0.1 to 1% sodium orthophenylphenate or the antibiotic mycostatin provided better decay control than did chlorine treatments (27). In 1960, 2,6-dichloro-4-nitroaniline (Botran) was introduced for control of *Rhizopus* and *Monilinia* and it continues to be the key chemical for control of both fungi (18, 24, 25, 40, 56, 65, 68). Mixtures of Botran with captan (58) gave excellent decay control (56) but benomyl gave even better control (60). Waxes containing these chemicals provide better distribution and increased chemical residues on fruit (54), and reduction in fruit shriveling (41, 92, 107). Recently, it was shown that established infections of *M. fructicola* and *R. stolonifer* may be suppressed by a proper application of Botran plus benomyl in water-soluble wax (47); these chemicals were found to penetrate into the mesocarp tissues (42, 80).

Studies have shown that Botran induces lysis of *Rhizopus* germ tubes (64). Botran is active against *R. stolonifer* at 2 ppm and against *M. fructicola* at 4 ppm. Benomyl does not prevent germination of Monilinia spores but it suppresses growth of the organism at 0.1 ppm. Neither fungucide is effective against *Alternaria* or *Aspergillus.* Tolerant isolates of *R. stolonifer, Botrytis cinerea,* and *G. persicaria* have been produced in a medium containing Botran (66, 104, 105), but in only one instance has Botran-tolerant *R. stolonifer* been found in the field and this was in a peach orchard not previously sprayed with Botran. Benomyl-tolerant *Monilinia* had not been found in culture or in nature (98) but was detected on fresh-market peaches in 1978.

Hot-water dips (32 °C for 0.3 to 1.5 min) (39, 49, 81, 90, 106, 107, 109, 110) suppress development of *Monilinia* and *Rhizopus.* Such treatment would therefore be beneficial for fruit with incipient infections. High-temperature storage (24 hours at 40 °C) of fruit picked 4 days before it was canning-ripe provides quality canned products without *Monilinia* or *Rhizopus* rot problems (99). Quick-cooling of fruit exposed to high temperatures is essential in order to retain its high dessert-quality.

Other decay control techniques introduced, but not proved as effective as the chemicals mentioned or the regulation of temperatures, are gamma radiation, use of polyethylene liners (43) (8), or treatment with ozone (93), ammonia (28), alcohols (59), or acetaldehydes (2).

The use of a modified atmosphere (69) containing as high as 40% CO_2 and as low as 2% O_2 at storage temtures, has reduced the incidence of decay. More recently, use of low atmospheric pressures of 1/15 to 1/10 atmospheres at 0 °C has been tested (26) in storage of apples.

Treatments of fruits for the fresh market currently involve use of chlorine in hydrocooling, followed by applications of Botran and benomyl in wax applied as a spray and uniformly distributed by brushing. Another method is to apply these chemicals as an oil mist; another is to apply them with a brush. Fruit for canning is usually dipped (56, 58) in Botran, thereby providing fungicidal residues of 20 ppm or even higher. Subsequent washing by lye-dipping of the fruit before canning removes the Botran residue.

Fungicide applications during bloom followed by postharvest applications have provided good decay control (63). As important, however, are postharvest treatments such as storage of fruit at a temperature near 0 °C, packaging only quality fruit of uniform maturity, and discarding infected fruit.

Plums

Monilinia fructicola and *Rhizopus stolonifer* are the fungi most commonly associated with decaying of harvested fruit (23, 81, 86). *Alternaria* rot develops on injured fruit, especially on that which is mechanically harvested. Decay caused by *Penicillium* and *Aspergillus* is rare.

Plums are hand-harvested and placed in wooden boxes (40 pounds) or in bins (800 pounds) for hauling to the packing shed, where they are either cooled or immediately packaged by the tight-fill (51) method after a fungicide treatment. Harvest extends from May to September in California.

Symptoms for each of the pathogens concerned are similar to those on other stone fruits. Inoculum for *Monilinia* comes from decayed fruit which has been injured and infected earlier. Blossom blight from *Monilinia* is not as common as that on other stone fruit, because the peduncle of blighted blossoms dehisce as the fungus moves down it.

Control of decay has been difficult because the fruit epidermis is smooth, which makes effective chemical deposition difficult. Until the introduction of 2,6-dichloro-4-nitroaniline, decay control was largely a matter of delaying the rate of decay by cold storage and modified atmospheres (3, 4, 19, 21, 22, 70). Chemical control tests showed that a 2,6-dichloro-4-nitroaniline spray alone does not provide sufficient fungicidal residues for control, but the addition of fruit waxes to the fungicide resulted in larger deposits and better control (72, 108, 110).

Prunes

Pathogens causing decay of fresh mechanically harvested prunes are similar to those causing decay of other stone fruit, while those attacking dehydrated prunes are heat tolerant or are favored by a substrate rich in sugars. Prunes are harvested when the soluble content is at a minimum of 24 to 25 percent. After drying, reducing moisture to 20 percent, the dried prunes range from 38.4 to 51 percent reducing sugars and 0.6 to 5.5 percent sucrose which is unsuitable for mold growth.

Decay of fresh prunes held in bins more than 1 day after harvest can be serious. Molds on dehydrated prunes (16 percent moisture) held in bulk bins are most critical in terms of quality and loss to the producer if invaded by insect pests which make conditions favorable for mold development.

Molds developing on fresh prunes are *Monilinia fructicola*, *M. laza*, *Rhizopus stolonifer*, *Alternaria alternata*, *Aspergillus*, *Cladosporium*, *Chrysosporium*, *Mucor*, and *Penicillium* (30). On dried fruit (95) organisms most isolated are *Aspergillus glaucus* [*A. chevalieri* (30)], followed by *A. niger*, *A. repens*, *A. amstelodami*, *Penicillium* spp., *Alternaria*, *Monilinia*, *Chaetomella* and *Mucor*. Yeast isolated (95) most commonly are *Saccharomyces rouxii*, followed by *S. mellis*, *Torulopsis magnoliae*, *T. stellata*, *Candida krusei*, *Trichosporon behrendii*, *Pichia fermentans*, *P. membranafaciens*, *C. chalmersi*, *S. rosei*, *S. cerevisiae*, *Sporobolomyces roseus* and *C. parapsilosis* (fig. 42D).

Tanaka and Miller (95) examined postharvest samples obtained from bulk stored, packaged, and processed prunes, while samples studied by El-Behadli and Ogawa (30) were from the orchard and bulk storage bins.

Prunes are largely mechanically harvested by shakers and the fruit is caught in frames attached to the shaker or on canvas laid on the ground. Before processing the fruit is held in bins of about 1,000 pounds capacity. During harvest and dehydration little sorting is done to remove decaying fruit. Mechanical injuries do occur and are sites for infection by *Monilinia*, *Aspergillus*, and *Alternaria*. The dehydration process (32, 82) involves moving single-layers of fruit in trays through a treatment tunnel with a flow of hot air parallel to the trays or a flow against the tray for 12 to 20 hours. The maximum temperature in the counter-flow tunnel is approximately 70.4 °C, while with the parallel-flow tunnel the warmest air in the front end of the tunnel is about 90 °C. The fruit itself is well below 70.4 °C to prevent carmelization of sugars. Phaff, Mrak, Alleman, and Whelton (71) reported that no viable yeasts and molds remain on prunes at the end of commercial dehydration (95). El-Behadli and Ogawa (30) showed that dehydration did not kill spores of *Aspergillus chevalieri* (*A. glaucus* group), and that fungus was the most common mold found in bulk bins.

Studies have been undertaken to find methods for preventing molds in dry- and wet-packaged fruits (44, 52), to determine heat resistance of xerophilous fungi (76, 77, 96), and to evaluate the effect of fruit moisture and relative humidity on spoilage (50). More recent attempts have been made to prevent molds on fresh fruit (6, 7) and on dehydrated fruit before processing (30). Chemicals showing the greatest promise are ethylene oxide, propylene oxide, and sorbic acid and its salts (52). One treatment is the exposure of prunes to 2 percent sorbic acid at 80.2 °C during hydration.

Preventing spoilage of the final product by application of K sorbate is practiced, but no real effort has been made to control decay just before or after dehydration in bulk bins.

A description of *Aspergillus chevalieri,* the most commonly occurring mold and the probable producer of mycotoxins, as given by Raper and Fennell (79) follows:

> *Aspergillus chevalieri* (Mangin) Thom and Church, synonyms *Eurotium chevalieri* Mangin and *A. allocutus* Batista and Maia, belong to the *A. glaucus* group. On Czapek's solution agar with 20 percent sucrose it grows best at 30 °C or above. The mycelium is spreading, plain to somewhat wrinkled in the central area of the colony with abundant conidial heads in shades of sage-green to andover-green or slate-olive. Yellow cleistothecia are enmeshed in orange-red hyphae at the agar surface. Conidiophores are 700 to 850 μm in length, with almost globose vesicular apices, 25 to 35 μm in diameter. Sterigmata are in a conidial single series, closely packed, 5 to 7 μm in width by 3.0 to 3.5 μm in length. Conidia ovate to elliptical with ends often flattened, are spinulose and 4.5 to 5.5 μm long. Cleisthothecia (100 to 140 μm in diameter) are abundant and closely enmeshed in a felt of orange-red encrusted hyphae. Asci are 9 to 10 μm long; ascospores are lenticular, 4.6 to 5.0 by 3.4-3.8 μm, with walls smooth to slightly roughened and with prominent equatorial crests that are thin and often recurved.

References

1. Adams, R. E., and S. E. Tamburo. 1959. A practical means of reducing storage rots of apple and postharvest rots of peach. West Virginia University Agr. Exp. Sta. Current Progress Rept. 22. 12 pp.

2. Aharoni, Y., and G. J. Stadelbacher. 1973. The toxicity of acetaldehyde vapors to postharvest pathogens of fruits and vegetables. Phytopathology 63:544-45.

3. Allen, F. W. 1948. Storage and shipping of plums. Calif. Fruit and Grape Grower 2(6):12-14.

4. Allen, F. W., W. T. Pentzer, and C. O. Bratley. 1944. Carbon dioxide investigations: Dry ice as a supplement to refrigeration of plums in transit. Amer. Soc. Hort. Sci. Proc. 44:141-47.

5. Anderson, H. W. 1925. Rhizopus rot of peaches. Phytopathology 5:122-24.

6. Archer, T. E., and J. B. Corbin. 1969. The site and fate of captan residues from dipping prunes prior to commercial dehydration. Food Technology 23(2):101.

7. _____ 1970. Captan residues on dipped prune fruits as affected by different adjuvants. Food Technology 24:710-12.

8. Beraha, L. 1959. Effects of gamma radiation on brown rot and Rhizopus rot of peaches and the causal organism. Phytopathology 49:354-57.

9. Boyes, W. W. 1955. Effect of polyethylene (polythene) wrappers on the keeping quality of apricots, peaches, and plums. Farming in S. Africa 30(346):13-19.

10. Bratley, C. O. 1931. Decay of sweet cherries from California. Plant Dis. Rep. 15:73-74.

11. Brooks, C., and J. S. Cooley. 1928. Time-temperature relations in different types of peach rot infection. J. Agr. Research 37:507-43.

12. Brooks, C., and D. F. Fisher. 1916. Brown rot of prunes and cherries in the Pacific Northwest. U.S. Dept. Agr. Bul. 368. 10 pp.

13. _____ 1924. Prune and cherry brown rot investigations in the Pacific Northwest. U.S. Dept. Agr. Bul. 1252. 22 pp.

14. Burton, C. L., and W. R. Wright. 1969. Sour rot disease of peaches on the market. Plant Dis. Rep. 53:580-82.

15. Bussel, J., N. F. Sommer, and T. Kosuge. 1969. Effect of anaerobiosis upon germination and survival of *Rhizopus stolonifer* sporangiospores. Phytopathology 59:946-52.

16. Bussel, J., P. M. Buckley, N. F. Sommer, and T. Kosuge. 1969. Ultrastructural changes in *Rhizopus stolonifer* sporangiospores in response to anerobiosis. J. Bacteriology 98:774-83.

17. Butler, E. E., J. M. Ogawa, and T. Shalla. 1960. Notes on *Gilbertella persicaria* from California. Bul. Torrey Bot. Club 87:397-401.

18. Cappellini, R. A., and A. W. Stretch. 1962. Control of postharvest decay of peaches. Plant Dis. Rep. 46:31-33.

19. Ceponis, M. J., and B. A. Friedman. 1957. Effect of bruising injury and storage temperature upon decay and discoloration of fresh, Idaho-grown Italian prunes on the New York City Market. Plant Dis. Rep. 41:491-92.

20. Chastagner, G. A., and J. M. Ogawa. 1973. Phytotoxicity to stone fruits from preharvest captan by postharvest wax treatment. 2nd International Congress of Plant Pathology. Minn., Minn. Sept. 2-12, 1973.

21. Couey, H. M. 1960. Effect of temperature and modified atmosphere on the storage life, ripening behavior, and dessert quality of El Dorado plums. Amer. Soc. Hort. Sci. Proc. 75:207-15.

22. _____ 1965. Modified atmosphere storage of Nubiana plums. Amer. Soc. Hort. Sci. Proc. 86:166-68.

23. Creelman, D. W. 1962. Summary of the prevalence of plant diseases in Canada in 1961. IV. Diseases of fruit crops. Plum. Canad. Plant. Dis. Survey 42(2):80.

24. Daines, R. H. 1965. 2,6-dichloro-4-nitroaniline used in orchard sprays, and dump tank, the wet brusher, and the hydrocooler for control

of Rhizopus rot of harvested peaches. Plant Dis. Rep. 49:300-04.

25. Dewey, D. H., and D. C. McLean. 1962. Post-harvest treatment with 2,6-dichloro-4-nitroaniline for fruit rot control on fresh market peaches. Mich. Agr. Expt. Sta. Quart. Bul. 44:679-83.

26. Dilley, D. R., and D. H. Dewey. 1973. Responses of apples to storage at subatmospheric pressures. 2nd International Congress of Plant Pathology Univ. of Minn., Minneapolis, Minn. USA Sept. 5-12, 1973.

27. DiMarco, G. R., and B. H. Davis. 1957. Prevention of decay of peaches with post-harvest treatments. Plant Dis. Rep. 41:284-88.

28. Eaks, I. L., J. W. Eckert, and C. N. Roistacher. 1958. Ammonia gas fumigation for control of Rhizopus rot of peaches. Plant Dis. Rep. 42:846-48.

29. Eckert, J. W. 1969. Chemical treatments for control of postharvest diseases. World Review of Pest Control 8(3):116-37.

30. El-Behadli, A., and J. M. Ogawa. 1974. Occurrence and survival of molds on fruit in California prune orchards and dehydrators. 66th Annu. Meeting American Phytopathological Society, August 11-15, 1974, Vancouver, Canada. Abstract No. 105.

31. English, H., and F. Gerhardt. 1942. Effect of carbon dioxide and temperature on the decay of sweet cherries under simulated transit conditions. Amer. Soc. Hort. Sci. Proc. 40:172-76.

32. Gentry, J. P., M. W. Miller, and L. L. Claypool. 1965. Engineering and fruit quality aspects of prune dehydration in parallel- and counter-flow tunnels. Food Technology 19(9):121-25.

33. Gerhardt, F., and L. A. Ryall. 1939. The storage of sweet cherries as influenced by carbon dioxide and volatile fungicides. U.S. Dept. Agr. Tech. Bul 631.

34. Gerhardt, F., H. English, and E. Smith. 1945. Cracking and decay of Bing cherries as related to the presence of moisture on the surface of the fruit. Amer. Soc. Hort. Sci. Proc. 46:191-98.

35. Gerhardt, F., H. A. Schomer, and T. R. Wright. 1956. Sealed film lug liners for packing Bing cherries. U.S. Agr. Mkt. Serv. AMS 121. 8 pp.

36. _____ 1957. Film lug liners lengthen market life of sweet cherries. U.S. Agr. Mkt. Serv. AMS 177. 3 pp.

37. Harding, P. L., and M. H. Haller. 1934. Peach storage with special reference to breakdown. Amer. Soc. Hort. Sci. Proc. 32:160-163.

38. Harter, L. L., and J. L. Weimer. 1922. Decay of various vegetables and fruits by different species of Rhizopus. Phytopathology 12:205-12.

39. Jenkins, P. T., I. D. Peggie, and G. B. Tindale. 1961. Brown rot in canning peaches. A heat therapy control. Plant Path. Waite Agr. Res. Inst., Adelaide Conf. 1(7):2.

40. Johnson, J. D. 1969. New techniques battle postharvest peach diseases. Texas Agr. Progress 15(1):24-25.

41. Kraght, A. J. 1966. Waxing peaches with the consumer in mind. Produce Mkt. 9(2):20-21.

42. Luepschen, N. 1964. Effectiveness of 2,6-dichloro-4-nitroaniline impregnated peach wraps in reducing Rhizopus decay losses. Phytopathology 54:1219-22.

43. Luvisi, D. A., and N. F. Sommer. 1960. Polyethylene liners and fungicides for peaches and nectarines. Amer. Soc. Hort. Sci. Proc. 76:146-55.

44. McBean, D. McG., and J. I. Pitt. 1965. Preservation of high-moisture prunes in plastic pouches. CSIRO Food Preservation Quarterly 25(2):27-32.

45. McClure, T. T. 1958. Brown and Rhizopus rots of peaches as affected by hydrocooling, fungicides, and temperature. Phytopathology 58:322-23.

46. McClure, T. T., and W. L. Smith, Jr. 1959. Postharvest decay of peaches as affected by temperatures after hydrocooling in water or Dowicide A solutions. Phytopathology 49:472-74.

47. Manji, B. T., J. M. Ogawa, and G. A. Chastagner. 1974. Suppression of established infections in nectarine and peach with postharvest fungicide treatment. 66th Annu. Mtg. American Phytopathological Society, Vancouver, Canada, August 11-15. Abstr. No. 104.

48. Matsumoto, T. T., and N. F. Sommer. 1967. Sensitivity of Rhizopus stolonifer to chilling. Phytopathology 57:881-84.

49. Miller, M. W., and H. Tanaka. 1963. Microbial spoilage of dried prunes. III. Relation of equilibrium relative humidity to potential spoilage. Hilgardia 34:183-90.

50. Miller, W. H., W. L. Smith, Jr., and H. D. Sisler. 1959. Temperature effects on Rhizopus stolonifer and Monilinia fructicola spores on potato dextrose agar. Phytopathology 49:546. (Abstr.).

51. Mitchell, F. G., N. F. Sommer, J. P. Gentry et al. 1968. Tight-fill fruit packing. Univ. Calif. Agr. Ext. Serv. Circ. 548.

52. Nury, F. S., M. W. Miller, and J. E. Brekke. 1960. Preservative effect of some antimicrobial agents on high-moisture dried fruits. Food Technology 14(2):113-15.

53. Ogawa, J. M. 1965. Postharvest diseases of peaches and their control. Proc. Peach Congress, Verona, Italy, July 20-24. 9 pp.

54. _____ 1965. Control of pre- and postharvest fruit decays in relation to residues of 2,6-dichloro-4-nitroaniline (DCNA). Symposium on Botran. Kalamazoo, Michigan. Nov. 3-5.

55. Ogawa, J. M., E. Bose, T. B. Manji, and W. R. Schreader. 1972. Bruising of sweet cherries resulting in internal browning and increases

susceptibility to fungi. Phytopathology 62: 579-80.

56. Ogawa, J. M., G. A. Boyak, J. L. Sandeno, and J. H. Mathre. 1964. Control of post-harvest fruit decays in relation to residues of 2,6-dichloro-4-nitroaniline and Difolatan. Hilgardia 35(14):365-73.

57. Ogawa, J. M., E. E. Butler, and S. D. Lyda. 1961. Relation of temperature to spore germination, growth, and disease development by *Gilbertella persicaria*. Phytopathology 51:572-74.

58. Ogawa, J. M., S. Leonard, B. T. Manji, E. Bose, and C. J. Moore. 1971. Monilinia and Rhizopus decay control during controlled ripening of freestone peaches for canning. J. Food Sci. 36:331-34.

59. Ogawa, J. M., and S. D. Lyda. 1960. Effect of alcohols on spores of *Sclerotinia fructicola* and other peach fruit-rotting fungi in California. Phytopathology 50:790-92.

60. Ogawa, J. M., S. D. Lyda, and D. J. Weber. 1961. 2,6-dichloro-4-nitroaniline effective against Rhizopus fruit rot of sweet cherries. Plant Dis. Rep. 45:636-38.

61. Ogawa, J. M., B. T. Manji, and E. Bose. 1968. Efficacy of fungicide 1991 in reducing fruit rot of stone fruits. Plant Dis. Rep. 52:722-26.

62. _____ 1974. Molds on fresh market Blenheim apricots controlled with fungicide mixtures. Annu. Meeting American Phytopathological Society, Aug. 11-15, Vancouver, Canada. Abstr. No. 99.

63. Ogawa, J. M., B. T. Manji, and D. J. Ravetto. 1970. Evaluation of preharvest benomyl applications on postharvest Monilinia rot of peaches and nectarines. Phytopathology 60:1306. (Abstr.).

64. Ogawa, J. M., and J. H. Mathre. 1964. Lysis of germinating sporangiospores of *Rhizopus stolonifer* by 2,6-dichloro-4-nitroaniline (DCNA)—A basis for control of fruit rot. 10th Int. Bot. Congress, Edinburgh, Scotland, August 1964. p. 438. (Abstr.).

65. Ogawa, J. M., J. H. Mathre, D. J. Weber, and S. D. Lyda. 1963. Effects of 2,6-dichloro-4-nitroaniline on Rhizopus species and its comparison with other fungicides on control of Rhizopus rot of peaches. Phytopathology 53:950-55.

66. Ogawa, J. M., R. H. Ramsey, and C. J. Moore. 1963. Behavior of variants of *Gilbertella persicaria* arising in medium containing 2,6-dichloro-4-nitroaniline. Phytopathology 53:97-100.

67. Ogawa, J. M., J. L. Sandeno, and J. H. Mathre. 1963. Comparisons in development and chemical control of decay-causing organisms on mechanical- and hand-harvested stone fruits. Plant Dis. Rep. 47:129-33.

68. Ogawa, J. M., and J. K. Uyemoto. 1962. Effectiveness of 2,6-dichloro-4-nitroaniline on develop-ment of Rhizopus rot of peach fruits at various temperatures. Phytopathology 52:23. (Abstr.).

69. O'Reilly, H. J. 1947. Peach storage in modified atmospheres. Proc. Amer. Soc. Hort. Sci. 49:99.

70. Pentzer, W. T., and F. W. Allen. 1937. Ripening and breakdown of plum as influenced by storage temperatures. Amer. Soc. Hort. Sci. Proc. 44:148-56.

71. Phaff, H. J., E. M. Mrak, R. Alleman, and R. Whelton. 1946. Microbiology of prunes during handling and drying. Fruit Prod. J. and Amer. Food Manufacture. 25:140-141.

72. Phillips, D. J., and M. Uota. 1971. Postharvest treatments to control brown rot on plums. Blue Anchor 48(3):20-21.

73. Pierson, C. F. 1958. Fungicides for reduction of postharvest decay of sweet cherries. Wash. State Hort. Assoc. Proc. 54:115-16.

74. _____ 1966. Effect of temperature on growth of *Rhizopus stolonifer* on peaches and agar. Phytopathology 56:276-78.

75. Pierson, C. F., A. M. Neubert, M. A. Smith, E. R. Wolford, and M. Thomson. 1958. Studies on Rhizopus rot of cannery peaches in the state of Washington. Wash. State Hort. Proc. 54: 179-82.

76. Pitt, J. I., and J. H. B. Christian. 1968. Water relations of xerophilic fungi isolated from prunes. Applied Microbiology 16(12)1853-58.

77. _____ 1970. Heat resistance of xerophilic fungi based on microscopical assessment of spore survival. Applied Microbiology 20(5):682-86.

78. Pryor, D. E. 1949. Reduction of post-harvest spoilage in fresh fruits and vegetables destined for long distance shipment. Food Technology 4(2):57-62.

79. Raper, K. B., and D. I. Fennell. 1965. The genus *Aspergillus*. Baltimore: The Williams & Wilkins Company. 686 pp.

80. Ravetto, D. J., and J. M. Ogawa. 1972. Penetration of peach fruit by benomyl and 2,6-dichloro-4-nitroaniline fungicides. Phytopathology 62:784 (Abstr.).

81. Richards, B. L., B. N. Wadley, and J. C. Barlow. 1953. Diseases of Italian prune in Utah. Farm and Home Sci. (Utah Agr. Expt. Sta.) 14:34-36.

82. Rodda, E. D., and J. P. Gentry. 1969. New concepts in fruit dehydrator construction. American Soc. Agr. Engineers 12(4):540-41.

83. Schomer, H. A., and K. L. Olson. 1964. Storage of sweet cherries in controlled atmospheres. U.S. Agr. Mkt. Serv. AMS 529. 7 pp.

84. Smith, M. A. 1930. Sulfur dust for the control of brown rot of peaches in storage. Phytopathology 20:122-23. (Abstr.).

85. _____ 1960. Etiology of sour pit of peaches. Applied Microbiology 8(4):256-61.

86. Smith, R. E. 1941. Diseases of fruits and nuts. Calif. Agr. Ext. Serv. Circ. 120. 16 pp (out of print).

87. Smith, W. L., Jr. 1962. Reduction of postharvest brown rot and Rhizopus decay of eastern peaches with hot water. Plant Disease Reptr. 46:861-65.

88. _____ 1962. Chemical treatments to reduce postharvest spoilage of fruits and vegetables. Bot. Rev. 28:411-45.

89. _____ 1971. Control of brown rot and Rhizopus rot of inoculated peaches with hot water or hot chemical suspension. Plant Dis. Rep. 55:228-30.

90. Smith, W. L., Jr., M. H. Haller, and T. T. McClure. 1956. Postharvest treatments for reduction of brown and Rhizopus rots of peaches. Phytopathology 46:261-64.

91. Smith, W. L., Jr., R. W. Penny, and R. Grossman. 1972. Control of postharvest brown rot of sweet cherries and peaches with chemical and heat treatments. USDA, ARS, Marketing Research Report 979.

92. Sommer, N. F., and F. G. Mitchell. 1959. Fruit shrivel control in peaches and nectarines. Am. Soc. Hort. Sci. 74:199-205.

93. Spalding, D. H. 1966. Appearance and decay of strawberries, peaches, and lettuce treated with ozone. USDA, ARS Marketing Research Report No. 756. 11 pp.

94. Stanton, T. H., and J. M. Ogawa. 1961. Susceptibility of detached Royal apricot fruits to various fungus pathogens. Plant Dis. Rep. 45:659.

95. Tanaka, H., and M. W. Miller. 1963. Microbial spoilage of dried prunes. I. Yeasts and molds associated with spoiled dried prunes. Hilgardia 34(6):167-70.

96. _____ 1963. Microbial spoilage of dried prunes. II. Studies of the osmophilic nature of spoilage organisms. Hilgardia 34(6):171-81.

97. Tate, K. G. 1973. Nitidulid beetles as vectors of Monilinia fructicola in stone fruits. Ph.D. dissertation. Department of Plant Pathology, University of California, Davis.

98. Tate, K. G., et al. 1974. Survey for benomyl tolerant isolates of Monilinia fructicola and M. laxa in stone fruit orchards of California. Plant Dis. Rep. 58:663-65.

99. Tindale, G. B., I. D. Peggie, P. T. Jenkins et al. 1968. Postharvest control. Rept. Res. work on brown rot of stone fruit—the brown rot research committee 1957-1962. A. C. Brooks, Gov. Printer, Melbourne 117 pp.

100. Togashi, K. 1949. Biological characters of plant pathogens. Temperature relations. 478 pp. Meibundo Co., Tokyo, Japan.

101. Van Blaricom, L. O. 1959. The effect on decay of adding various reagent to the water for hyrdocooling peaches. South Carolina Agr. Exp. Sta. Cir. 124.

102. Wade, G. C. 1956. Investigations on brown rot of apricots caused by Sclerotinia fructicola (Wint.) Rehm. I. The occurrence of latent infection in fruit. Austral. J. Agr. Res. 7: 504-15.

103. Weber, D. J., and J. M. Ogawa. 1965. The mode of action of 2,6-dichloro-4-nitroaniline in Rhizopus arrhizus. Phytopathology 55:159-65.

104. Webster, R. K., J. M. Ogawa, and E. Bose. 1970. Tolerance of Botrytis cinerea to 2,6-dichloro-4-nitroaniline. Phytopathology 60:1489-92.

105. Webster, R. K., J. M. Ogawa, and C. J. Moore. 1968. The occurrence and behavior of variants of Rhizopus stolonifer tolerant to 2,6-dichloro-4-nitroaniline. Phytopathology 58:997-1003.

106. Wells, J. M. 1970. Postharvest hot water and fungicide treatments for reduction of decay of California peaches, plums, and nectarines. U.S. Dept. Agr. Market, Res. Rept. 908. 10 pp.

107. _____ 1972. Heat wax-emulsions with benomyl and 2,6-dichloro-4-nitroaniline for control of postharvest decay of peaches and nectarines. Phytopathology 62:129-33.

108. _____ 1973. Postharvest wax fungicide treatments of nectarines, peaches and plums for: reducing decay, reducing moisture loss, and enhancing external appearance. USDA Marketing Research Report No. 981.

109. Wells, J. M., and M. H. Gerdts. 1971. Pre- and postharvest benomyl treatments for control of brown rot of nectarines in California. Plant Dis. Rep. 55:69-72.

110. Wells, J. M., and J. M Harvey. 1970. Combination heat and 2,6-dichloro-4-nitroaniline treatments for control of Rhizopus and brown rot of peaches, plums and nectarines. Phytopathology 60:116-20.

111. Wells, J. M., and M. Uota. 1970. Germination and growth of five decay fungi in low oxygen and high carbon dioxide atmospheres. Phytopathology 60:50-53.

112. Wiant, J. S., and C. O. Bratley. 1948. Spoilage of fresh fruits and vegetables in rail shipments unloaded at New York City 1935-1942. U.S. Dept. Agr. Circ. 773. 62 pp.

113. Yarwood, C. E., and H. T. Harvey. 1952. Reduction of cherry decay by washing. Plant Dis. Rep. 36:389.

114. Young, W. J., and E. S. Beneke. 1952. Treatments to prevent fruit storage rot. Phytopathology 42:24. (Abstr.).

115. Zycha, H., R. Siepmann, and G. Linnemann. 1969. Mucorales. Lehre, Verlag Von J. Cramer. 355 pp.

III. DISEASES ATTACKING SEVERAL GENERA OF FRUIT AND NUT TREES

BACTERIAL DISEASES OF FRUIT AND NUT TREES

Bacterial Canker or Blast of Fruit and Nut Trees
Pseudomonas syringae van Hall

The disease variously known as "bacterial canker," "bacterial gummosis" or "bacterial blast" attacks most species of *Prunus* and *Pyrus* and has been found on these hosts in many parts of the world. It is particularly severe on stone fruit in England, Europe, Australia, New Zealand and the Pacific Coast of North America (15, 16, 18, 49, 50, 60, 61, 66, 67, 68). The blossom blast form of disease occasionally occurs on pear in the coastal regions and Sierra foothills of California and on almond, cherry and peach in the interior valleys.

Symptoms on stone fruit (63, 64, 68). The most destructive form of the disease occurs on trunks and branches of apricots, peaches, plums and cherries in the form of roughly elliptical cankers which may exude large amounts of gum or a watery material (fig. 43A). The latter exudate has led to the term "sour-sap" because of its disagreeable sour smell. Cankers may extend down the trunk of the tree but seldom very far below ground. Consequently, though the above-ground parts of the tree may be killed, the roots remain alive and send up new shoots. Individually affected branches may fail to start growth in the spring, or they may produce leaves and then die in early summer.

The dormant or semi-dormant buds of infected cherry, plum, and apricot may fail to grow in the spring (fig. 43B) and are brown and, often, covered with gum. Such symptoms are similar to those produced by *Coryneum beijerinckii* on apricot. Blossoms of almond and apricot, in particular, may suddenly wither and turn dark brown. Necrosis in the bark tissue of these species may extend into the supporting branch, forming a canker which may or may not exude gum.

The pathogen sometimes attacks the young green fruit of cherry (fig. 43C) and apricot forming dark brown sunken lesions which severely malform the fruit at maturity.

Roughly circular to somewhat angular lesions 2 to 4 mm in diameter develop on the leaves (fig. 43D). A yellowish halo usually surrounds the brown necrotic centers of the lesions. A sudden withering of the ends of the leafy terminals sometimes occur in plum and peach (16). Santa Rosa, Wickson and Duarte plums are most commonly affected. This phase of the disease is seldom serious in California but is reported to be quite common in England (67).

Symptoms on pear. Blossom infection (blast) of certain pear cultivars occurs in the north coastal counties of California and sometimes in the Sierra Nevada foothills. In Oregon, the disease occurs in the Willamette and Hood River valleys. Affected blossoms turn dark brown but necrosis seldom extends very far into the supporting twig. This, and the fact that no bacterial exudate is present on the blossom parts, distinguishes blast from fire blight.

Blighting of buds similar to that in stone fruit has occurred on pear but this is not common. The thickened ends of spurs that have borne fruit may become infected, and a section through such tissue reveals a water-soaked area extending back from the fruit-stem scars.

Active cankers may occur on the branches of certain pear cultivars. The infected cortex is spongy, cracked and sometimes loosened. Because the diseased area is commonly confined to the cortex, the branch is not usually killed but may be weakened.

The causal organism. The organism causing cherry gummosis was originally named *Pseudomonas cerasi* by Griffin (49). Wormald described two organisms which he claimed caused cankers and shoot blight of cherry and plum in England. One he named *Pseudomonas prunicola* (67), the other *P. mors-prunorum* (69). Erickson (43, 44, 45) later made a study of *P. mors-prunorum* and its pathogenicity to plum trees. Wilson (59) later showed that *P. prunicola* was similar to the organism causing bacterial canker of stone fruit in California and to that described by Griffin as *P. cerasi.* Studies by C. O. Smith (56, 57) showed a close relationship between the organisms causing citrus blast, blight of lilac, and stone fruit bacterial canker. Such studies, including those by Clara (13) and others, have revealed that many named species pathogenic to annual as well as perennial hosts could be grouped under one species name, that of *Pseudomonas syringae* van Hall, originally described as a pathogen of lilac (6, 7, 58).

Pseudomonas syringae is a gram-negative rod, 0.75 to 1.5 × 1.5 to 3.0 μm with one to several polar flagella, occurring singly in pairs, or in short chains. It is a facultative anaerobe, capable of utilizing a large number of compounds as energy sources. On certain media it produces a green, fluorescent, water-soluble pigment. Isolates differ with respect to intensity of pigment production.

Otta and English (53) showed that pathogenicity of *P. syringae,* regardless of its host origin, can be tested by inoculation of Lovell peach seedlings. and that serological tests for pathogenicity are limited because 10 or more serotypes exist (46, 53). DeVay, Lukezic, Sinden, English, and Coplin (29) showed that loss in pathogenicity was related to the ability of *P. syringae* to produce an antibiotic. However, Baigent (1) showed that some nonpathogenic isolates produce an antibiotic which can suppress growth of *Geotrichum.*

Disease development. Branch cankers, and in pear the infected bases of fruit clusters, harbor the bacteria. In spring the bacteria are numerous in branch cankers, but in summer they are sparse. They can survive for a time in the gummy exudate. They are washed about by rain and probably spread short distances in wind-blown rain water. Evidently they can live as epiphytes on the leaves and bark of stone and pome fruits. Wounds, leaf scars (14) and stomata appear to be the chief infection courts.

Infection of branches and dormant buds occurs during fall, winter and early spring; well-developed cankers are present in the tree in spring. Growth of the host appears to check canker development. Infection of blossoms, leaves, and fruit occurs in the growing season but in California this type of infection is important only in years with frost during this period (fig. 43E). Leafscar infection occurs during the leaf-fall period (60, 64).

On cherries (10) infection was found to occur at the bases of the outer bud scales during the winter (November-February). On peaches 3-year-old pruning cuts were highly susceptible from October through November but became almost immune to infection by February (30).

The incubation period has not been studied in detail. Wound inoculations of branches in spring required 10 to 14 days to produce visible necrosis of the tissue. Leaf lesions appeared in 5 to 10 days (63). Length of incubation time is probably influenced greatly by temperature.

In early stages of infection the bacteria are largely intercellular. After cells of infected tissue begin to separate and collapse the bacteria probably enter them. Particularly noticeable are streaks extending from the margins of the cankers along the cambium, a tissue which appears to be especially susceptible to the bacteria. Streaks of affected tissue also occur in the cortex. Cameron (9) reported that bacteria have been isolated 8 feet from the nearest visible canker in the xylem of young Mazzard cherries. As canker activity wanes in early summer, the diseased tissue is surrounded by a phelloderm which may be several cells thick.

The optimum temperature for multiplication of the bacteria in culture media is between 21 and 25 °C. Certain tests indicated that temperatures of 18.3 to 21.1 °C are more favorable to canker extension than 10 °C or lower (63). Rain is responsible for spreading the bacteria about the trees and wounds moistened by rain are probably more readily infected than are dry wounds. Leaf infection and shoot wilt are serious in England, where rainfall is abundant during the growing season, but blossom and shoot infection in California have occurred only during years of exceptionally cold winters and prolonged spring rains. Blossom parts injured by freezing are suspected infection sites.

Trees treated with a nitrogenous fertilizer were found better able to recover from the effects of bacterial canker than those not fertilized (60, 63), but fertilization did not appear to affect the tree's susceptibility to infection. Beard and Wormald (5) and Wormald and Garner (70) found no effects of N, P, and K on susceptibility of plum trees to infection by *Pseudomonas mors-prunorum*, but liming the soil appeared to increase susceptibility. This latter observation does not conform with experience with *P. syringae* in California. Here, in the foothill district (Placer County) where bacterial canker is the most destructive, the soil is neutral to slightly acid. In peach, sandy soils appear to be more conducive to canker development than are heavier soils. Unpublished evidence in California indicates that adequate N, P and K favors resistance of peach trees to bacterial canker.

Cultural practices. Low available phosphate in the soil apparently reduces susceptibility of trees to canker. In the Pacific Northwest, top-working Mazzard cherry scaffolds 8 inches from the trunk when they are at least 1/4 inch in diameter has resulted in much lower incidence of canker on the commercial cultivar. In California, *Prunus mahaleb* is often similarly used as a cherry rootstocks which has reduced the incidence of canker on the scion cultivars.

Control. Removal of affected branches and diseased bark tissue is recommended. Dipping of scion wood in Bordeaux or streptomycin, and spraying the nursery with these chemicals has been recommended in England (20, 22).

Planting of Beauty plum to avoid the loss from bacterial canker was widely practiced in certain California orchards a few years ago. In Oregon, the Corum sweet cherry is the most resistant commercial cultivar (12). Resistance in certain other cultivars is not sufficient to warrant planting them.

Experimental evidence indicates that plum and French prune trees on peach roots suffer less from bacterial canker than do trees on plum root (12, 42). If the bud union is covered by soil, the scion will form its own root system and in so doing becomes more susceptible to the disease. British workers have reported that the use of certain rootstocks has reduced the severity of bacterial canker in plums and cherries. Seedling rootstocks vary in their susceptibility to bacterial canker.

Dowler and Petersen (31) showed that early-pruned peach trees developed the most severe winter injury and greatest susceptibility to *P. syringae*. Daniell

(25) stated that late pruning resulted in greater growth and longevity of the trees.

Chemical treatment of the cankers has been tried with little benefit. Spraying the trees with Bordeaux mixture in the fall may reduce infection to some extent. British researchers (52) recommend an autumn and spring application of Bordeaux for controlling bacterial canker caused by *Pseudomonas mors-prunorum*. More recently, New Zealand (32) and British workers (20) have reported that streptomycin offers promise: streptomycin appeared to be somewhat more effective than Bordeaux in reducing the spring blast phase, whereas Bordeaux was more effective than streptomycin when used during the leaf-fall period for the prevention of leaf-scar infection. Proper timing of the fall application has not been determined. In California, sprays have not provided adequate canker control.

Preplant soil fumigation with materials such as chloropicrin, dichloropropene-dichloropropane mixture and dibromochloropropane has been followed by a reduction in severity of canker in young trees and an increase in their growth. Chloropropane, reduced significantly the severity of canker in young peach trees in California on sandy soils; however, the beneficial effects of fumigation have not been consistent in reducing canker severity in prune orchards. Postplant fumigation with Fumazone (dibromochloropropane) reduces the severity of canker on peach and further tests are being tested on other stone fruit crops (38, 39). Preplant fumigation has become a standard procedure in establishing new peach and almond orchards on sandy soil.

References

1. Baigent, N. L. 1963. Bacteriophages of *Pseudomonas syringae*. New Zealand J. Sci. 6:75-100.
2. Barss, H. P. 1913. Cherry gummosis. A preliminary report. Oregon Crop Pest and Hort. Bien. Rpt. 1911-1912:199-217.
3. _____ 1915. Bacterial gummosis or bacterial canker of cherries. Ore. Crop Pest and Hort. Bien. Rpt. 1913-1914:224-40.
4. _____ 1918. Bacterial gummosis of stone fruits. Calif. State Comm. Hort. Mo. Bul. 7:121-36.
5. Beard, F. H., and H. Wormald. 1936. Bacterial canker of plum trees in relation to nutrition. Experimental results in sand culture. East Malling Res. Sta. Ann. Rep. (Sec. III) 1936:146-54.
6. Breed, R. S., E. G. D. Murray, and A. Parker Hitchens. 1948. Bergey's manual of determinative bacteriology. 6th Ed. p. 119-20.
7. Bryan, M. K. 1928. Lilac blight in the United States. J. Agr. Research 36:225-35.

8. Cameron, H. R. 1960. Death of dormant buds in sweet cherry. Plant Dis. Rep. 44:139-43.

9. _____ 1962. Diseases of deciduous fruit trees incited by *Pseudomonas syringae* van Hall. Oregon State Univ. Agr. Expt. Sta. Tech. Bul. 66: 64 pp.

10. _____ 1962. Mode of infection of sweet cherry by *Pseudomonas syringae*. Phytopathology 52:917-21.

11. _____ 1970. *Pseudomonas* content of cherry trees. Phytopathology 60:1343-46.

12. _____ 1971. Effect of root or trunk stock on susceptibility of orchard trees to *Pseudomonas syringae*. Plant Dis. Rep. 55:421-23.

13. Clara, F. M. 1934. A comparative study of the green-fluorescent bacterial plant pathogens. Cornell Agr. Expt. Sta. Mem. 1959:3-36.

14. Crosse, J. E. 1951. The leaf scar as an avenue of infection for the cherry bacterial canker organism, *Pseudomonas mors-prunorum*. Nature 168:560-61.

15. _____ 1953. Bacterial diseases of stone fruit trees in Britain. IX. Bacteriosis of apricot. Trans. Brit. Mycol. Soc. 36:38-45.

16. _____ 1954. Bacterial canker leaf spot and shoot wilt of cherry and plum. East Malling Res. Sta. Ann. Reptr. 1953:202-07.

17. _____ 1955. Bacterial canker of stone fruits. I. Field observations on the avenues of autumnal infection of cherry. J. Hort. Sci. 30:131-42.

18. _____ 1956. Bacterial canker of stone fruits. II. Leaf scar infections of cherry. J. Hort. Sci. 31:212-24.

19. _____ 1957. Bacterial canker of stone fruits. III. Inoculum concentrations and time of inoculation in relation to leaf-scar infection in cherry. Ann. Appl. Biol. 45:19-34.

20. _____ 1957. Streptomycin in the control of bacterial canker of cherry. Ann. Appl. Biol. 45:226-28.

21. _____ 1963. Bacterial canker of stone fruits. V. A comparison of leaf-surface populations of *Pseudomonas mors-prunorum* in autumn on two cherry varieties. Ann. Appl. Biol. 52:97-104.

22. _____ 1966. Epidemiological relations of the pseudomonad pathogens of deciduous fruit trees. Annu. Rev. Phytopathology. 4:291-310.

23. Crosse, J. E., and C. M. E. Garrett. 1963. Studies on the bacteriophagy of *Pseudomonas mors-prunorum*, *Ps. syringae* and related organisms. J. of Appl. Bact. 26:157-177.

24. Crosse, J. E., and C. M. E. Garrett. 1966. Bacterial canker of stone-fruits. VII. Infection experiments with *Pseudomonas mors-prunorum* and *P. syringae*. Ann. Appl. Biol. 58:31-41.

25. Daniell, J. W. 1973. Effect of time of pruning on growth and longevity of peach trees. J. Am. Soc. Hortic. Sci. 98:383-86.

26. Davis, J. R., and H. English. 1969. Factors involved in the development of peach seedling cankers induced by chilling. Phytopathology 59:305-13.

27. Day, L. H. 1947. The influence of rootstocks on the occurrence and severity of bacterial canker *Pseudomonas cerasi*, of stone fruits. Amer. Soc. Hort. Sci. Proc. 50:100-02.

28. DeVay, J. E. *et al.* 1965. Effects of thermal neutron irradiation of the frequency of crown gall and bacterial canker resistance in seedlings of prunus rootstocks. Radiation Bot. 5:197-204.

29. DeVay, J. E., F. L. Lukezic, S. L. Sinden, H. English, and D. L. Coplin. 1968. A biocide produced by pathogenic isolates of *Pseudomonas syringae* and its possible role in the bacterial canker disease of peach trees. Phytopathology 58:95-101.

30. Dowler, W. M., and F. D. King. 1967. Dormant season susceptibility of peach to bacterial canker not related to movement of *Pseudomonas syringae*. Phytopathology 57:809-10. (Abstr.).

31. Dowler, W. M., and D. H. Petersen. 1966. Induction of bacterial canker of peach in the field. Phytopathology 56:989-90.

32. Dye, D. W. 1953. Control of *Pseudomonas syringae* with streptomycin. Nature, London. 172, 4380:683-84.

33. _____ 1954. Blast of stone fruit in New Zealand. New Zealand J. Sci. and Tech. Ser. A. 35:451-61.

34. _____ 1954. Preliminary field trials to control blast of stone fruit (*Pseudomonas syringae* van Hall). New Zeal. J. Sci. & Tech. Ser. A. 36:331-34.

35. _____ 1956. Suggestions for controlling blast of stone fruit. The Orchardist of New Zeal. 29(4):2-3.

36. _____ 1957. The effect of temperature on infection by *Pseudomonas syringae* van Hall. New Zealand J. Sci. and Technol., Sec. A, 38:500-05.

37. Dye, D. W., and M. H. Dye. 1954. Effectiveness of therapeutants including antibiotics in preventing development of blast of stone fruit. New Zeal. J. Sci. and Tech. Ser. A. 36:21-26.

38. English, H., and J. E. DeVay. 1964. Influence of soil fumigation on growth and canker resistance of young fruit trees in California. Down to Earth 20:6-8.

39. English, H., and C. J. Hansen. 1954. Experiments on the control of bacterial canker of stone fruit trees. Phytopathology 44:487.

40. _____ 1955. Bacterial canker—serious threat to stone fruits. Western Fruit Grower 9(1):17-19.

41. English, H., J. M. Ogawa, and J. R. Davis. 1957. Bacterial blast, a newly recognized disease of almonds in California. Phytopathology 47:520.

42. English, H., J. E. Devay, F. J. Schick, and B. F. Lownsbery. 1974. Factors affecting bacterial canker in prune trees. 66th Annu. Meeting Amer. Phytopath. Soc., August 11-15, 1974, Vancouver, Canada. Abstr. No. 234.

43. Erickson, D. 1945. Certain aspects of resistance of plum trees to bacterial canker. I. Some biochemical characteristics of *Pseudomonas mors-prunorum* (Wormald) and related phytopathogenic bacteria. Ann. Appl. Biol. 32:44-52.

44. _____ 1945. Certain aspects of resistance of plum trees to bacterial canker. II. On the nature of the bacterial invasion of *Prunus* sp. by *Pseudomonas mors-prunorum* Wormald. Ann. Appl. Biol 32:112-17.

45. _____ 1945. Certain aspects of resistance of plum trees to bacterial canker. III. The action of cell-free filtrates of *Pseudomonas mors-prunorum* Wormald and related phytopathogenic bacteria of plum trees. Ann. Appl. Biol. 32:117-23.

46. Friedman, B. A. 1953. Serological tests with some phytopathogenic species of *Pseudomonas*. Phytopathology 43:412-14.

47. Garrett, C. M. E., and J. E. Crosse. 1963. Observations of lysogeny in the plant pathogens *Pseudomonas mors-prunorum* and *Ps. syringae*. J. Appl. Bact. 26:27-34.

48. Garrett, C. M. E., C. G. Panagopolous, and J. E. Crosse. 1966. Comparison of plant pathogenic pseudomonads from fruit trees. J. Appl. Bacteriol. 29:342-56.

49. Griffin, F. L. 1911. A bacterial gummosis of cherries. Science (N.S.) 34:615-16.

50. McKen, W. E. 1955. Pear blast on Vancouver Island. Phytopathology 45:629.

51. Mills, G. Barbara. 1949. A biochemical study of Pseudomonas prunicola Wormald. I. Pectin esterase. Biochem. J. 44:302-05.

52. Montgomery, H. B. S., and N. H. Moore. 1945. The control of bacterial canker and leaf spot of sweet cherry. J. Pom. and Hort. Soc. 21:155-63.

53. Otta, J. D., and H. English. 1970. Epidemiology of the bacterial canker disease of French prune. Plant Dis. Rep. 54:332-36.

54. _____ 1971. Serology and pathology of *Pseudomonas syringae*. Phytopathology 61:443-52.

55. Perlasca, G. 1960. Relationships among isolates of *P. syringae* pathogenic on stone fruit trees. Phytopathology 50:889-99.

56. Smith, C. O. 1926. Similarity of bacterial diseases of avocado, lilac, and citrus in California. Phytopathology 16:235-36.

57. Smith, C. O., and H. S. Fawcett. 1930. A comparative study of the citrus blast bacterium and some allied organisms. J. Agr. Research 41:233-46.

58. Van Hall, C. J. 1902. Bijdragen tot de kennis der bakterieele plantenziekten. Thesis, Univ. Amsterdam.

59. Wilson, E. E. 1931. A comparison of *Pseudomonas prunicola* with a canker-producing bacterium of stone fruit trees in California. Phytopathology 21:1153-61.

60. _____ 1933. Bacterial canker of stone fruit trees in California. Hilgardia 8:83-123.

61. _____ 1934. A bacterial canker of pear trees new to California. Phytopathology 24:534-37.

62. _____ 1936. Symptomatic and etiologic relations of the canker and blossom blast of Pyrus and the bacterial canker of Prunus. Hilgardia 10:213-40.

63. _____ 1939. Factors affecting development of the bacterial canker of stone fruits. Hilgardia 12:259-98.

64. _____ 1953. Bacterial canker of stone fruits. Plant Diseases. The Yearbook of Agriculture. USDA. Pp 722-729.

65. Wilson, E. E., and W. B. Hewitt. 1939. Host organs attacked by bacterial canker of stone fruits. Hilgardia 12:249-58.

66. Wormald. H. 1928. Bacterial diseases of stone fruit trees in Britain. I. Preliminary note on bacteriosis in plum and cherry trees. East Malling Res. Sta. Ann. Rpt. (Suppl. II). 1926-27:121-27.

67. _____ 1930. Bacterial diseases of stone fruit trees in Britain. II. Bacterial shoot wilt of plum trees. Ann. Appl. Biol. 17:725-44.

68. _____ 1931. Bacterial diseases of stone fruit trees in Britain. III. The symptoms of bacterial canker of plum trees. J. Pom. and Hort. Sci. 9:239-56.

69. _____ 1932. Bacterial diseases of stone fruit trees in Britain. IV. The organism causing bacterial canker of plum trees. British Mycol. Soc. Trans. 17:157-69.

70. Wormald, H., and R. J. Garner. 1938. Manurial trial on nursery trees with reference to effect on plum to bacterial canker. East Malling Res. Sta. Ann. Rept. 1937:194-97.

Crown Gall of Fruit and Nut Trees
Agrobacterium tumefaciens (Smith & Townsend) Conn.

Crown gall, also known as "root tumors" and "plant cancer" attacks a wide range (142 genera) of dicotyledonous hosts including stone fruit, pome fruit, grape and brambles (17). The importance of the disease in California was reported in 1892 by Wickson and Woodworth (64).

The disease is worldwide but is especially prevalent in temperate regions and is probably responsible for the loss of more nursery trees than any other disease. The economic loss sustained after planting is difficult to evaluate, but in 1963 alone, it was estimated to cause $7 million loss in California on 14 major crops (63).

Symptoms. Galls occur on roots, crown, stems or leaves, but most typically on large roots where they arise from the crown (fig. 44). The smooth young galls enlarge rapidly and on perennial hosts become hard, woody tumors with irregular surfaces. Galls vary in size from nearly microscopic to 12 inches or more in diameter. The exterior color matches that of the host bark and the interior color that of the normal wood of the host. Eventually, the galls become necrotic and portions slough or break off. Secondary invasions result in masses of galls which girdle the roots and crown. Secondary heartrot organisms quickly enter these injuries, causing further debilitation of the host. *Armillaria* may also enter the gall tissue. Galls commonly form on aerial parts of quince, brambles, and grapes.

Although crown gall is very important on young nursery trees, methods for detecting incipient infections have not been developed.

The causal organism is *Agrobacterium tumefaciens* (Smith and Townsend) Conn., formerly *Bacterium tumefaciens*. Recently, Keane, Kerr, and New (22), using biochemical tests, serology, and pathogenicity on isolates of the organism reported two distinct biotypes. Biotype 1 contains tumor-inducing, root-proliferating, and non-pathogenic forms; biotype 2 contains both tumor-inducing and root-proliferating forms but no pathogenic forms. Species *A. radiobacter* is proposed by Kerr (24) on the basis that this species can be converted to typical *A. tumefaciens* through transfer of virulence. Pathogenicity is then indicated by varietal epithet and the biotype specified. The Califoria pathogenic variety could be indicated as *A. radiobacter* var. *tumefaciens* biotype 2 (50). In Greece (35) biotype 2 is as common as in California, and biotype 1 is found on grape. Seven heterogeneous types did not conform with biotypes 1 or 2. In 1930 Riker *et al.* (44) gave the name of *A. rhizogenes* to the organism producing hairy root. See a discussion of the hairy root disease of apple.

The bacteria form circular, smooth, creamy, shiny colonies on rich media (20). They are bacilliform rods, 0.4 to 0.8 × 0.8 × 2.5 to 3.0 μm, motile with 1 to 6 peritrichous flagella, gram negative, and with capsules. The optimum growth is around 32 °C with generation time of about 60 minutes. Actions of B-glucoside-3-dehydrogenase, catalase, oxidase, urease, nitrate reductase and B-galactosidase is evi-

dent. On a basal medium, acid is produced from arabinose, cellobiose, fructose, gallactose, lactose or salicin. Selective media for the organism in which the pathogenic and nonpathogenic forms can be separated by their appearance have been developed (20, 32, 50). Cultures kept in water at room temperature retain their pathogenicity for over 4 years, and indefinitely in lyophilized state.

Identification of *A. tumefaciens* is most easily accomplished by inoculating carrot slices, young tomato, or sunflower plants, on which tumors develop in 7 to 10 days (4). Soil population studies of a pathogenic variety of the organism (50) on selective medium excluded over 99 percent of the common soil microorganisms but tests recovered only 38 percent of the pathogens introduced. Schroth *et al.* (51) detected *A. tumefaciens* in 18 out of 28 soils tested, in many instances where no host plants were grown. Hildebrand (18) reported that the organism is not a good soil inhabitant, but Dickey (12) considered the organism successful in this respect.

Disease development. *A. tumefaciens* survives from one year to the next in galls and in soil. The greatest incidence of the disease occurs in nurseries, with infection occurring during the time seeds germinate, when liners and nursery trees are harvested, and during storage in heal-in beds. On apples the union produced from the root-scion grafting is readily infected (3). The bacteria can infect nonmechanically injured roots of peach (14). Most commonly the galls formed on the undamaged root lenticels (25) are difficult to detect. Shipment of affected nursery stock is probably the most important means of long-distance dissemination, and local dissemination is accomplished by soil water or movement of soil, by cultivation, or by wind. Release of bacteria from galls can occur when galls are wet or are disintegrating.

In established orchards the bacteria most commonly enter through growth cracks or wounds caused by hoeing, discing, or removal of suckers (46). On such crops as pea, mung bean, tomato, and barley, Schroth and Ting (49) showed that *A. tumefaciens* was attracted to root hairs and to zones of root elongation. Broken root hairs also appeared to be a major site where the bacteria accumulated, whereas root-cap zones repulse the bacteria. Acidity of medium also effected attraction sites. At pH 5.4, the bacteria accumulated at cut ends of roots; at pH 6.0 they accumulated at root hairs and zones of elongation.

Because development of galls depends upon growth of the trees, these overgrowths appear only during the growing season. Riker (42) reported that incubation periods in the field ranged from 2 to 11 weeks depending on time of year. Such variations reflected the influence of temperature on gall formation, as the longest incubation periods occurred in the spring and the shortest ones occurred in mid-summer. Still longer incubation periods are possible because infection in autumn will not result in gall formation until growth starts in spring.

The bacterium is invasive, spreading intercellularly from the site of initial invasion. During infection cells adjacent to the invaded areas are transformed and begin dividing actively. As abnormal division continues in an undifferentiated manner, a tumor-like growth becomes visible. Such neoplasms develop into massive tumors which are called crown gall.

The cause of cellular transformation by *A. tumefaciens* is unknown. According to Nitsch (34) it is believed that auxin and phytokinin are needed for the inception of crown gall tumors. Crown gall tumors generally have been shown to contain more auxin than does corresponding normal tissues and also contain water-soluble phytokinin (6). Tumor cells contain only about one-fourth of the amount of phospholipid present in normal cells, and thus there is an increase in permeability of cell membranes (65). Tumor tissues also have unusually high concentrations of free lysopene and especially of free proline (19). Several hypotheses are proposed as tumor-inducing agents: a) auxin or cytokinin-like substances, b) proteinaceous material, c) ribonucleic acid, d) deoxyribonucleic acid, e) bacteriophage, and f) toxins. More recent efforts in research have been concerned with nucleic acids (14, 20), with possible virus carried by the inciting bacterium, and with plasmids.

The bacteria are intercellular but may occur to some extent within the vessels (45). They are especially abundant in the hyperplastic islands near the periphery of active galls. Both hypertrophy and hyperplasia of cells occur. The hyperplastic islands apparently have centers of gall enlargement. Smith's view of "tumor strands" giving rise to secondary galls at a distance from the point of infection has been considerably modified by Riker (36).

A soil temperature of 22 °C appears most favorable for gall formation; the maximum appears to be near 30 °C. Soil moisture of 60 percent is most favorable for gall formation at all temperatures (40). Fertility, tilth, and other soil characteristics are of minor importance in development of this disease. Infestation by the pathogen is not limited to any noticeable extent by soil types. Siegler (52) found gall formation more abundant at a pH of 6.8 than at 5.0.

This may account for the greater severity of the disease in some soils than in others.

Host susceptibility. Almond and peach root are the most susceptible of the stone fruits. C.O. Smith

Host susceptibility. Almond and peach root are the most susceptible of the stone fruits. C. O. Smith (54) found both bitter and sweet almonds to be highly susceptible, as was the peach commonly used for rootstocks. Japanese plums were more susceptible than the European sorts. Because of susceptibility to crown gall, propagation of walnuts on *Juglans regia* stock was abandoned in favor of *J. californica* or *J. hindsii* stock.

Control. Cultural techniques, followed by nurseries, involved soaking the seeds in sodium hypochlorite or calomel and stratifying seeds directly in planting rows instead of under refrigeration (1, 46, 53). At harvest, diseased nursery trees are discarded and apparently healthy trees are planted soon after delivery instead of using the heeling-in procedure. Little benefit has resulted from fertilization or irrigation, but use of sulfur to lower the pH of neutral or alkaline soils has been suggested (42).

Resistance has been shown only for black walnut. DeVay *et al.* (11) attempted to increase resistance in peach, almond, and cherry seedlings by thermal neutron irradiation of seeds. They obtain some resistance in irradiated as well as nonirradiated peach and almond seedlings but none in cherry seedlings.

Soil fumigation with methyl bromide-chloropicrin reduced the bacterial population but does not effectively control the disease (8, 9, 13, 31). Furthermore, fumigants do not kill bacteria in the gall tissues (28).

Treatments to kills the galls at the root-crown region, thereby preventing further girdling, received much attention. Ark (1) obtained good results with a sodium dinitro-cresol-methanol mixture on almonds. Steptomycin or tetracycline as a 60-minute dip failed.

Bacticin, a hydrocarbon containing 2,4 xylenol and metacresol, has produced good results (47). On crops such as peach, cherry, almond, pear and walnuts (47, 51) this treatment is suggested for use during the first 3 years of tree growth. The crown area of the plant is exposed by hydraulic means (46) so as not to injure the host tissue. The dry gall is treated once with the chemical and left exposed for several weeks. The gall dies within a 3 to 4 month period. Galls over 4½ inches in diameter may require two applications. Except for walnuts, removal of any part of the gall prior to treatment has not been necessary. The chemical penetrates the diseased but not the healthy tissue, and therefore does not retard formation of new callus. Such a treatment has prevented regrowth or production of new tumors. Though effective when applied to tumors, bacticin cannot be used as a dip for nursery stock because of phytotoxic effects.

Biological control of crown gall has been under consideration by many researchers. Recently New and Kerr (25, 33) used the nonpathogenic isolate of *A. radiobacter* var. *radiobacter* biotype 2 (strain 84) to reduce gall incidence in seedlings from seeds inoculated with the pathogen and nonpathogen. In inoculation tests on pinto bean leaves (28), the ratio of pathogenic to nonpathogenic populations required for control was 1:1. Prevention of crown gall on *Prunus* roots with strain 84 of *A. radiobacter* has been confirmed by Schroth and Moller (51) and Moore (30). The mechanism of action has been related to presence of bacteriophage (27), production of an antibiotic by the strain used (26), and to the exclusion of the pathogen from the infection or attachment site (28). Evidence by Moore (30) indicates that protection is afforded by the *A. radiobacter* production of an antibiotic bacteriocin.

References

1. Ark, P. A. 1941. Chemical eradication of crown gall on almond trees. Phytopathology 31:956-57.
2. _____ 1942. Crown gall of deciduous fruit trees and its control. Blue Anchor 19(1). February.
3. Ark, P. A., and C. E. Scott. 1951. Elimination of crown gall: treating small galls on young trees with elgetol-methanol mixture assures control in almond, peach, walnut orchard. Calif. Agr. 5(7):3.
4. Ark, P. A., and M. N. Schroth. 1958. Uses of slices of carrot and other fleshy roots to detect crown gall bacteria in soil. Plant Dis. Rep. 42:1279-81.
5. Bernaerts, M., and J. DeLey. 1963. A biochemical test for crown gall bacteria. Nature 197:406-07.
6. Braun, A. C. 1962. Tumor inception and development in the crown gall disease. Ann. Rev. Plant Physiology 13:533-58.
7. Breed, R. S., E. G. D. Murray and N. R. Smith. 1957. Bergey's Manual of Determinative Bacteriology, 7th Ed. London: Balliere, Tindall and Cox.
8. Deep, I. W., and R. A. Young. 1965. The role of preplanting treatments with chemicals in increasing the incidence of crown gall. Phytopathology 55:212-16.
9. Deep, I. W., R. A. McNeilan, and I. C. MacSwan. 1968. Soil fumigants tested for control of crown gall. Plant Dis. Rep. 52:102-05.
10. DeVay, J. E., and W. C. Schnathorst. 1963. Single-cell isolation and preservation of bacterial cultures. Nature, Lond. 199:775-77.
11. DeVay, J. E., G. Nyland, W. H. English, F. J. Schick, and G. D. Barbe. 1965. Effects of thermal neutron irradiation on the frequency of crown gall and bacterial canker resistance in seedlings of Prunus rootstocks. Radiation Botany 5:197-204.
12. Dickey, R. S. 1961. Realtion of some edaphic factors to *Agrobacterium tumefaciens*. Phytopathology 51:607-14.
13. _____ 1962. Efficacy of five fumigants for the control of *Agrobacterium tumefaciens* at various depths in the soil. Plant Dis. Rep. 46:73-76.
14. Drlica, K. A., and C. I. Kado. 1974. Quantitative estimation of *Agrobacterium tumefaciens* DNA in crown gall tumor cells. Proc. Nat. Acad. Sci. 71:3677-81.
15. Dye, D. W. 1952. The effects of chemicals and antibiotic substances on crown-gall (*Agrobacterium tumefaciens* [Smith and Townsend] Conn.) Part IV. New Zealand J. Sci, and Tech. 33:104-08.
16. Dye, D. W., P. B. Hutchinson, and A. Hastings. 1950. Effect of chemicals and antibiotic substances on crown-gall (*Agrobacterium tumefaciens* [Smith and Townsend] Conn.) Part I. Colchicine and penicillin. New Zealand J. Sci. and Tech. 31:31-39.
17. Elliott, C. 1951. Manual of bacterial plant pathogens. 2nd ed. Waltham, Mass.: Chronica Botanica Co. 186 pp.
18. Hildebrand, E. M. 1941. On the longevity of the crown gall in soil. Plant Dis. Rep. 25:200-02.
19. Hochster, R. M. 1964. Perspectives on the biochemistry of *Agrobacterium tumefaciens*. *In* DeVay and Wilson, Proc. Conf. on Abnormal Growth in Plants. Univ. of California, Berkeley. Nov. 5-6, 1964 pp. 26-35.
20. Kado, C. I., and M. G. Heskett. 1970. Selective media for isolation of *Agrobacterium*, *Corynebacterium*, *Erwinia*, *Pseudomonas*, and *Xanthomonas*. Phytopathology 60:969-76.
21. Kado, C. I., M. G. Heskett, and R. A. Langley. 1972. Studies on *Agrobacterium tumefaciens*: Characterization of strains 1D135 and B6, and analysis of the bacterial chromosomes, transfer RNA and ribosomes for tumor inducing ability. Physiol. Pl. Path. 2:47-57.
22. Keane, P. J., A. Kerr, and P. B. New. 1970. Crown gall of stone fruit. II. Identification and nomenclature of *Agrobacterium* isolates. Aust. J. Biol. Sci. 23:585-95.
23. Kerr, A. 1969. Crown gall on stone fruit. I. Isolation of *Agrobacterium tumefaciens* and related species. Aust. J. Biol. Sci. 22:111-16.

24. _____ 1971. Acquisition of virulence by nonpathogenic isolates of *Agrobacterium radiobacter*. Physiol. Pl. Path. 1:241.

25. _____ 1972. Biological control of crown gall: seed inoculation. J. Appl. Bact. 35:493-97.

26. Kerr, A. and A. Htay. 1974. Biological control of crown gall through bacteriocin production. Physiol. Plant Pathol. 4:37-44.

27. Leff, J., and R. E. Beardsley. 1970. Action tumorigene de l'acide nucleique d'un bacteriophage present dans les cultures de tissu tumoral de Tournesol (Helianthus annus.). C. R. hebd. Seanc. Acad. Sc., Paris, Ser. D., 270:2505.

28. Lippincott, J. A., and B. B. Lippincott. 1969. Bacterial attachment to a specific wound site as an essential stage in tumour initiation by *Agrobacterium tumefaciens*. J. Bact. 97:620-28.

29. _____ 1969. Tumor growth complementation among strains of *Agrobacterium*. J. Bact. 99:496-502.

30. Moore, L. W. 1977. Prevention of crown gall on *Prunus* roots by bacterial antagonists. Phytopathology 67:139-44.

31. Munnecke, D. E., and J. Ferguson. 1960. Effect of soil fungicides upon soil-borne plant pathogenic bacteria and soil nitrogen. Plant Dis. Rep. 44:552-55.

32. New, P. B., and A. Kerr. 1972. A selective medium for *Agrobacterium* radiobacter biotype 2. J. Appl. Bact. 34:233.

33. _____ 1972. Biological control of crown gall: Field measurements and glasshouse experiments. J. Appl. Bact. 35:279-87.

34. Nitsch, J. P. 1964. Endogenous auxins and phytokinins in abnormal plant tissues. *In:* DeVay and Wilson, Proc. Conf. on Abnormal Growth in Plants. Univ. of California, Berkeley.

35. Panagopoulous, C. G., and P. G. Psallidas. 1973. Characteristics of Greek isolates of *Agrobacterium tumefaciens* (E. F. Smith and Townsend) Conn. J. Appl. Bact 36:233-40.

36. Riker, A. J. 1923. Some relations of the crown gall organism to its host tissue. J. Agr. Research 25:119-32.

37. _____ 1923. Some morphological responses of the host tissue to the crown gall organism. J. Agr. Research 26:425-36.

38. _____ 1925. Crown gall in relation to nursery stock. Science 62:184-85.

39. _____ 1925. Second report of progress on studies of crown gall in relation to nursery stock. Phytopathology 15:805-6.

40. _____ 1926. Studies on the influence of some environmental factors on the development of crown gall. J. Agr. Research. 32:83-96.

41. _____ 1927. Cytological studies of crown gall. Am. J. Bot. 14:25-37.

42. _____ 1934. Seasonal development of hairy-root and crown gall, and wound overgrowth of apple trees in the nursery. J. Agr. Research 48:997-912.

43. Riker, A. J. and G. W. Keitt. 1926. Studies of crown gall and wound overgrowth on apple nursery stock. Phytopathology 16:765-808.

44. Riker, A. J., W. M. Banfield, W. H. Wright, G. W. Keitt, and H. E. Sagen. 1930. Studies on infectious hairy root of nursery apple trees. J. Agr. Research 41:507-40.

45. Robinson, W. and H. Walkden. 1923. A critical study of crown gall. Ann. Bot. 37:299-324.

46. Ross, N., M. N. Schroth, R. Sanborn, et al. 1970. Reducing loss from crown gall disease. Calif. Agr. Exp. Sta. Bul. 1845:1-10.

47. Schroth, M. N. and D. C. Hildebrand. 1968. A chemotherapeutic treatment for selectively eradicating crown gall and olive knot neoplasms. Phytopathology 58:848-54.

48. Schroth, M. N. and W. J. Moller. 1976. Crown gall controlled in the field with a nonpathogenic bacterium. Plant Dis. Rep. 60:275-78.

49. Schroth, M. N. and W. P. Ting. 1966. Attraction of *Agrobacterium* spp. to roots. Phytopathology 56:889-900. (Abstr.).

50. Schroth, M. N., J. P. Thompson, and D. C. Hildebrand. 1965. Isolation of *Agrobacterium tumefaciens-A. radiobacter* group from soil. Phytopathology 55:645-47.

51. Schroth, M. N., A. R. Weinhold, A. H. McCain D. C. Hildebrand, and N. Ross. 1971. Biology and control of *Agrobacterium tumefaciens*. Hilgardia 40:537-52.

52. Siegler, E. A. 1938. Relations between crown gall and pH of the soil. (Note) Phytopathology 28:858-59.

53. Siegler, E. A. and J. J. Bowman. 1940. Crown gall of peaches in the nursery. Phytopathology 30:417-26.

54. Smith, C. O. 1917. Comparative resistance of Prunus to crown gall. Amer. Nat. 51:47-60.

55. _____ 1944. A method of inoculating peach seedlings with crown gall without using punctures. Phytopathology 34:764-65.

56. Smith, E. F. 1907. A plant tumor of bacterial origin. Science 25:671-73.

57. _____ 1917. Mechanism of tumor growth in crown gall. J. Agr. Research 8:165-88.

58. Smith, E. F., N. A. Brown, and C. O Townsend. 1911. Crown gall of plants: Its cause and remedy. USDA Bur. Plant Indus. Bul. 213.

59. Smith, E. F., N. A. Brown, and L. McCulloch. 1912. The structure and development of crown gall, a plant cancer. USDA Bur. Plant Indus. Bul. 225.

60. Stonier, L. 1960. *Agrobacterium tumefaciens* II. Production of an antibiotic substance. J. Bact. 79:880-98.

61. Stonier, T., J. McSharry, and T. Speitel. 1967. *Agrobacterium tumefaciens* Conn. IV. Bacteriophage PB2, and its inhibitory effect on tumor induction. J. Virology 1:268-73.

62. Stroun, M., P. Anker, P. Gahan, A. Rossier, and H. Greppen. 1971. *Agrobacterium tumefaciens* ribonucleic acid synthesis in tomato cells and crown gall induction. J. Bacteriology 106: 634-39.

63. University of California Plant Pathology Statewide Conference on Plant Disease Losses Committee. J. M. Ogawa, Chairman. 1965. Estimates of crop losses and disease-control costs in California, 1963. Univ. Calif. Agr. Expt. Sta. and Agr Ext. Serv. 102 p (multilith).

64. Wickson, E. J. and C. W. Woodworth. 1892. Root knots on fruit trees and vines. Calif. Agr. Exp. Sta. Bul. 99:1-4 (out of print).

65. Wood, H. N. 1964. Cell membranes as regulators of biosynthetic metabolism and the biochemistry of a mitotic triggering substance in plant tumor cells. *In* DeVay and Wilson, Proc. Conf. on Abnormal Growth in Plants. Univ. of California, Berkeley, Nov. 5-6, 1964, pp. 20-6.

FUNGAL DISEASES OF FRUIT AND NUT TREES

Armillaria Root Rot of Fruit and Nut Trees
Armillaria mellea (Vahl.) Quel.

Armillaria root rot, also known as "mushroom root rot," "shoestring fungus rot," and "oak root fungus disease," occurs on a wide range of hosts including woody and herbaceous plants throughout both temperate and tropical regions. According to Gardner and Raabe (8) the disease was first recognized by Hartig on pine trees in Germany in 1873. In the U.S. the disease is of greatest importance on fruit trees west of the Rocky Mountains. In California it was first recorded on lemon, then on grape in Sonoma County in 1881, and at Oakville in Napa Valley in 1887. It was of great concern to walnut growers in Santa Barbara County in 1886-88, and was reported on peach and prune in Santa Clara County in 1901. A 1945 survey showed 34 of 65 orchards in Santa Clara County had one or more infected sites (26). The importance of Armillaria root rot is emphasized by the host list compiled by Raabe, who also named the years and countries in which the disease was first reported (24).

Symptoms. External symptoms of the disease are poor shoot growth, premature yellowing and dropping of leaves, and eventual death of the tree. Sudden collapse of the tree can occur during the dry summer months, an occurence that can be confused with rodent injury and Phytophthora root rot. Symptoms usually appear on one or two limbs, then in 2 or 3 years spread throughout the tree. The root (up to and including the crown) are dead. Between the brown dead bark and the wood are white to slightly yellow, flat, fanshaped, felt-like plaques of mycelia (fig. 45A). Dark-brown somewhat shiny rootlike strands of rhizomorph, which arise from the diseased areas, extend along the surface of the bark (fig. 45B) and a short distance into the soil. Rhizomorphs are not so consistently present as to be a ready means of diagnosis, especially on crops like grapes. Sporophores of the fungus are also not common in California, but when they do occur they develop clusters about the base of the diseased trees between October and February (fig. 45C, 45D). The decayed bark is not sour or putrid but has a sharp, rather agreeable mushroom odor. The fungus also penetrates into the underlying wood causing it to develop a uniformly white rot (27).

Another fungus, a species of *Poria* (7), is often confused with *Armillaria*. This fungus produces somewhat more wefty or cottonly plaques, irregular in shape and not confined between the wood and bark but occurring throughout the bark and into the wood. It is primarily a wood-rotting fungus and usually can be distinguished from *Armillaria* by means of its powdery mycelium and the soft crumbling condition of the wood it attacks, as contrasted with the firm condition of the wood attacked by *Armillaria*. Furthermore, this fungus does not develop rhizomorphs nor does it have the fresh mushroom odor produced by *Armillaria*.

Causal organism. The rhizomorphic stage of *Armillaria*, first described as *Rhizomorpha subterranea* Pers. and *R. subcorticalis* Pers., was later shown (12, 13) to give rise to the mushroom stage, then known as *Agaricus melleus* but now named *Armillaria (Armillariella) mellea* (Vahl.) Quel.

The characteristic rhizomorphs of the fungus are not always produced on tree-hosts and have never been observed on grapes. In culture, rhizomorph formation was shown to occur when ethanol and related compounds were present in the medium (34). Certain naturally-occurring materials in woody plants have also been shown to stimulate rhizomorph formation. Ethanol in glucose media was found to inhibit production of phenols which are thought to prevent thallus growth (33).

The mushrooms, which vary in size, are usually honey-colored and have a delicate annulus (ring) on a stout stem. They are borne in clusters at the base of the tree trunk. The caps are from 3 to 15 cm wide, spores are colorless, elliptical or round, 7 to 10 μm in dimension and borne on white or dull-white gills. Wolpert (37) found that *Armillaria* grows at a range of pH between 2.9 and 7.4, about 5.0 being optimum (for germination of spores, however, growth optimum is 6.5). The fungus first destroys the cellulose of cells and associated pentosans and later the lignin. Lanphere (16) found that rhizomorphs of *A. mellea* produce the enzymes amylase, catalase, inulase, lipase, pepsin, and sucrase.

Clones of the fungus collected from various areas of California exhibited different degrees of pathogenicity on Elberta peaches in the orchard (36) or on plants in containers (23).

Disease development. The pathogen survives from one year to the next in the soil on roots of affected hosts. Unassociated with the host, it may survive for several years on woody materials in the soil. The rhizomorphs are principal agents of infection. Under California conditions the basidiospores, being both comparatively rare and certainly more evanescent than the rhizomorphs, probably play no part in secondary infection. Rhizomorphs are moderately abundant and are produced whenever the fungus finds conditions favorable for growth. The fungus is disseminated on infected material by man and by movement of surface water. The basidiospores are doubtless carried considerable distances in air currents. In soil, the fungus spreads by growing out along the roots of affected trees; if such roots touch those of healthy trees, the fungus may move into the latter. The rhizomorphs do not extend for great distances in the soil, as was formerly believed. No wounds are necessary for infection: Thomas (28) found the rhizomorphs capable of penetrating directly through the bark of roots. Infection occurs and the disease develops at an optimum soil temperature of 17 to 24°C. Such temperatures occur during spring and early summer in California (2).

Thomas (28), dealing primarily with the early stages of infection, found some evidence of destruction of the suberized cells of the bark and death of cells of the cortex ahead of the invading rhizomorph. After gaining entrance, the rhizomorph grows rapidly and kills the cells. The cellulose of cells is destroyed, followed later by destruction of lignin, where this is present. In resistant hosts the invaded regions are frequently walled off by a phelloderm.

Trees usually die in 1 to 3 years, depending on the susceptibility of the tree. Death is hastened by summer heat and lack of soil moisture.

Host susceptibility. The pathogen has a wide host range and is distributed throughout the world (23). Apples, cherries, almonds, olives, peaches, prunes, plums, and apricots are highly susceptible. The pear and fig are comparatively resistant. The resistance of the California black walnut (*Juglans hindsii*) has led to its wide use as a rootstock for Persian (English) walnuts (*J. regia*), the roots of the latter species being highly susceptible. Certain selections of myrobalan plums exhibit resistance.

Control. Soil fumigation and the use of resistant rootstocks have been used with moderate success (21). The value of such control measures as destruction of the mushrooms, use of nitrogen to stimulate growth of affected trees, and care not to introduce the fungus, are difficult to evaluate.

Fumigation of soil before planting trees eliminates most of the *Armillaria* fungus, but spot treatment is necessary later to disinfest trees where the fungus was not killed. Most important in fumigation is low soil moisture (3, 30) and proper application of the fumigants, carbon disulfide or methyl bromide. In preparation for fumigation diseased trees should be removed during the winter months and, along with them, all roots greater than 1½ inches in diameter in the top 2 feet of soil. Diseased roots and stumps should be burned in place. It is necessary to remove partially affected trees and an entire row of apparently unaffected trees around the margin of the *Armillaria* site. After tree removal, an entire summer without irrigation is needed for the soil to dry out. Planting deep-rooted unirrigated cover crop, such as mustard, sudangrass, or safflower, will help reduce the soil moisture to the level necessary for optimum diffusion of fumigating gas throughout the soil. In heavy soils the moisture should be tested to a depth of at least 5 to 6 feet. Fumigation is done in the fall while the soil is still warm and low in moisture. The soil should be prepared for fumigation by cultivation to break up the clods; if a plow pan or hardpan is present, subsoiling or deep chiseling is necesssary. Following the final cultivation and before carbon bisulfide application, the top 6 to 8 inches of soil should be moistened lightly as an aid to penetration by the soil-fumigation equipment and to help prevent escape of the fumigant.

The equipment used for applying the fumigant depends upon the size of the area to be treated. For small areas, hand equipment is most feasible. A self-measuring, force-fed hand-applicator, is used to inject 2 liquid ounces 6 to 8 inches deep at 18-inch intervals in each direction. To obtain maximum soil diffusion of the gas, injection sites are staggered so that the pattern of injection is diagonal or diamond-shaped. Immediately after injection the soil should be firmly tamped to prevent escape of the fumes. Carbon disulfide is injurious to tree roots so treatment should not be made nearer uninfected trees than the overhead branches extend—the branch of apricot and peach extend 8 to 10 feet; walnut extends 15 to 25 feet. After treating the area, give a light irrigation sufficient to wet the soil to a depth of about 3 inches.

For larger areas, tractor-operated equipment is used. The applicator consists of three or more chisels, 18-inches apart, to inject the fumigant 8 inches deep in sandy soil and 6 inches in heavier soils. If using carbon disulfide, a minimum of 302 gallons (3025 pounds) per acre has been applied. Following application, a drag and a heavy steel roller are used to pack and seal the soil surface.

Care must be taken in handling and storage of carbon disulfide as it is both explosive and toxic. The gas is 2½ times heavier than air. Safety rules are a) store in a cool place and use at temperatures below 29.4 °C; b) do not light matches or smoke near the chemical; c) never use hammer and chisel to loosen the bung—use a wrench made to open barrels, and then allow the gas pressure to equalize slowly; d) prevent accumulation of static electricity by grounding the barrels when they are in a truck when the liquid is being removed.

Methyl bromide has done as well as carbon disulfide on light sandy soil when applied at the rate of 870 pounds per acre under a plastic tarp (14, 15, 17). The chemical is injected as deep as possible with chisel applicators at the rate of 2 pounds per 100 square feet and then the treated area is covered with a gas-proof plastic sheet. With clay soils, the dosage should be increased to 4 pounds per square foot. The plastic cover is removed after 2 weeks and the treated area is aerated 1 month before trees are planted.

Complete eradication is rarely achieved and localized treatment may be necessary. Neither fumigant treatment is successful if soil is wet or if extensive unpenetrable clay layers are present to depths reached by the roots. Methyl bromide has been used almost exclusively in California because it is easier to handle, but is toxic and must be handled with caution.

Control of *Armillaria* by soil fumigation is apparently related to weakening of the pathogen followed by the increase in population of *Trichoderma viride,* which is antagonistic towards the pathogen (3, 11, 18, 25).

Resistant rootstocks offer less expensive and more practical method of coping with this disease. Resistant rootstocks are plum (Marianna 2624), persimmon, fig, northern California black walnut, and domestic French pear. Moderately resistant are plum (Myrobalan 29-C, Mazzard cherry, St. Julien and Damson plum *(P. insititia)* and apple. Seedlings of peach, apricot, and almond are susceptible, as are Mahaleb and Stockton Morello cherries and all rootstocks of grape and quince. The Oriental pear rootstocks are, as a group, more susceptible than domestic French rootstocks. Havens 2B almond interstock is used with Nonpareil, a variety which is not compatible with the resistant plum rootstock Marianna 2624. Cultivars compatible with Marianna 2624 are Jordanolo, Ne Plus Ultra, Mission (Texas) (5, 6, 21). Mission (Texas) (5, 6, 21).

References

1. Bliss, D. E. 1944. Controlling Armillaria root rot in citrus. Univ. of California, Agr. Exp. Sta. Lithoprint 50.
2. _____ 1946. The relation of soil temperature to the development of Armillaria root rot. Phytopathology 36:302-18.
3. _____ 1951. The destruction of *Armillaria mellea* in citrus soils. Phytopathology 41:665-83.
4. Campbell, A. H. 1934. Zone lines in plant tissues. II. The black lines formed by *Armillaria mellea* (Vahl.) Quel. Ann. Appl. Biol. 21:1-22.
5. Chester, D. E., C. J. Hanson, and C. Panetsos. 1962: Plum rootstocks for almonds. California Agriculture 16(6):10-11.
6. Day, L. H. 1947. Apple, quince and pear rootstocks in California. California Agr. Exp. Stn. Bul. 700 (out of print).
7. DeVay, J. E. *et al.* 1968. Poria root and crown rot of cherry trees. Phytopathology 58:1239-41.
8. Gardner, M. W., and R. D. Raabe. 1963. Early references to Armillaria root rot in California. Plant Dis. Rep. 47:413-15.
9. Garraway, M. O., and A. R. Weinhold. 1968. Influence of ethanol on the distribution of glucose-^{14}C assimilated by *Armillaria mellea.* Phytopathology 58:1652-57.
10. Garrett, S. D. 1956. Rhizomorph behavior in *Armillaria mellea* (Vahl.) Quel. II. Logistics of infection. Ann. Bot. London 20:193-209.
11. _____ 1958. Inoculum potential as a factor limiting action by Trichoderma viride Fr. on *Armillaria mellea* (Fr.) Quel. Trans. Brit. Mycol. Soc. 41:157-64.
12. Hartig, R. 1873. Vorlaufig Mittheilung uber den Parasitismus von *Agaricus melleus* und dessen Rhizomorphen. Bot. Ztg. 31:295-97.

13. _____ 1874. Wichtige krankheiten der Waldbaume. Beitrage zur Mycologie und Phytopathologie fur Botaniker und Forstmanner. 127 pp. Berlin.

14. Kolbezen, M. J., and F. J. Abu-El-Haj. 1972. Fumigation with methyl bromide. I. Apparatus for controlled concentration, continuous flow laboratory procedures. Pestic. Sci. 3:67-71.

15. _____ 1972. Fumigation with methyl bromide. II. Equipment and methods for sampling and analyzing deep field soil atmospheres. Pestic. Sci. 3:73-80.

16. Lanphere, W. M. 1934. Enzymes of the rhizomorphs of *Armillaria mellea*. Phytopathology 24:1244-49.

17. LaRue, J. H., et al. 1962. Armillaria root rot fungus controlled with methyl bromide soil fumigation. California Agriculture 16(8):8-9.

18. Munnecke, D. E., M. J. Kolbezen, and W. D. Wilbur. 1963. Effect of methyl bromide or carbon disulfide on *Armillaria* and *Trichoderma* growing on agar medium and relation to survival of Armillaria in soil following fumigation. Phytopathology 63:1352-57.

19. _____ 1970. Dosage response of Armillaria mellea to methyl bromide. Phytopathology 60:992-93.

20. Ohr, H. D., D. E. Munnecke, and J. L. Bricker. 1973. The interaction of *Armillaria mellea* and *Trichoderma* spp. as modified by methyl bromide. Phytopathology 63:965-73.

21. O'Reilly, H. J. 1963. Armillaria root rot of deciduous fruits, nuts, and grapevines. California Agr. Exp. Sta. Circ. 525. 15 pp (out of print).

22. Piper, C. V., and S. W. Fletcher. 1903. Root diseases of fruit and other trees caused by toadstools. Washington State Coll. Agr. Exp. Sta. Bul. No. 59, 14 pp.

23. Raabe, R. D. 1962. Host list of the root rot fungus, *Armillaria mellea*. Hilgardia 33(2):25-88.

24. _____ 1967. Variation in pathogenicity and virulence in *Armillaria mellea*. Phytopathology 57:73-75.

25. Saksena, S. B. 1960. Effect of carbon disulphide fumigation on *Trichoderma viride* and other soil fungi. Trans. Brit. Mycol. Soc. 43:111-16.

26. Schneider, H., E. W. Bodine, and H. E. Thomas. 1945. Armillaria root rot in the Santa Clara Valley of California. Plant Dis. Rep. 29:495-96.

27. Smith, R. E. 1941. Diseases of fruits and nuts. California Agr. Ext. Serv. Circ. 120. p. 144-50 (out of print).

28. Thomas, H. E. 1934. Studies on *Armillaria mellea* (Vahl.) Quel., infection, parasitism, and host resistance. J. Agr. Research 48:187-218.

29. _____ 1938. Suggestions for combating oak root fungus. Almond Facts (October-November).

30. Thomas, H. E., and L. O. Lawyer. 1939. The use of carbon disulfide in the control of Armillaria root rot. Phytopathology 29:827-28.

31. Thomas, H. E., H. E. Thomas, C. Roberts, and A. Amstutz. 1948. Rootstock susceptibility to *Armillaria mellea*. Phytopathology 38:152-54.

32. Thomas, H. E., S. Wilhelm, and N. A. MacLean. 1953. Two root rots of fruit trees. *In* Plant Diseases. U. S. Dept. Agr. Yearbook 1953: 702-05.

33. Vance, C. P., and M. O. Garraway. 1973. Growth stimulation of *Armillaria mellea* by ethanol and other alcohols in relation to phenol concentration. Phytopathology 63:743-48.

34. Weinhold, A. R., and M. O. Garraway. 1963. Rhizomorph production in *Armillaria mellea* induced by ethanol and related compounds. Science 142:1065-66.

35. _____ 1966. Nitrogen and carbon nutrition of *Armillaria mellea* in relation to growth promoting effects of ethanol. Phytopathology 56:108-12.

36. Wilbur, W., D. E. Munnecke, and E. F. Darley. 1972. Seasonal development of Armillaria root rot of peach as influenced by fungal isolates. Phytopathology 62:567-70.

37. Wolpert, F. S. 1924. Studies in the physiology of the fungi. XVIII. The growth of certain wood-destroying fungi in relation to the H-ion concentration of the media. Ann. Missouri Bot. Garden 11:43-97.

Phytophthora Crown and Root Rot of Fruit and Nut Trees
Phytophthora sp.

Most deciduous fruit and nut species are affected by a disease known as "crown rot," "collar rot," "Phytophthora collar rot," "Phytophtora trunk rot" and, in the earlier literature, "Pythiacystis canker." All species of stone fruit, pome fruit, and walnut are more or less affected. A similar diseases of citrus is known as "gummosis" or "brown rot canker."

Crown rot disease occurs in many fruit-growing areas of the world, and it seems certain that crown rot has been present since orchard trees were first cultivated. Early horticultural records give accounts of such a disease. Baines (1), for example, cited a description in 1858 of "collar injury" of apple in the midwestern states. Although, at that time the malady was believed to be caused by winter injury to the trunk, a means of avoiding it—that of double-working the trees—had been successfully employed.

Crown rot and root rot has been a source of major loss to Pacific Coast orchards for many years. In

California, it kills more almond, apple, cherry, nectarine, and peach trees than perhaps any other disease and, has long been a concern to walnut growers. On pears and prunes, however, the occurence of the disease is sporadic.

Symptoms. The disease is troublesome both in the nursery and in the orchard (fig. 46A). Fruit infection occurs in sprinkler-irrigated orchards (fig. 46B). In the nursery, the principal loss occurs when the young trees are dug, tied into bundles, and the bundles heeled-in (the roots and crown buried in sawdust or soil) pending their sale. Under such conditions, cankers (which in stone fruit trees, exude copious gum, and in pome fruit or walnut trees exude a watery or slimy material) develop at various places along the trunk. In the orchard, cankers usually are centered at the crown or lower part of the trunk of the tree, but may—depending on the species of host —extend some distance up the trunk and down into the large roots (fig. 46C).

Affected bark is brown and dead, gum-soaked in stone fruit trees and moist or slimy in pome fruit trees. A shallow layer of outer sapwood underlying the cankers may be discolored, but discoloration does not extend very far beyond the upper and lower limits of the necrotic area in the bark.

These symptoms are frequently not apparent without close examination of the crown of the tree. Thus the first indication of infection may be failure of the tree to start growth in the spring, or sparse light-green or bronze foliage after the tree starts growth and subsequent rapid decline and death of the tree.

Phytophthora cactorum on pear does not confine its attack to the crown and large roots but may infect the small feeder roots (26, 31). The newly affected bark develops various shades of light and dark brown and has a marbled appearance. There is usually a well-defined margin between the diseased and healthy bark. Diseased trees occur at random throughout the planting, evidence that the disease is not transmitted from one affected tree to another. When young vigorously growing trees become infected their leaves develop a purplish cast in autumn. Infected mature trees which have poorly developed chlorotic foliage produce little or no new growth, and bear small highly colored fruit. The relationship of this type of infection to the pear decline complex is under investigation (26). Pythiaceous fungi were not found to be the primary cause of pear decline in California (36).

Information on pathological histology of the disease is meager. Baines (1) reported that the protoplasts of infected cells, particularly the parenchymatous cells, are disorganized and the cell walls disrupted. Mycelium is both intercellular and intracellular. According to Cooper (13), however, the mycelium is intercellular but haustoria penetrate into the adjacent cells.

The causal organism. Although it is generally believed that species of *Phytophthora* are involved in most crown rot situations, it would be premature to say that other agents cannot produce similar symptoms. For example, Magness (23) believed that various factors, including low temperature and excessive soil moisture, might cause collar rot symptoms on apple trees.

The frequent association of *Phytophthora* spp. with crown rot symptoms in various crops and at various places strongly suggests that the fungus is the primary cause of the disease. Though studies on this genus of fungus were started by Rosenbaum (37) in 1917, and extended by Leonian (20, 21) and Leonian and Greer (22), and by Tucker (49, 50), the status of the species is still in a state of change. Earlier workers employed morphological characters of the sexual and asexual structures in classifying species. Tucker (49) considers these of limited value and believes that cultural and environmental criteria offer better means for identification. Most investigators agree that *P. cactorum* (Leb. & Cohn) Schroet. is commonly the cause of the disease in walnut and apple (3, 4, 11, 14, 24, 25, 30, 38, 53). McIntosh (27) found it to be widely distributed in the irrigated soils of the apple-growing areas of British Columbia, but it was not found in the virgin soils nor in nonirrigated cultivated soils. Young and Milbrath (54) later found that *P. syringae* Kleban will attack nursery stock of peach, apricot, cherry, and crabapple under similar conditions in Oregon. Both *P. cactorum* and *P. cinnamomi* Rands attack pear in Oregon (12). Mircetich and Keil in 1970 (33) implicated *P. cinnamomi* in root rot of peach in Maryland and southern Pennsylvania, and extensive isolations from California stone fruit orchards since then have revealed the following association by host: peach and almond: *P. megasperma, P. drechsleri, P. cambivora, P. syringae* and four unidentified *Phytophthora* spp. (29, 30, 31); apricot: *P. cambivora, P. syringae, P. megasperma, P. drechlseri, P. citricola* and seven unidentified *Phytophthora* spp.; cherry: *P. cambivora, P. drechsleri, P. megasperma* and three unidentified *Phytophthora* spp. (34; prune: *P. megasperma, P. cambivora,* and *P. syringae;* apple: *P. cambivora, P. megasperma, P. drechsleri,* and six unidentified *Phytophthora* spp.; walnut: *P. cactorum, P. cinnamomi, P. megasperma,* and *Phytophthora* sp.

Variation with respect to morphological and pathogenic characters have contributed greatly to the problem of identifying species of *Phytophthora*. The information on variation was reviewed by Erwin *et al.* (15).

The following account is based on Blackwell's (7) description of the life cycle of *P. cactorum*. Aerial sporangiophores, bearing sympodially a succession of sporangia, 36 × 28 μm in dimensions, are produced when the atmosphere is moist and they project above the surface of the infected host-part. Under favorable conditions the sporangium produces zoospores which emerge into a vesicle at the apex of the sporangium. The pear-shaped, uninucleate, biflagellate zoospores are liberated when the wall of the vesicle breaks. Production of sporangia and liberation of zoospores may occur within 6 or 7 hours. Under unfavorable conditions the sporangium may develop into a structure, which Blackwell calls a conidium. Once the sporangium develops into a conidium it does not produce zoospores but germinates by means of a germ tube which usually emerges from the apex of the structure. If kept dry it will remain dormant for months and then germinate when moisture is present.

Blackwell describes another resting structure produced by some strains of *P. cactorum* which she calls a chlamydospore. The chlamydospore is produced terminally, rarely intercalary, on mycelia and is easily confused with an oospore.

The oogonium and antheridium, sexual reproductive structures of the fungus, are produced on separate hyphal branches. Oogonia vary from 25 to 40 μm (av. 33 μm) in diameter and oblong antheridia average about 13 to 14 μm in greatest dimension. Blackwell (7) reported that the anteridia of *P. cactorum* are largely paragynous. The oogonium and antheridium are multinucleate, and the nuclei are arranged evenly throughout the protoplasm; eventually, however, one nucleus becomes most prominent and with a portion of surrounding protoplasm forms an oosphere, which is separated from the rest of the nuclei by a thin periplasm. Upon its contact with the oogonium wall the antheridium forms a fertilization tube, which appears to be an extension of the walls of the antheridium and oogonium. This tube presses into the oogonium and finally gives way, liberating a nucleus which fertilizes the oosphere. The resulting oospore undergoes a period of dormancy, apparently comparable to the dormant period of seeds. During this period, which may last for several months, it must be in a moist environment or it will not survive. At the end of dormancy the oospore germinates by one to three germ tubes.

Various methods of isolation of *Phytophthora* from soil have been described (2, 8, 36, 47). The key to

Phytophthora species is found in papers by Waterhouse (51, 52).

Development of the disease. The fungus can live in the soil without a host plant for extended periods, probably obtaining nutriments from dead plant material. In nursery sales-yards, where for year after year bundles of nursery trees are heeled-in pending sale, the disease may become epidemic, indicating that the fungus finds conditions favorable for both multiplication and infection. In such situations it is not known whether the fungus increases on the host tissue only, or on the host tissue and dead organic matter in the soil. Seemingly, the most effective means whereby the fungus could increase would be through the production of sporangia and the liberation of zoospores. Oospores are commonly produced by some *Phytophthora* spp. in infected host tissue. Sporangia also may be present on such tissue. Some investigators apparently believe that sporangia may be produced on fallen fruit or on dead organic debris in the soil and, consequently, that zoospores play an important part in disseminating the fungus and in buildup of infection in the orchard.

The disease is more likely to occur when the soil remains wet for extended periods. Welsh (53) found that colony growth of *P. cactorum in vitro* ceased when the relative humidity fell below 90 percent and that at relative humidity levels below 60 percent the fungus soon died. Welsh also found that the disease in apple trees was not influenced by different soil-moisture but is favored by temperatures between 23 and 32 °C. In *P. cactorum*-infested soils approaching saturation, the disease increased with successive increases in soil temperature between these limits. At lower soil-moisture levels, disease development did not increase as soil temperature increased. At 61 percent saturation, for example, disease development was low at all temperatures between 23 and 32 °C. Cardinal temperatures for growth of the fungus in culture are: minimum 4 to 7 °C, optimum about 27 °C, maximum 32 °C. The fungus survives only a few days at 32 °C.

Welsh (53) believed that high soil moisture possibly favors development of Phytophthora crown rot because it impairs the vigor of the tree by injuring the root system. Low soil moisture, he believed, is unfavorable to development of the disease because the vegetative phase of the fungus cannot survive under such conditions. Only the resting structures of the fungus would survive, and these would be unable to germinate and develop sporangia at low moisture levels.

The effect of high soil moisture on production, liberation, and dissemination of zoospores has not been explored thoroughly. Sporangial production and zoo-

142

spore maturation are favored by high humidity, and certainly the mobility of the zoospores would depend upon free soil water. In addition, there is evidence that spattering of some part of the fungus, possibly zoospores, leads to infection of the stems of young nursery trees when these are heeled-in in the nursery yard. In such trees individual cankers of the disease often develop not only on the base of the trunk in contact with the soil but a foot or more above the soil level. Baines (1) described infection of apple trees where cankers develop on the trunk well above the soil level. It is likely that the fungus reaches such sites in spattered water during rainy weather.

Phytophthora crown rot epidemics in stone fruit trees occur in California in years when rainfall is plentiful in winter and spring and temperatures are moderate. Smith and Smith (46) mentioned the heavy losses that occurred in nursery trees in California during the winter of 1921-22, a season of excessive rainfall which began in early November. Apparently, infection occurred in the nursery row before the trees were dug for sale. Thousands of trees were lost during January and February. The greatest losses occurred among apricot and peach trees that had been heeled-in in out-of-door trenches. Many almond, plum, apple and pear trees were also lost.

Susceptibility of apple cultivars. With Phytophthora crown rot, as with other root and crown diseases, susceptibility of the above-ground portions of the tree to infection by the pathogen may or may not determine the severity of the disease in the orchard. This is because fruit trees are propagated on a rootstock which is from a different variety or even a different species than that of the top. Since it is the lower trunk of the tree (crown) which is attacked by *P. cactorum* and since, in trees propagated by budding the lower trunk may be rootstock tissue, the susceptibility of the rootstock determines the severity of the disease in the orchard. In trees propagated by grafting the scion of the commercial variety onto a root from a different cultivar or species, the lower trunk is tissue of the scion. Consequently, the susceptibility of the commercial cultivar will be important in determining the severity of the disease in the orchard.

Baines (1) reported that collar rot of apples in Indiana was largely confined to Grimes Golden. He said little about the rootstock in general use at that time, but alludes to seedlings of French crab which he intimated were resistant to infection by *P. cactorum*. It is clear, however, that the site of infection was not in rootstock tissue but in the trunk tissue of commercial cultivars and thus it can be assumed that the rootstock was either resistant or escaped infection because of some special attribute.

Baines noted that the disease was occasionally found in Baldwin, Tompkins King, Roxbury Russett, Rhode Island Greening, Esopus Spitzenburg, and Hubbardston.

Welsh (53) described a situation in British Columbia in which the fungus attacked the trees at or slightly below soil level. He noted that the rootstocks were seedlings of various apple cultivars, and while he did not mention the method of propagation it is probable that the trees were budded into the seedling trees a few inches above the soil level. Consequently when they were transplanted to the orchard the union between rootstock and scion of some would be above the soil level, while with others the union would be at or below soil level. In such a situation the susceptibility of the commercial cultivar will influence the incidence of infection in trees planted with the bud union at or near the soil level. Susceptibility of the rootstock will be the more influential factor in trees planted with the bud union well above the soil level.

Seasonal susceptibility of apples, and variations in activity of the fungi in the soil, have also been studied to provide better timing of fungicide applications for control and the evaluation of rootstocks for resistance (8, 17, 27, 39).

Susceptibility of pear cultivars. McIntosh (25) cited d'Anjou as the pear most often affected by Phytophthora crown rot in British Columbia. Bartlett is sometimes affected. In experiments in Oregon, Bartlett and Winter Nelis proved susceptible (12) whereas Old Home, Old Home X Farmingdale, and *Pyrus calleryana* "... were not severely damaged."

Susceptibility among stone fruit species. Smith and Smith (46) noted that apricot and peach nursery trees were most often infected by *P. citrophora* during the 1921-22 epidemic. Almond and plum trees were also highly susceptible to infection. It has become more and more evident that the incidence of disease under one set of conditions may lead to erroneous conclusions regarding inherent susceptibility among the different host plants. One reason for this is that certain hosts or rootstocks may merely escape infection while others do not. Another reason is the existence of pathogenic races of the fungus. This aspect of the problem will be discussed presently.

Mahaleb seedling rootstock for sweet cherries was susceptible to severe root and crown rot as well as stem cankers when inoculated with *P. megasperma* and *P. cambivora*, but no stem cankers developed when inoculated with *P. drechsleri*. *P. drechsleri* caused decay of feeder roots with resultant growth stunting. Field isolations supported this data. Mazzard cherry rootstocks were more resistant to these pathogens (34). On almond the root and crown rot phase was predominately caused by *P. megasperma* and *P. drechsleri*, but *P. syringae* caused most extensive trunk cankers on almond rootstock, with the next in order being almond X peach hybrid, Nemaguard and Lovell (35).

Susceptibility among walnut species. Barrett (4) lists the southern California black walnut *(Juglans californica)* as somewhat more susceptible than the northern California black walnut *(J. hindsii)* to attack by *P. cactorum*. The Persian (English) walnut *(J. regia)* is quite resistant. Black walnut species, especially *J. hindsii*, have been widely employed in California as rootstocks for the commercial Persian walnut cultivars. More recently the Paradox hybrid *(J. hindsii × J. regia)* have come into use as a rootstock. Susceptibility of the paradox has not been fully explored. After infecting the black walnut rootstock the fungus may sometimes invade the trunk of the Persian walnut above the bud union. Nevertheless, susceptibility of the rootstock is more important than susceptibility of the commercial cultivar in determining the severity of walnut disease in the orchard.

In addition to *J. hindsii*, *J. californica*, and *J. regia*, Smith and Barrett (41) found that *P. cactorum* produced symptoms on *J. nigra*, *J. mandschurica*, *J. sieboldiana*, *J. major*, *J. pyriformis*, and a Paradox hybrid from the cross *J. californica × J. regia*.

Age of tree. Among most fruit and nut tree hosts the young nonbearing trees seem to be somewhat less susceptible to infection than are the older bearing trees (25, 53).

Control. Measures recommended for the control of the disease in orchard trees can be divided into three categories: a) use of resistant understock for the commercial cultivar, b) removal of the soil from around the crown of the tree, and c) drainage measures in areas of the orchard where water tends to accumulate and 4) application of fungicides.

Baines (1) noted that the French crabapple root, commonly in use in the 1930's as a rootstock for apples, was resistant to infection by *P. cactorum*. A measure practiced by some nurseries is that of "double-working" the trees—a resistant cultivar is grafted onto the French crab root, and the scion of the susceptible commercial cultivar is grafted or budded onto the French crab root, and the scion of the sussoil level.

Smith and Barrett (41) reported that the white or Persian walnut *(J. regia)* was sufficiently resistant to

P. cactorum to be a suitable rootstock. The objection to the use of seedlings of this species as a rootstock is that it is highly susceptible to attack by *Armillaria mellea*. In recent years a rootstock known as the Paradox hybrid has come into use because of its vigor and apparent resistance to *A. mellea* and its tolerance of soil salinity (it also appears to be fairly resistant to crown rot disease).

In 1930, Braucher (9) reported that removal of the soil around the crown of infected walnut trees would check the disease. This method has been used quite widely in California with apparently good results.

Preventing soil around the crown of the tree from staying wet for long periods should help prevent infection.

Much can be done to prevent infection of nursery trees after they have been dug and are being held at the sales yard. By heeling-in trees in fresh peat moss or fresh sawdust one eliminates soil as a source of contamination, and by protecting heeled-in trees from rain one avoids the moisture needed for pathogen's activities.

Protective fungicides, especially copper compounds, have been placed at the crown of the tree with variable results. Copper crystals hung at the intake of pumps for sprinkler irrigation provided control of fruit decay in Washington (23). Maneb and Difolatan have been recommended (28) and Dexon has been tested. Because most fungicides have short half-life in wet soil, critical studies on periods of host susceptibility have not been determined (15, 27, 31). On apples in Missouri, inner bark tissues are highly susceptible to fungus colonization at or near the blossoming period (17), so this may be the proper time to provide protective measures.

References

1. Baines, R. C. 1939. Phytophthora trunk canker or collar rot of apple trees. J. Agr. Research 59:159-84.
2. Banihashemi, Z. 1970. A new technique for isolation of *Phytophthora* and *Pythium* species from soil. Plant Dis. Rep. 54:261-62.
3. Barrett, J. T. 1917. Pythiacystis related to *Phytophthora*. Phytopathology 7:150-51. (Abstr.)
4. _____ 1928. *Phytophthora* in relation to crown rot of walnut. Phytopathology 18:948-49. (abstr.)
5. _____ 1948. Induced oospore production in the genus *Phytophthora*. Phytopathology 38:2. (Abstr.)
6. Bingham, F. T., and G. A. Zentmyer. 1954. Relation of hydrogen ion concentration of

nutrient solution to Phytophthora root rot of avocado seedlings. Phytopathology 44:611-14.

7. Blackwell, E. 1943. The life history of *Phytophthora cactorum* (Leb. & Cohn) Schroet. Trans. British Mycol. Soc. 26:71-89.

8. Borecki, Z., and D. F. Millikan. 1969. A rapid method for determining the pathogenicity and factors associated with the pathogenicity of *Phytophthora cactorum. Phytopathology* 59:247-48.

9. Braucher, O. L. 1930. Field trials in crown rot control. That success is based on keeping the tree crown dry. Diamond Walnut News 12(4):9.

10. Braun, H., and F. Nienhaus. 1949. Fortgefuhrte Untersuchungen uber die Kragenfaule des Apfels *(Phytophthora cactorum).* Phytopathol. Zeit. 36:169-208.

11. Braun, H. and F. J. Schwinn. 1963. Fortgefuhrte Untersuchungen uber den Erreger der Kragenfaule des Apfelbaumes (Phytophthora cactorum). Phytopathol. Zeit. 47:327-370.

12. Cameron, H. R. 1962. Susceptibility of pear roots to *Phytophthora.* Phytopathology 52:1295-97.

13. Cooper, D. 1928. Paragynous antheridia of *Phytophthora* spp. Phytopathology 18:149. (Abstr).

14. Dunegan, J. C. 1935. Phytophthora disease of peach seedlings. Phytopathology 25:800-09.

15. Erwin, D. C., G. A. Zentmyer, J. Galindo, and J. S. Niederhauser. 1963. Variation in the genus *Phytophthora. In* Annual Review of Phytopathology 53:375-96.

16. Fitzpatrick, R. E., F. C. Mellor, and M. F. Welsh. 1944. Crown rot of apple trees in British Columbia—Rootstock and scion resistance trials. Sci. Agr. 24:533-41.

17. Gates, J. E., and D. F. Millikan. 1972. Seasonal fluctuations in susceptibility of the inner bark tissues of apple to colonization by the collar rot fungus *Phytophthora cactorum.* Phytoprotection 53:76-81.

18. Houten, J. G. ten. 1958. Resistance trials against collar rot of apples caused by *Phytophthora cactorum.* Tijdschr. Plantenziekten 65:422-31.

19. Hunt, J. F. 1921. Pythiacystis "brown rot" affecting deciduous trees. California Dept. Agr. Monthly Bul. 10:143-45.

20. Leonian, L. H. 1925. Physiological studies on the genus *Phytophthora.* Amer. J. Botany 12:444-98.

21. Leonian, L. H. 1936. Control of sexual reproduction in *Phytophthora cactorum.* Amer. J. Botany 23:188-90.

22. Leonian, L. H., and H. L. Geer. 1929. Comparative values of the size of *Phytophthora* sporangia obtained under standard conditions. J. Agr. Research 39:293-311.

23. Magness, J. R. 1929. Collar rot of apple trees. Washington Agr. Exp. Sta. Bul. No. 236, 19 pp.

24. McIntosh, D. J. 1953. A trunk and crown rot of sweet cherry in British Columbia. Phytopathology 43:402-03.

25. _____ 1959. Collar rot of pear trees in British Columbia. Phytopathology 49:795-97.

26. _____ 1960. The infection of pear rootlets by *Phytophthora cactorum.* Plant Dis. Rep. 44:262-64.

27. _____ 1964. *Phytophthora* spp. in soils of the Okanagan and Similkameen Valleys of British Columbia. Canadian J. Bot. 42:1411-15.

28. _____ 1971. Dilution plates used to evaluate initial and residual toxicity of fungicides in soils to zoospores of *Phytophthora cactorum,* the cause of collar rot in apple trees. Plant Dis. Rep. 55:213-16.

39. McIntosh, D. L., and I. C. MacSwan. 1966. The occurrence of collar rot caused by *Phytophthora cactorum* in a planting of apple trees aged 1 to 7 years. Plant Dis. Rep. 50:267-70.

30. McIntosh, D. L., and F. C. Mellor. 1953. Crown rot of fruit trees in British Columbia. II. Rootstock and scion resistance trials of apple, pears, and stone fruits. Can. J. Agr. Sci. 33:615-19.

31. McIntosh, D. L., and H. J. O'Reilly. 1963. Inducing infection of pear rootlets by *Phytophthora cactorum.* Phytopathology 53:1447. (Abstr.)

32. Mircetich, S. M., and H. W. Fogle. 1968. Occurrence and pathogenicity of *Pythium* in peach orchard soil. Phytopathology 58:886. (Abstr.)

33. Mircetich, S. M., and H. L. Keil. 1970. *Phytophthora cinnamomi* root rot and stem canker of peach trees. Phytopathology 60:1376-82.

34. Mircetich, S. M., M. E. Matheron, and W. R. Schreader. 1974. Sweet cherry root rot and trunk canker caused by *Phytophthora* spp. 66th Annu. Meeting American Phytopathological Society, August 11-15, 1974. Vancouver, British Columbia. Abstr. No. 173.

35. Mircetich, S. M., W. J. Moller, and D. H. Chaney. 1974. *Phytophthora* crown rot and trunk canker of almond trees. 66th Annu. Meeting American Phytopathological Society, August 11-15, 1974. Vancouver, British Columbia. Abstr. No. 174.

36. Nichols, C. W., S. M. Garnsey, R. L. Rackham, S. M. Gotan, and C. N. Mahannah. 1964. Pythiaceous fungi and plant-parasitic nematodes in California orchards. I. Occurrence and pathogenicity of Pythiaceous fungi in orchard soils. Hilgardia 35:577-602.

37. Rosenbaum, J. 1917. Studies of the genus *Phytophthora.* J. Agr. Research 8:233-76.

38. Sewell, G. W. F., and J. F. Wilson. 1959. Resistance trials of some apple rootstock varieties to *Phytophthora cactorum* (L. & C.) Schroet. J. Hort. Sci. 34:51-58.

39. _____ 1973. Phytophthora collar rot of apple: seasonal effects on infection and disease development. Ann. Appl. Biol. 74:149-58.

40. Sewell, G. W. F., J. F. Wilson, and J. T. Dakwa. 1974. Seasonal variations in the activity in soil of *Phytophthora cactorum, P. syringae,* and *P. citrocola* in relation to collar rot disease of apple. Ann. Appl. Biol. 76:179-86.

41. Smith, C. O., and J. T. Barrett. 1931. Crown rot of Juglans in California. J. Agr. Research 43:885-04.

42. Smith, E. H. 1915. Pythiaceous infection of deciduous nursery stock. Phytopathology 5:317-22.

43. Smith, E. H., and J. F. Hunt. 1922. *Pythiacystis* blighting of nursery stock. Calif. Agr. Exp. Sta. Ann. Rept. 1920-21:63.

44. Smith, H. C. 1950-1951. Collar rot of apples and gooseberries. Orchardist. New Zealand 23(11):11, 13-14.

45. _____ 1955. Collar-rot and crown rot of apple trees. Orchardist New Zealand 28:16.

46. Smith, R. E., and E. H. Smith. 1925. Further studies on Pythiaceous infection of deciduous fruit trees in California. Phytopathology 15:389-404.

47. Tsao, P. H. 1960. A serial dilution end-point method for estimating disease potentials of citrus *Phytophthoras* in soil. Phytopathology 50:717-24.

48. Tsao, P. H., and J. M. Menyonga. 1966. Response of *Phytophthora* spp. and soil microflora in the pimaricin-vancomycin medium. Phytopathology 56:152. (Abstr.)

49. Tucker, C. M. 1931. Taxonomy of the genus *Phytophthora* de Bary. Missouri Univ. Agr. Exp. Sta. Res. Bul. 153, 208 pp.

50. _____ 1933. The distribution of the genus *Phytophthora.* Missouri Univ. Agr. Exp. Sta. Research Bul. No. 184. 80 pp.

51. Waterhouse, G. M. 1956. The Genus *Phytophthora.* Commonwealth Mycological Institute, Kew, Surrey. 120 pp.

52. Waterhouse, G. M. 1963. Key to the species of *Phytophthora* de Bary. Commonwealth Mycological Papers. No. 92. 22 pp.

53. Welsh, M. F. 1942. Studies of crown rot of apple trees. Can. J. Research 20 Sec. 457-90.

54. Young, R. A., and J. A. Milbrath. 1959. A stem canker disease of fruit tree nursery stock caused by *Phytophthora syringae.* Phytopathology 49:114. (Abstr.)

Silver Leaf Disease of Stone Fruit
Stereum purpureum (Pers.) Fr.

Silver leaf or silver blight is rarely found in California although it is of considerable importance on apples in the Pacific Northwest (24). In temperate climates it is known to affect crops such as pome fruits, stone fruits, currants, chestnuts, and gooseberries. Wild hosts are willow, lilac, sycamore, rhododendron, poplar, birch, oak, and conifers. It was first reported by Prillieux in France in 1885 (29) and later by Sorauer in Germany in 1886 and by Aderhold in 1895. The disease has also been reported from England, Australia, New Zealand, South Africa, and Canada. In France and New Zealand it is of major economic importance.

Symptoms. Leaves of affected trees become silvery in appearance (fig. 47A) due to separation of the upper epidermis from the palisade layer, and consequent admission of a layer of air and interference with normal reflection of light. Severely affected leaves may turn necrotic before normal leaf fall (28). Some plants such as hawthorn, rhododendron, roses, beech, and birch are killed without any silvering of leaves (8). Discoloration of the heartwood is one of the most characteristic symptoms, and after death of the branches or tree leathery basidiocarps occur on the surfaces. The upper portion of the basidiocarps frequently extend out from the host in a form of a small shelf. The hymenium is smooth and generally purplish or lilac in color.

The causal organism. *Stereum purpureum* (Pers.) Fr. in the family Thelephoraceae forms a thin leathery sporophore of 2 to 8 cm in width which is brown or brownish purple but fades with age (fig. 47B). It appears as a small circular resupinate or profusely imbricate structure with a hairy upper surface. The hymenium is smooth, lilac to purplish in color. The basidiospores are hyaline, oval, apiculate at one end, and 6 to 8 × 3 to 4 μm in dimension. One of the characteristic histological features of this fungus is the presence of vesiculose, subhymenial cystidia measuring 15 to 30 μm in length × 12 to 25 μm in width which extend above the basidia. The sporophores appear in autumn and sporulate freely when wetted (8).

Disease development. The fungus, a wound parasite, enters through a pruning cut and moves rapidly along the root through the vessels and finally penetrates the sapwood. A gummy substance is finally formed in the vessel and forms a gum barrier around the fungus, thus preventing its further spread (10, 12, 13).

Although the fungus cannot be isolated from the silvered leaves, substantial evidence exists to prove that *S. purpureum* causes the leaf symptoms. Bendford and Pickering (1) produced silver leaf symptoms by inoculating trees with sporophores of *S. purpureum.* Injections of trees with filtered extracts of the fungus induced the silver symptom in plum trees (11). Naef-Roth, Kern and Toth in 1963 (25) reported that a similar symptom can be produced in plum trees by using a phytolysin, a high-molecular-weight water-soluble compound prepared from cultures of the fungus.

It has been suspected that silver leaf disorder on apricots in California is caused by *S. purpureum,* and the fungus has been definitely implicated in an 8-year-old Sacramento Valley cling peach orchard (14). The disease was later found on another peach orchard about 30 miles away. Both orchards were located near rivers where alternate hosts of the fungus such as poplar (*Populus* sp.) were present.

Control. Control is difficult due in part to the pathogen having a wide host range of perennial plants, inoculum being produced over a long period, and the virtual impossibility of protecting all wounded surfaces. Therefore, chemotherapeutic treatments have been suggested. Iron sulphate was used by Brooks in 1911 (5) and oxyquinoline sulphate was used by Grosjean in 1951 (22) with variable results from both treatments. Control by applying spore suspensions of *Trichoderma viride* Pers. ex. Fr. to pruning wounds has been reported (16, 19, 20). Infected parts can best be removed during summer before the middle of July, because trees are then comparatively resistant to infection. In areas of warm summer temperatures, as in Oregon and the Netherlands (22, 31), recovery of infected trees has been noted.

Further precautions suggested are use of clean nursery stock, burning of all infected material after removal, and soil sterilization before replanting healthy trees in diseased areas. Resistance has been reported for crops such as plums and apples (3, 10, 18). Some rootstocks also impart resistance to the scion variety.

References

1. Bedford, D., and S. U. Pickering. 1910. Silver leaf disease. Woburn Exp. Fruit Farm 12th Rept. Pp. 1-34.
2. Bennett, M. 1962. An approach to the chemotherapy of silver leaf disease *(Stereum purpureum)* of plum trees. Ann. Appl. Biol. 50:515-24.
3. _____ 1962. Susceptibility of Victoria plum trees to different isolates of *Stereum purpureum.* J. Hort. Sci. 37:235-38.
4. Binter, J. 1919. Silver leaf disease. Kew Bull. Misc. Inf. pp. 241-63.
5. Brooks, F. T. 1911. Silver leaf disease. I. J. Agr. Sci. 4:133-44.
6. _____ 1913. Silver leaf disease. II. J. Agr. Sci. 5:288-308.
7. Brooks, F. T. 1928. Plant Diseases. Oxford University Press, London. 386 pp.
8. Brooks, F. T., and M. A. Bailey. 1919. Silver leaf disease. III. J. Agr. Sci. 9:189.
9. Brooks, F. T., and G. H. Brenchley. 1929. Injection experiments on plum trees in relation to *Stereum purpureum* and silver leaf disease. New Phytol. 28:218.
10. _____ 1931a. Silver leaf disease. VI. J. Pomol. 9:1-15.
11. _____ 1931b. Further injection experiments in relation to *Stereum purpureum.* New Phytol. 30:128. (Abstr.)
12. Brooks, F. T., and W. C. Moore. 1926. Silver leaf disease. V. J. Pomol. 5:11-97.
13. Brooks, F. T., and H. H. Storey. 1923. Silver leaf disease. IV. J. Pom. and Hort. Sci. 3:1.
14. Chaney, D. H., W. J. Moller, and S. M. Gotan. 1973. Silver leaf of peach in California. Plant Dis. Rep. 57:192.
15. Cunningham, G. H. 1923. Silver blight, *Stereum purpureum,* its appearance, cause and preventative treatment. New Zealand J. Agr. 24:276-83.
16. Dubos, B., and J. L. Richard. 1974. Curative treatment of peach trees against silver leaf disease *(Stereum purpureum)* with *Trichoderma viride* preparations. Plant Dis. Rep. 58:147-50.
17. Dye, M. H. 1974. Basidiocarp development and spore release by *Stereum purpureum* in the field. New Zealand J. Agric. Res. 17:151-61.
18. Grosclaude, C. 1971. Silver leaf disease of fruit trees. VIII. Contribution to the study of varietal resistance in plum. Ann. Phytopathol. 3(3):283-98.
19. Grosclaude, C., B. Dubos and J. L. Ricard. 1974. Antagonism between ungerminated spores of *Trichoderma viride* and *Stereum purpureum.* Plant Dis. Rep. 58:71-74.
20. Grosclaude, C., J. Ricard, and B. Dubos. 1973. Inoculation of *Trichoderma viride* spores via pruning shears for biological control of *Stereum purpureum* on plum tree wounds. Plant Dis. Rep. 57:25-28.
21. Grosjean, J. 1952. Natuurlijk herstel van loodglansziekte. Tijdschrift over Plantenziekten 58:109-20.
22. _____ 1951. Investigations on the possibility of silver leaf disease control by the borehole method. Tijdschr. Plziekt. 57:103-08. (English summ.)
23. Heimann, M. 1962. *At* 34th German Plant Protection Conference of the Biol. Bundesanst. (g) Spread of silver leaf by nursery material Review of Appl. Myc. 43:454, 1964.

24. Hord, H. H. V., and R. Sprague. 1950. Silver leaf disease of apple in Washington. Washington Agr. Exp. Sta. Cir. 119. 5 pp.

25. Naef-Roth, S., H. Kern, and A. Toth. 1963. On the pathogenesis of parasitogenic and physiological silver leaf of stone fruit. Phytopath. Z. 48:232-39. (Eng. summary).

26. Overholtz, L. O. 1939. The genus *Stereum* in Pennsylvania. Bul. Torrey Bot. Club 66:515-37.

28. Percival, J. 1902. Silver leaf disease. J. Linn. Soc. Bot. 35:390-95.

27. Pratella, G., and A. Kovaca. 1960. Systemic activity of 8-oxyquinoline sulphate in young peach plants. Ann. Sper. Agr. 14:171-83. (Eng. summary).

29. Prillieux, E. 1885. Le plomb des arbes fruitiers. Bul. des. Seances de la Soc. Nat. d'Agr. de France.

30. Setliff, E. C., and E. K. Wade. 1973. *Stereum purpureum* associated with sudden decline and death of apple trees in Wisconsin. Plant Dis. Rep. 57:473-74.

31. Williams, H. E., and H. R. Cameron. 1956. Silver leaf of Montmorency sour cherry in Oregon. Plant Dis. Rep. 40:954-56.

Verticillium Wilt of Stone Fruit and Nut Trees
Verticillium dahliae Kleb.

This disease, popularly known as "black heart" in trees of certain cultivated fruits, has also been called "verticilliosis," "Verticillium hadromycosis," and "vascular wilt." It occurs in many parts of the world and causes much economic loss. According to Rudolph (22) the disease was observed in California as early as the first decade of the present century. There it was noticed that in orchards of young apricot, peach, plum and almond where tomatoes had been interplanted a disease known as "black heart" frequently developed. The condition was first considered to be associated with heavy irrigation of the tomatoes, which led to souring of soil caused by rotting of tomatoes left on the ground after harvest. However, in 1916 Czarnecki first presented proof of the fungus origin of the disease and in 1923 she stated (5) that it was caused by a fungus belonging to the genus *Verticillium*. According to Rudolph (22), as early as 1879 Reinke and Berthold (20) noted that a disease of Irish potato in Germany was caused by a fungus which they named *Verticillium albo-atrum*. The association of *Verticillium* with diseases of many species of plants was later established. In 1957, Englehard (7) published a host index of plants affected by *Verticillium albo-atrum* (including *V. dahliae*). Besides the plants named above, the cultivated tree fruits affected are sweet and sour cherry (*Prunus avium* and *P. cerasus*), pear (*Pyrus com-*

munis), apple (*Malus pumuli*), Japanese persimmon (*Diospyros kaki*), Persian walnut (*Juglans regia*), and olive (*Olea europea*). In addition stone fruits used as rootstocks such as myrobalan plum, mahaleb cherry, *Prunus mume*, and *P. davidiana* are susceptible. The disease also occurs on brambles (especially raspberry), melons, cotton and many other cultivated plants (4, 6, 8, 15, 19, 25).

Symptoms. The following symptoms are largely those developing on apricot and almond (fig. 48A). The initial external evidence is a sudden wilting of the foliage on one or more branches in summer. Leaves turn a dull gray, wither, and infrequently fall from the tree. Sometimes the lower leaves wither and fall first and a progressive development of leaf symptoms up the branch follows.

On affected sweet cherry, the first symptom may be a withering of leaves of one or more spurs of the leaders on 1-year-old wood. The trees become unthrifty, the remaining leaves are off-color and small, and the fruit is abnormally small (14).

Although very young apricot and almond trees may be killed outright by the fungus, older trees are not —in fact, the defoliated twigs and branches show no other external symptoms. In the cool California coastal areas some of the youngest twigs die, but the older wood remains normal-looking throughout summer and the following year again puts out foliage. However, terminal growth is subnormal; these branches may again be attacked by the fungus and defoliated, thereby severely stunting their growth. Thus the primary effect of the disease on trees several years old is generally poor growth and low productivity.

When the bark of affected branches is removed, the underlying sapwood is found to be brown to black in color (fig. 48B). This symptom has led to the name "black heart" for the disease in apricot and almond. In olive, however, the wood of affected branches is rarely off-color, although symptoms with respect to withering of foliage are the same as in apricot and almond.

In winter, following an attack by the fungus, the dead younger twigs become covered by masses of black micro-sclerotia of the causal fungus. These bodies are also present in the lumina of the vessels as is the mycelia.

The causal organism. As noted earlier, Reinke and Berthold (20) in 1879 described a disease in Irish potato caused by a fungus which they named *Verti-*

cillium albo-atrum. In 1913, Klebahn (10) isolated a fungus from a diseased dahlia and named it *Verticillium dahliae.* The difference between *V. albo-atrum* and *V. dahliae* was said to be that the latter species produces microsclerotia whereas the former does not. According to Rudolph, whether or not the fungus described by Reinke and Berthold produced microsclerotia depends upon interpretation of the description and drawings of those authors. Rudolph (22) gave an extensive review of the literature up to 1930 pertaining to the two species. He cited the work of Bewley (3) who isolated six strains of a fungus he regarded as *V. albo-atrum* from plants suffering from hadromycosis. Some of the strains produced no microsclerotia; others produced microsclerotia in abundance. Rudolph concluded that the fungus isolated by Klebhan from dahlia was *V. albo-atrum,* and went on to say that morphological, physiological and genetic studies and cross inoculation tests of different forms of *Verticillium* were needed.

Although many workers have accepted *Verticillium albo-atrum* Reinke & Berth. as the name for the pathogen which produces hadromycosis in perennial as well as annual hosts (18, 19), others have maintained that *Verticillium dahliae* Kleb. is the correct name (21). The difference of opinion hinges on the question of whether or not Reinke and Berthold observed true microsclerotia—although these workers claimed that microsclerotia of the organism gave rise to the hyaline mycelium when placed in moist environment, certain other workers believe that their drawings do not represent true microsclerotia. Rather, they believe that the structures Reinke and Berthold (20) illustrated were composed of dark-celled torulose resting mycelia. Schnathorst (23) reviews this question in the light of recent studies by himself and others.

The question regarding the identity of the fungus clearly cannot be answered at this time. For one thing, the conditions under which the fungus is grown may affect its production or lack of production of microsclerotia. Wilhelm (26) found that at temperatures of 10 to 20 °C the fungus produced numerous microsclerotia, whereas at 25 to 31 °C it produced a creamy white growth and only sparse microsclerotia. He concluded that differences in temperature at which various studies are made could lead to the morphological differences on the basis of which Klebahn separated *V. dahliae* and *V. albo-atrum.* Studies such as those of Berkeley, Maden, and Willison (2), Hall (9), and Reiss (21) appear to show certain fundamental distinctions between isolates purported to be *V. dahliae* and *V. albo-atrum.*

For example, Berkeley and his coworkers claimed that the latter is much more pathogenic to tomato, potato, and cucumber than the former. Hall found that the two "species" were clearly distinguishable by the patterns of their buffer-soluble proteins. Ludbrook (12) found that *V. albo-atrum* grew at the same rate as *V. dahliae* at 22 °C but only about one-fourth as fast at 28 °C.

Verticillium dahliae, the name now used for this fungus, produces in culture a hyaline mycelium. Conidia are one-celled and borne in verticilliately (whorled) branched conidiophores. Branches of the conidiophores are shaped like very slender Indian clubs or ten pins attached to whorls in a central stalk. Microsclerotia are produced in varying amounts depending on growth conditions.

Disease development. The fungus lives from one year to the next in the soil. Wilhelm (27) found that it occurred to a depth of 30 to 36 inches, with the greatest concentration in the upper 6 to 12 inches. No relation was found between soil type, climatic environment, or past crop history and vertical distribution of the fungus. In *Verticillium*-infested plant debris such as that of potato and tomato the fungus can survive for at least a year and perhaps longer. It has been found to persist in soil (probably as microsclerotia) for an equal length of time depending on conditions (14). Nadakavikaren and Horner (16) found that microsclerotia "survived poorly" in soils with temperature above 25 °C and that in soils which were flooded, the microsclerotia population was reduced rapidly. Survival was highest at 5 to 15 °C and 50 to 75 percent moisture-holding capacity. At favorable soil moisture the microsclerotia could survive up to several months even though soil temperature rose to 30 °C.

The fungus can be disseminated in various ways—for example, it can be carried to uninfested areas in diseased plants. The role of tomato in introducing the fungus into apricot orchards was noted by Rudolph (22) in California as early as 1931, and this has been found to occur in other states according to Parker (17). Development of *Verticillium* hadromycosis in olives following their planting in soils in which cotton has grown has been experienced in the San Joaquin Valley of California. Wilhelm (27) and others have suggested that microsclerotia and *Verticillium*-infested plant debris may be blown about by wind, thereby infesting new areas.

Parker (17) reviewed the spread of the fungus both in infected buds used in propagation of perennials and on knives used in propagation. The fungus was reported to be spread from diseased to healthy maple trees by pruning.

McKeen (14) found that the fungus from such diverse plants as barberry, peach, rose, potato, muskmelon, and chrysanthemum differed only slightly in morphology and pathogenicity. Under greenhouse conditions at optimum soil moisture conditions, the disease was severe at 21 to 27 °C with a sharp peak at 24 °C. This coincided with the optimum temperature for growth of the fungus in culture.

McKeen found the fungus to persist and remain aggressive in sandy and clay soils and in soils that were cropped or remained fallow. Growth of an immune crop had no apparent effect on survival of the fungus. Low soil-moisture conditions did, however, reduce the aggressiveness of the fungus. According to Parker (17) others also have found that infection is less in dry than in moist soils.

Wilhelm (28) reported that Verticillium wilt of various crops occurred in California soils which ranged in pH from 4.6 to 6.7. He quoted the studies of Van der Meer in Holland, who also found the disease to attack plants growing in soils with a pH of 4.4 to 6.6.

The disease develops quite characteristically in fruit trees. That is, symptoms appear early in the growing season but seldom appear first in late summer although they intensify during that time; this coincides with the development of the fungus in olive. In early summer the fungus can be readily isolated from the diseased tissue, whereas in late summer and autumn it appears to be nonviable in those parts (31). If new infection through the roots does not occur the trees recover and grow normally the next year. Somewhat the same course of disease development occurs in apricot and almond (22).

Control. The most effective means for preventing fruit tree hosts from infection by *Verticillium dahliae* is to avoid interplanting such susceptible crops as tomatoes, cotton, and potatoes in the orchard. If such crops have been grown in soil in which fruit trees are to be planted, it is advisable to delay planting trees for several years, allowing the soil to lie fallow and cultivating it to prevent growth of susceptible weed hosts. Parker (17), reviewing the work of others, reported that soil-inhabiting fungi belong to the general *Gliocladium* and *Blastomyces,* and that *Bacillus vulgatus* are antagonistic to *V. dahliae.* Allowing the soil to remain fallow would give such microorganisms a chance to reduce the inoculum of *V. dahliae.*

Only trees known to be free of infection by *V. dahliae* should be planted. Very young fruit trees are those generally developing the most severe cases of hadromycosis. Proper fertilization and irrigation of the orchard better enables trees to recover from attack of the fungus. According to Parker (17) there is some evidence that fertilization with nitrogen and potassium reduces the disease in susceptible plants. Yearly applications of sulfur are said to decrease, and lime applications to increase, *Verticillium* wilt of eggplant (8).

There is little that can be done in the way of selecting resistant fruit varieties. Not only are most edible cultivars of stone fruit susceptible, but the root-stock used in propagating these varieties is susceptible to infection thereby allowing the fungus to gain entrance to the wood of edible cultivars.

There is some evidence that sod culture may reduce the severity of *Verticillium* hadromycosis in olive (1), but whether the effect of the sod is on *Verticillium* or on the olive tree is not clear.

Examples of attempts to find chemicals that can be used to control the disease are those of LeTourneau, McLean, and Guthrie (11) who tested phenols and quinones in culture, and Waggoner (25) who applied growth regulators, such as 2,4-D to potato plants.

Wilhelm (29) found that large amounts of blood meal, fish meal, cotton seed meal and ammonium sulfate applied to the soil substantially reduced the inoculum potential of the fungus, as did Fermate and Dithane Z78. Wilhelm and Ferguson (30) found that chloropicrin applied at the rate 2 to 2.5 ml per square foot and at a depth of 12 inches to soil was effective in destroying *V. dahliae* inoculum. Chloropicrin diffused in all directions, whereas allyl bromide and 55 percent chlorobromopropene though effective diffused laterally and downward but not upward.

References

1. Ashworth, L. J., and S. Wilhelm. 1971. Verticillium wilt of olive: sod culture offers a promise of control. California Olive Industry News 25.
2. Berkeley, G. H., G. O. Maden, and R. S. Willison. 1931. Verticillium wilt in Ontario. Sci. Agr. 11:739-59.
3. Bewley, W. F. 1922. "Sleepy disease" or wilt of the tomato. Ann. Appl. Biol. 9:116-34.
4. Carter, J. C. 1938. Verticillium wilt of woody plants in Illinois. Plant Disease Rep. 22:253-54.

5. Czarnecki, H. 1923. Studies on the so-called black heart disease of apricot. Phytopathology 13:216-24.

6. Dufrenoy, J., and M. L. Dufrenoy. 1927. Hadromycosis. Ann. Epiphyt. 13:195-212.

7. Englehard, A. W. 1957. Host index of *Verticillium albo-atrum* Reinke & Berth. (including *Verticillium dahliae* Kleb.) Plant Dis. Rep. Supplement No. 244:23-49.

8. Haenseler, C. M. 1928. Effect of soil reaction on Verticillium wilt of eggplant. New Jersey Agr. Exp. Sta. Ann. Rept. 41:267-73.

9. Hall, R. 1969. *Verticillium albo-atrum* and *V. dahliae* distinguished by acrylamide gel-electrophoresis of protein. Canadian J. Bot. 47:2110-111.

10. Klebahn, H. 1913. Beitrage zur Kenntnis der fungi imperfecti. I. Eine *Verticillium*-krankheit auf Dahlien. Mycol. Centralbl. 3(2):49-66.

11. Le Tourneau, D., J. G. McLean and J. Guthrie. 1957. The effect of phenols and quinones on the growth in vitro of *Verticillium albo-atrum*. Phytopathology 47:602-06.

12. Ludbrook, M. V. 1933. Pathogenicity and environal studies on Verticillium hadromycosis. Phytopathology 23:117-54.

13. McIntosh, D. L. 1954. Verticillium wilt of sweet cherry in British Columbia. Plant Disease Rep. 38:74-75.

14. McKeen, C. D. 1943. A study of some factors affecting the pathogenicity of *Verticillium albo-atrum*. R & B Canadian J. Research Sec. C 21: 95-117.

15. Mills, W. D. 1932. Occurrence of Verticillium wilt of peach in New York. Plant Disease Rep. 16:132-33.

16. Nadakavikaren, M. J., and C. E. Horner. 1961. Influence of soil moisture and temperature on survival of *Verticillium* microsclerotia. Phytopathology 51:66. (Abstr.)

17. Parker, K. G. 1959. Verticillium hadromycosis of deciduous tree fruits. Plant Disease Rep. Supplement 255:39-61.

18. Presley, J. T. 1941. Saltants from a monosporic culture of *Verticillium albo-atrum*. Phytopathology 31:1135-39.

19. ————— 1950. Verticillium wilt of cotton with particular emphasis on variation of the causal organism. Phytopathology 40:497-511.

20. Reinke, J., and G. Berthold. 1879. Die Zersetzung der Kartoffel durch Pilze. Untersuch. Bot. Lab. Univ. Gottingen. 1:1-100.

21. Reiss, J. 1969. Beitrag zum Problem der systematischen Abgrenzung von *Verticillium albo-atrum* Rke. et Berth. und *Verticillium dahliae* Kleb. Z. Pflanzenkrank. Pflanzenpathologie. Pflanzenschutz 8:480-84.

22. Rudolph, B. A. 1931. Verticillium hadromycosis. Hilgardia 5:197-353.

23. Schnathorst, W. C. 1965. Origins of new growth in dormant microsclerotial masses of *Verticillium albo-atrum*. Mycologia 57:343-51.

24. Taylor, J. B., and N. J. Flentje. 1968. Infection, recovery from infection and resistance of apricot trees to *Verticillium albo-atrum*. New Zealand J. Bot. 6:417-26.

25. Waggoner, P. E. 1956. Chemotherapy of Verticillium wilt of potatoes in Connecticut. 1955 American Potato J. 33:223-25.

26. Wilhelm, S. 1948. The effect of temperature on the taxonomic characters of *Verticillium albo-atrum* Reinke & Berthe. Phytopathology 38: 919. (Abstr.)

27. ————— 1950. Vertical distribution of *Verticillium albo-atrum* in soils. Phytopathology 40: 368-76.

28. ————— 1950. Verticillium wilt in acid soils. Phytopathology 40:776-777.

29. ————— 1951. Effect of various soil amendments on the inoculum potential of the Verticillium wilt fungus. Phytopathology 41:684-90.

30. Wilhelm, S., and J. Ferguson. 1953. Soil fumigation against *Verticillium albo-atrum*. Phytopathology 43:593-96.

31. Wilhelm, S., and J. B. Taylor. 1965. Control of Verticillium wilt of olive through natural recovery and resistance. Phytopathology 55:310-16.

IV. ENGLISH WALNUT AND ITS DISEASES

THE ENGLISH WALNUT

The English walnut (*Juglans regia* L.) also known as the Persian walnut, apparently originated in the Caucasus and Turkestan areas of Persia. In ancient times trees of the species were taken to Greece and later to Rome where the tree became known as "Jovis Glans" from which the genus name *Juglans* is derived. In relatively early times trees of *J. regia* were taken to England and then to America, where it was called the English walnut to distinguish it from the American native species.

The native American species are called black walnut because of the color of the hard, thick shell. The American black walnut, *J. nigra,* is native to the eastern and midwestern U.S., while the species found in California are *J. hindsii* (northern California black walnut) and *J. californica* (southern California black walnut). Two other species of black walnut, *J. rupestris* and *J. major,* are native to the U.S. and are found in Arizona, New Mexico, and Texas.

Although trees of *J. regia* were grown in the eastern U.S., commercial cultivation has become almost exclusively confined to the West Coast, largely in California and Oregon. The California English walnut industry owes its origin to the efforts of Joseph Sexton, of Santa Barbara, who propagated the Santa Barbara soft shell type of nut from seeds brought from Chile, and to Felix Gellet of Nevada City, who introduced varieties from France (Franquette, etc.). One of the earliest orchards in California was the Kellog orchard near Napa which was planted in 1846 (if trees are planted in good soil and well cared for they may be in production for 200 years). In 1974, California cultivated over 99 percent of the walnuts in the western U.S. with 211,242 acres which produced about one-third of the world's supply of walnuts. Other producing countries are France, Italy, Rumania, China, Turkey, Yugoslavia, Bulgaria, and Hungary. California's center of walnut acreage has moved from southern California to the San Joaquin Valley and Sacramento Valley. Tulare, Stanislaus, and San Joaquin counties cultivate about 40 percent and Sutter, Tehama, and Butte Counties about 19 percent of the crop. Largest acres are in Hartley variety (58,586) followed by Payne (36,130), Franquette (35,791), Eureka (20,664) and Ashley (15,065). Other varieties planted to 1,000 acreas or more are Mayette, Nugget, Blackmer, Poe, Waterloo, and Concord.

Propagation of trees is through budding a patch of bark with a leaf-bud on the trunk of a young seedling tree suitable for a rootstock. Although seedlings of the English walnut were formerly used, these were abandoned in favor of seedlings of *J. hindsii,* the northern California black walnut, partly because the regia seedlings are highly susceptible to Armillaria root rot and did not do well on marginal soil types. The southern California black walnut tends to sucker profusely at the base of the trunk. In recent years Paradox hybrid (*J. regia* × *J. hindsii*) seedlings have been used to some extent as a rootstock because of their rapid growth. One objection is the high degree of variability in growth among its seedlings.

The pistillate and pollen-bearing flowers of walnut are produced in different locations on the same plant. The former arise from terminal buds on the ends of shoots produced the current year, the latter arise as long, pendulous catkins from naked buds in the axils of leaves of shoots produced the previous year. Catkins develop in the spring (April-May) shortly before the pistillate flowers emerge, and pollen from the former is transferred by wind to the stigma of the latter. As shall be discussed at more length later, these features must be taken into consideration in controlling walnut blight. Mature nuts are mechanically shaken and gathered during September and October.

References

1. Batchelor, L. D. 1921. Walnut culture in California. California Agric. Exp. Sta. Bul. 332: 142-217 (out of print).
2. Lelong, B. M. 1896. California walnut industry. Dept. State Board of Horticulture for 1895-96. Sacramento. 44 pp.
3. Lewis, C. I. 1906. The walnut in Oregon. Oregon Agric. Exp. Sta. Bul. 92:1-43.
4. Smith, R. E., C. O. Smith, and H. J. Ramsey. 1912. Walnut culture in California. Walnut blight. Calif. Agr. Exp. Sta. Bul. 231:119-398 (out of print).
5. Wood, M. N. 1934. Pollination and blooming habits of the Persian walnut in California. U.S.D.A. Tech. Bul. 387:1-56.

BACTERIAL DISEASES OF ENGLISH WALNUT

Bark Canker of the English Walnut
Erwinia nigrifluens Wilson, Starr & Berger

Bark canker (shallow bark canker) was discovered in the Sacramento Valley in 1955. Few cases of the disease have been found in other areas of the state and none has been reported from other parts of the world. Judging from the extensive nature of the cankers, one might expect the disease capable of seriously damaging the tree. Although the trunks of some trees are completely encircled by the cankers, few trees show evidence of injury, apparently because the bark is not killed to the cambium, except in a few places (1).

Symptoms. Irregular dark-brown necrotic areas develop in the bark of the trunk and scaffold branches (fig. 49). These originate as small more or less circular spots in the cortical tissue just beneath the corky outer layer of bark (fig. 49) (periderm). Extensive cankers are formed by the enlargement and coalescence of these spots. The outline of the canker is not visible from the surface, but its presence can be detected by a dark-colored watery exudate which stains the affected trunk or limb. In general the canker is relatively shallow, extending only about one-fourth to one-third the depth of the bark. Occasionally, a break occurs in the bark underlying the infected area, and the bark adjacent to the break becomes involved to a greater depth.

Some features of bark canker resemble Melaxuma *(Dothiorella gregaria)* on large branches. For example,

both diseases are characterized by limb cankers which exude a dark watery material. With Melaxuma, the cankers occur most commonly at the crotches between the trunk and scaffold branches, while bark canker occurs most commonly on the trunk in no particular relation to crotches. Moreover Melaxuma involves the bark down to the wood and causes underlying wood to be discolored; this seldom happens in bark canker. Upon examination, however, the points of similarity are more easily perceived than are the points of difference. Consequently, bark canker undoubtedly has been often mistaken for Melaxuma in the past.

Susceptibility of walnut species and cultivars. Bark canker has been found on trees of the following cultivars of English walnut: Hartley, Mayette, Payne, Mammoth, Meylan, and Myrtleford. In one orchard the disease was found on the trunk of a Paradox hybrid (Persian × Northern California black walnut). Northern California black walnut *(Juglans hindsii)* apparently is resistant if not immune to the disease. Franquette trees growing near diseased trees of other cultivars are seldom affected. Inoculation tests indicate, however, that certain clones of this cultivar are more susceptible than others.

The causal organism. The pathogen is a bacterium belonging to the genus *Erwinia*. It resembles *E. amylovora* in some features but differs in certain important characteristics and has therefore been given the designation *Erwinia nigrifluens* sp. nov. *Erwinia nigrifluens* is a peritrichous, gram-negative, rod-shaped organism ranging in size from 0.8 to 1.3 μm wide by 1.6 to 3.5 μm long. The rods are slightly pointed at the ends and sometimes somewhat curved. There are at least five flagella and these are two to three times the length of the cell. No endospores or capsules are formed. The bacterium grows and produces acid, but no gas, in media containing the following carbon sources: glucose, fructose, galactose, mannose, ribose, xylose, arabinose, rhammose, sucrose, cellobiose, and raffinose. It does not utilize ammonium chloride as the sole nitrogen source, but can use amino acids as the sole source of both carbon and nitrogen. Optimum temperature for growth of the bacterium in culture is about 28 °C. It grows very slowly below 20 °C and slowly or not at all at 37 °C and above.

Disease development. The bacterium survives from one year to the next in the bark canker and escapes from the cankers in the dark-colored watery exudate. The manner in which the bacteria are disseminated has not been determined, nor has the most common mode of entry into the host been established. In one orchard, the holes produced in the bark by sapsuckers were found to be affected. In other orchards, how-

153

ever, such injuries were not avenues of entry. The cankers spread rapidly in summer and are essentially quiesent during the fall and winter. Serological and bacteriophage studies are reviewed in the section on phloem canker (2, 3).

Control. Methods for preventing infection have not yet been devised. However, the following method is effective in preventing extension of established cankers. In spring, the corky outer bark overlying the diseased area is shaved off with a carpenter's draw-knife. A few weeks after this treatment the necrotic bark will have dried out, and this causes the bacteria to die—their margins are usually well-defined so one can easily determine the limit of the cankers and thus avoid removing no more of the periderm than that which overlies diseased bark (1).

References

1. Wilson, E. E., M. P. Starr, and Joyce A. Berger. 1957. Bark canker a bacterial disease of the Persian walnut tree. Phytopathology 47: 669-73.
2. Zeitoun, F. M. and E. E. Wilson. 1966. Serological comparison of *Erwinia nigrifluens* with certain other *Erwinia* species. Phytopathology 56:1381-85.
3. _____ 1969. The relation of bacteriophage to the walnut-tree pathogens *Erwinia nigrifluens* and *Erwinia rubrifaciens*. Phytopathology 59: 756-61.

Blight of English Walnut
Xanthomonas juglandis (Pierce) Dowson

The disease known as "walnut bacteriosis," "walnut blight," "black spot," and "black plague" affects English (Persian) walnut, *Juglans regia* but rarely occurs on English walnut hybrids (paradox seedlings). The black walnut species (*Juglans nigra, J. californica* and *J. hindsii*) have been infected artificially but are seldom affected in nature.

Although first observed in southern California in 1891, the first published reference to the disease was in 1893 (8). Oregon was the second state to report it (9). Thereafter it was reported in chronological order as follows: New Zealand (1900), Russia (1904), Canada (1911), Tasmania (1912), Australia (1914), Mexico (1915), Chile (1917), South Africa (1918), Italy (1923), Holland (1923), Switzerland (1924), England (1927), France (1931), Rumania (1940), and the West Indies (1943). In California, Pierce (16) was the first to direct attention to walnut blight in Los Angeles County and in 1896 was credited as being the first to prove that the incitant is a bacterium. By 1903 the disease became so destructive

that the California Walnut Growers Association offered a reward of $20,000 to anyone who could find a practical method of control, but no successful claimant for the prize appeared (25). During the same year, which was soon after the establishment of the first Division of Plant Pathology at the University of California, Berkeley, the Association voted funds to the University to investigate the disease. In 1905, the California State Legislature appropriated $4,000. Later plant pathologists at the Plant Disease Laboratory at Whittier provided new insights on the disease (22, 23) but had little success in finding a satisfactory method of control. In 1912, C.O. Smith estimated that for the previous 10 years the average annual loss from the disease was 50 percent of the crop. In the Pacific Northwest losses ranging from 40 percent to 60 percent are not uncommon according to Miller (11). It was not until 1928 that progress was made in the development of a satisfactory control program (17). In Oregon, the 1933 loss estimate was 35 percent and in 1950 only 4 percent, and this is probably related to effective spraying.

Symptoms. The bacteria are known to attack the catkins, fruit, green shoots, leaves and buds (7, 11, 13, 16, 17, 22) (fig. 50A, 50B).

Catkins, although not as susceptible as the fruit, become infected as soon as they break dormancy and symptoms are commonly expressed after they are elongated. A single floret or all the florets on one side or at the top or bottom of the catkin may show symptoms. Infected florets first appear water-soaked and wilted and later turn black. Similarly, the rachis may be attacked at any point along its length. Distortions and deformities in catkins results from killing of local areas.

Fruit infection accounts for the major part of the economic loss (fig. 50C). Fruit may become infected at any time after its formation until harvest, and this long period of susceptibility is one of the chief obstacles to control of the disease. The first symptom of the disease usually appears in the bracts, bracteoles, or involucres at the apical end. A tiny black spot develops on the blossom end of the fruit (13). The spot enlarges rapidly and may then involve the entire young fruit. After the stigma shrivels, new infection at the blossom-end usually ceases and lateral or side infections are found. Lesions produced on partly grown nuts enlarge rapidly, and the somewhat shrunken and depressed areas rupture and exude a black shiny liquid (white specks when dry) containing large numbers of bacteria. During rains this spatters onto healthy nuts and shoots. Nuts infected before, during, or immediately after pollination period (nuts 1/8 to 1/2 inch in diameter) almost invariably are shed from the tree. Nuts attacked before the shell hardens tend to remain on the tree. The kernel at this time may be destroyed or blackened and shriveled. These nuts are referred to as "blanks" or (sometimes) "blows." The shell finally attains a toughness impenetrable to the bacteria but a substance formed in the lesion can cause discoloration or even a partial shriveling of the kernel, and the shell may be badly stained, with the nut becoming a cull. Even after the shell becomes impenetrable to the bacteria, or to by-products of the lesion, the shell can still be stained.

The mere blackening or shriveling of the kernel is not always attributable to walnut blight disease. Drought may cause shriveling, and sunburn may do likewise. Sunburned husks are dry and leathery while diseased husks are soft and water-soaked. Also sunburned husks show symptoms only on exposed sides of the fruit.

Infection of green shoots is possible only for a comparatively short time after their appearance. Infection is more common at or near the extreme tip of the shoot, and the entire end may then be killed back for a few inches. More often the infection is localized and the shoot grows away from the lesion. If the localized lesions are deep-seated, the bacteria have a better chance for survival in winter. The dying tissue sometimes exudes a mixture of decomposed cellular products and bacterial slime. When dry, it is a frosty, whitish, flaky precipitate.

All parts of the leaf may be attacked, including the parenchyma tissue of the leaflet, the midrib, lateral veins, veinlets, rachis, and petiole. Typical disease spots are dark brown in color with yellowish-green margins; they are usually only a few millimeters in diameter but several young ones may coalesce to form a single large one. Severe infections of tender young leaflets result in considerable killing of tissue, which causes malformation of leaflets as they develop. Defoliation is rare, although killing of the rachis or petiole can lead to death of the leaflet or leaf.

The causal organism. The pathogen is now classified as *Xanthomonas juglandis* (Pierce) Dowson. Earlier the genus ranged from *Pseudomonas, Bacillus, Phytomonas,* to *Bacterium.* The bacterium is a rod (0.5 to 0.7 × 1.1 to 3.8 μm) gram negative, capsulated and occurs singly or in pairs and with no endospores. The organism is motile by means of a long, single polar flagellum (13). Acid, but no gas, is formed from the common diagnostic sugars, mannitol, glycerol, and starch (6, 8). The colony is pale-yellow on nutrient dextrose agar. Temperature growth optimum is 28 °C, the minimum about 1 °C and maximum 35 to 37 °C. The thermal death point is approximately 53 °C (13). The optimum pH for growth is 6.4 to 7.2. Enzymes produced by the bacteria in culture are diastase, rennin, proteolase and pectinase but not cellulase (6, 13). The pathogen retained its virulence in culture at room temperature for over 3 years without repassage through the host (13).

Disease development. The pathogen survives from one year to the next in twig lesions, affected buds (13), and nuts which remain hanging in the tree. Between fall and spring Smith (22) was able to isolate it from the diseased epidermis, wood and pith of shoots, and from infected nuts hanging in the tree. Pollen from diseased catkins was also shown to carry the bacteria. In isolations from August through February, Ark (2) found that 15 percent of the healthy catkins and 10 to 26 percent of the blighted leaf buds contained living bacteria. During rainy seasons bacteria exude to the surface and are washed about the tree, and the first infection usually occurs on the young leaflets and catkins. Once the catkins are infected the pollen grains become filled with bacteria, thereby allowing the bacteria to spread about in wind-blown pollen. When contaminated pollen falls upon the stigmatic surfaces of the pistillate flower, the bacteria invaded those parts. Miller (13) believed that, since distribution of infected nuts in the tree is not uniform, the severity of infection is related to moisture not to time of pollen shedding, and infection is highly improbable. The point generally agreed upon is that the first symptoms appear on the fruit at the blossom end.

When bacteria exude to the surface of twig lesions they may remain viable for 72 hours if they remain in shade, but if desiccated and exposed to direct sunlight they die within an hour. Smith (22) recovered the pathogen in sterilized inoculated soil after 18 days at 20 °C but only after 6 to 9 days in unsterilized soil. Rudolph (19) believed that erinose mites carry the bacteria from one place to another (this is a small anthropod that produces galls on leaves of the black walnut). Flies, aphids and other insects that feed upon the bacterial exudate probably pick up the bacteria on their feet and transfer them to susceptible parts of the tree (24). Although certain insects probably do carry the bacteria, they have not yet been shown to play an important part in disease dissemination.

Stomata are probably the principal infection courts on leaves and fruit (13). Insect punctures and mechanical injuries have also been suspected as infection courts but not proved as such. Fruit and leaf infections can occur at any time in early spring. In California the disease is most prevalent in years when rains and fog occur during the early part of the growing season (25). It is particularly severe in coastal areas and portions of the central valley such as San Joaquin County which is exposed to ocean influences.

Free moisture is the most important environmental factor required for initiation and development of disease. This was clearly stated by Pierce in 1896 "... moisture of the atmosphere is favorable to the disease, and dry atmosphere is unfavorable to it." The presence of moisture for only 5 to 15 minutes was followed by infection of stomata in laboratory tests (13). So long as temperature was within a range between 5 to 27°C, bacterial infection of nuts was favored. The time required for lesion development was 4 days at 27°C and 8 days at 15°C. Inoculated leaves developed lesions in 6 days at 21°C and 13 days at 16°C.

Cultivar susceptibility. Cultivars reported most susceptible to infection are Payne, Ashley, Santa Barbara soft shell, Chase, Placentia, and Santa Rosa, while Mayette, Poe, Hartley, and Concord are less susceptible. Eureka, Waterloo, Franquette, San Jose, and Ehrdardt are least affected. The early blooming cultivars are more susceptible because climatic conditions are favorable to infection at that time. As an example, Eureka was once classified as highly resistant to immune in southern California but when exposed to wet weather during bloom it was highly susceptible; in Oregon it is regarded commercially as a failure because of its susceptibility to blight (12, 13). Thus resistance could very well be related to blooming and foliation in dry weather.

Control. Little in the way of fertilization, irrigation, or cultivation can be done to control walnut blight. Removal of affected shoots and fruit would probably help in reducing the disease but such an operation is impractical. Use of late-blooming varieties would be beneficial.

Chemical sprays and dusts are now the most effective controls of blight. Rudolph (17) found that two applications of 16-8-100 Bordeaux mixture was effective. The first, a prebloom spray, has been applied at a time when few or no nuts have appeared and the catkin are out but not shedding pollen. He stated that this spray is "absolutely indispensable." The second spray has been applied when fruit is the size of a pea or small olive. Other investigators later tried copper-lime dust and proprietary copper sprays; still later, sprays containing 50 ppm streptomycin and streptomycin-pyrophyllite dusts were employed (3, 14). If there was a high incidence of disease the previous year, the first spray has been applied during catkin elongation and the

has been applied during catkin elongation and the second spray when the 25 to 75 percent of the pistillate flowers are in bloom. However, if the disease was not severe, only one spray has been applied when 25 to 75 percent of the pistillate flowers are showing. Bordeaux mixture (16-10-100) has been used before the pistillate flowers are showing but sprays during bloom require a weaker mixture of 4-2-100. Fixed copper materials are used in accordance with the manufacturer's direction.

References

1. Anderson, H. W. 1950. Bacterial blight of Persian walnut in Illinois. Plant Dis. Rep. 34:352.
2. Ark, P. A. 1944. Pollen as a source of walnut bacterial blight infection. Phytopathology 34: 330-34.
3. _____ 1955. Use of streptomycin-pyrophyllite dust against pear blight and walnut blight. Plant Dis. Rep. 39:926-28.
4. Ark, P. A., and C. E. Scott. 1950. Walnut blight—symptoms and control. Diamond Walnut News 32: March Issue.
5. Barss, H. P. 1928. Bacterial blight of walnuts. Oregon Ext. Cir. 239:1-15.
6. Burkholder, W. H. 1932. Carbohydrate fermentation by certain closely related species of the genus *Phytomonas*. Phytopathology 22: 699-707.
7. Clayton, C. O. 1921. Some studies relating to infection and resistance to walnut blight. Calif. Dept. Agr. Mo. Bul. 10:367-71.
8. Galloway, B. T. 1894. Walnut disease. USDA Report 1893. P. 272.
9. Lewis, C. I. 1906. The walnut in Oregon. Oregon Agr. Exp. Sta. Bul. 92:1-43.
10. McMurran, S. M. 1917. Walnut blight in the Eastern United States. USDA, Bur. Plant Indus. Bul. 611:1-7.
11. Miller, P. W. 1934. Walnut blight and its control in the Pacific Northwest. USDA Cir. 331:13.
12. Miller, P. W. *et al.* 1940. The pathogen of filbert bacteriosis compared with *Phytomonas juglandis,* the cause of walnut blight. Phytopathology 30:713-33.
13. Miller, P. W., and W. B. Bollen. 1946. Walnut bacteriosis and its control. Ore. Agr. Exp. Sta. Tech. Bul. 9:1-107.
14. Miller, P. W. 1959. A preliminary report on the comparative efficacy of copper-lime and agrimycin dust mixtures for the control of walnut blight in Oregon. Plant Dis. Rep. 43:401-02.
15. Miller, P. W. and B. G. Thompson. 1935. Walnut and filbert blight and insect pests and their control. Ore. Agr. Exp. Sta. Ext. Bul. 476:1-16.

16. Pierce, N. B. 1901. Walnut bacteriosis. Bot. Gaz. 31:272-73.

17. Rudolph, B. A. 1933. Bacteriosis (blight) of the English walnut in California and its control. Calif. Agr. Exp. Sta. Bul. 564:3-88.

18. _____ 1940. A blight control spray. Red cuprous oxide. Diamond Walnut News. Vol. 22. March Issue.

19. _____ 1943. The walnut erinose mite a carrier of walnut blight. Diamond Walnut News. Vol. 25. November Issue.

20. _____ 1946. Attempts to control bacterial blights of pear and walnut with Penicillium. Phytopathology 36:717-25.

21. Scott, C. E. 1948. Does it pay to spray for blight? Diamond Walnut News. Vol. 30. March Issue.

22. Smith, C. O. 1922. Some studies relating to infection and resistance to walnut blight, *Pseudomonas juglandis*. Phytopathology 12:106. (Abstr.)

23. _____ 1931. Pathogenicity of *Bacillus amylovorus* on species of Juglans. Phytopathology 21:219-23.

24. Smith, R. E., J. F. Hunt, and W. H. Nixon. 1913. Spraying walnut trees for blight and aphis control. Calif. Agr. Exp. Sta. Circ. 107:1-8 (out of print).

25. Smith, R. E., C. O. Smith, and H. J. Ramsey. 1912. Walnut culture in California. Walnut blight. Calif. Agr. Exp. Sta. Bul. 231:119-398 (out of print).

26. Wormald, H., and J. B. Hammond. 1931. The distribution of bacterial blight of walnut. Gard. Chron. 3rd Ser. 90(2348):476-77.

Crown Gall of English Walnut
Agrobacterium tumefaciens (Smith & Townsend) Conn.

Susceptibility to crown gall is considered one of the reasons why California black walnut rootstock has replaced both English and Paradox hybrid as rootstocks for commercial cultivars (fig. 51).

A control measure recently introduced is a hydrocarbon containing 2,4 xylenol and metacresol treatment of galls for young trees. Under study is a biological control measure using a nonpathogenic *Agrobacterium radiobacter* on seedling trees before planting. If these treatments are effective, in areas with problems of *Phytophthora* crown and root rot (black walnut rootstocks are susceptible), the English or Paradox hybrid could be considered. Again the *Armillaria*-resistance in the black walnut should be considered for the specific orchard planting.

A general discussion of crown gall appears in section III of this publication.

Phloem Canker of English Walnut
Erwinia rubrifaciens Wilson, Zeitoun & Fredrickson

In 1967, a heretofore undescribed disease of English walnut trees was identified (11) in the San Joaquin Valley of central California. Although the symptoms had been noted as early as 1962, they were not recognized as those of a distinct disease because they occurred in trees that were also affected by the bark canker disease caused by *Erwinia nigrifluens* (10). Later, characteristic symptoms of the disease were found in trees free of bark canker, and a bacterial organism, differing in important characteristics from those of *E. nigrifluens* was obtained from the diseased tissue (11, 12, 13). This disease has also been called "deep bark canker" to differentiate it from bark canker.

So far, phloem canker has been an important disease only on Hartley in the San Joaquin and Sacramento valleys. Although Hartley is grown to some extent in northern coastal districts (Santa Clara, Hollister, Napa, and Sonoma valleys) the disease has not been found there. However, Hartley trees with the disease were found in the Ojai Valley 20 miles from the coast in southern California.

The importance of the disease was shown by surveys conducted in the Sacramento Valley on 3,680 trees in 27 orchards over a period of four years. In 1968 only 1.7 percent of the trees showed disease, in 1969 4 percent, in 1970 9 percent and in 1971 11.6 percent which would project an average increase of 3 percent per annum (1). Some orchards in the San Joaquin Valley showed 70 percent of the trees infected (8).

Symptoms. Dark brown to black streaks of varying width extend through the inner bark of the trunk and scaffold branches of affected trees (fig. 52). Because these streaks occur in the region of the phloem, the disease was named "phloem canker" to distinguish it from bark canker, the diseased areas of which occur almost exclusively in the outer bark just below the phelloderm. Individual discolored streaks of phloem canker commonly merge into bands which may extend for several feet up the trunk and into the scaffold branches.

Another characteristic internal symptom is the occurrence of numerous small more or less circular discolored spots in the outer xylem immediately beneath the cankered areas in the bark. These spots are not more than 1 to 2 millimeters in diameter. ter.

A symptom of the disease which is visible on the outside of the branch or trunk is a crack in the bark phelloderm from which exudes a dark reddish brown, often slimy, substance. This material, which is produced abundantly in summer, runs down the surface of the bark and dries, leaving discolored deposits somewhat similar to those on trees affected by bark canker.

Causal organism. The pathogen is a peritrichous, gram-negative, rod-shaped organism 0.37 to 0.6 μm in breadth and 0.92 to 1.52 μm in length. It grows well at temperatures of 24 to 39°C, with an optimum of 30 to 33°C. Its pH optimum is 6.0 to 7.2. It utilizes arabinose, glucose, glycerol, mannose, and sucrose as carbon sources, but apparently not lactose or xylose. On YDC agar (yeast extract dextrose, calcium carbonate, agar) the organism grows profusely and produces a red pigment which diffuses through the medium surrounding the colonies. In other diagnostic cultural tests the organism differs significantly from *E. nigrifluens* and *E. rhapontici,* the latter being the only other known *Erwinia* species to produce a red pigment on the YDC medium. A bacteriophage obtained from exudate from cankers produced by *E. nigrifluens* was found to have lysed that organism but not the phloem canker pathogen. Concentrated suspensions of the phage placed in contact with the phloem canker pathogen did, however, modify the cell wall of the bacterium to such an extent that it became spherical in shape (9). Such a phenomenon is known to occur with other bacteria and has been termed "lysis from without" and "abortive infection."

The phloem canker pathogen differs serologically from other *Erwinia* species, including *E. nigrifluens* (11, 12). In view of the differences in cultural and serological relationships, the phloem canker organism was considered an unidentified species and was named *Erwinia rubrifaciens* n. sp. (red-producing *Erwinia*).

Hosts. *E. rubrifaciens* has been identified only on English walnut *(Juglans regia)*. Among cultural (cultivars) species the Hartley is most commonly affected. While black walnut, *J. hindsii,* is not known to be a host of this organism, cankers originating in the trunk of Hartley sometimes have been found to extend several inches into the tissues of the black walnut rootstock. When interplanted with Hartley the Franquette and Payne are sometimes attacked. The disease has never been recorded in other cultivars, artificial inoculations indicate that Gustine and Howe may exhibit some degree of susceptibility. However, phloem canker, like bark canker, is an important disease only of Hartley.

Hartley originated in the Napa Valley in California and was introduced in 1925. Its parentage is unknown except that in 1909 it was produced from a seedling grown from seeds planted in 1892. The tree comes into leaf after Payne and is a pollinator for Payne, and is one of the most popular commercial cultivars in California.

Disease development. The pathogen survives from year-to-year in infected trees and is released from such trees in large numbers through cracks in the bark. The slimy exudate, which is most abundant in summer and early autumn, runs down the surface of the bark and dries. The bacteria may remain viable in the dried exudate for as long as 123 days (6). Wind-blown rains disseminate the bacteria as far as 20 feet (8).

Under some conditions the pathogen can survive for as much as 3 months during the winter in infested soil. Whether infested soil does or does not constitute an important overwintering site of the bacteria has not been determined (5).

The bacteria gain entrance to the inner bark of infected trees through breaks in the outer bark (phelloderm). Growth cracks, which occur quite frequently in the trunks and scaffold branches of Hartley, as well as pruning cuts and holes made by woodpeckers, are avenues of entry. Another type of injury which may be a site of infection is that made by the harvest shaker (6) whose role in transferring the pathogen from infection to uninfected trees warrants careful investigation.

Disease activity in the form of systemic canker extension and exudation of bacteria from infected areas of the tree is greatest during April through October. This, in turn, corresponds to the relatively high temperature requirement of the bacterium (optimum temperature) 30 to 33°C. Increase in canker length is found to be most rapid during the summer months, the rate of extension corresponding to the increase in average temperature from spring to summer. The trees are not infected in winter (9).

Prevalence of the disease has differed greatly even within the Central Valley, being much more widespread in the southern (San Joaquin Valley) half than in the northern (Sacramento Valley) half (8). One possible factor contributing to this is a difference in the age of Hartley trees in the two sections: they are considerably younger in the north than in the south. Another possible contributing factor is temperature: minimum and maximum air temperatures in summer are higher in the central San Joaquin Valley than at Davis in the southern Sacramento Valley. In comparative tests, cankers from inoculations developed more rapidly in the San Joaquin Valley than at Davis.

The pathogen invades the sieve tubes of the nonfunctional secondary phloem, development of which appears to be characteristic of *Juglans regia* (3, 4). As the nonfunctional secondary phloem elements become involved, the bacteria pass into the laterally-occurring parenchyma cells. Invaded adjacent sieve tubes and parenchyma merge and produce bands of discolored tissue. Because the sieve plate pores are large enough to allow passage of the bacterial cells, vertical invasion of the sieve elements readily occurs. This results in long streaks and bands of diseased tissue extending sometimes for several feet up and down the inner bark outside of the cambial and the functional phloem regions.

In addition to the vertical movement of the pathogen there is a lateral movement inward from the secondary nonfunctional phloem. This occurs along the ray elements and terminates in the outer xylem region. If the bark is pulled away the surface of the outer xylem (wood tissue) is found to be covered by numerous dark-colored more or less circular pits 1 to 2 milimeters in diameter. The inner surface of the bark overlying this area is covered by small protrusions which correspond in locations to the pits in the xylem. The pits are therefore the termini of the infected ray elements. Further invasion of the xylem by the bacteria has not been found to occur—apparently, vertical movement of bacteria in the tree occurs only in the secondary nonfunctional phloem elements.

Control. When cankers are small, surgical removal is possible but it is impractical to remove all of the cankered tissue when trees are extensively involved. Bordeaux mixture and copper sprays applied to the trees were shown to kill the pathogens in the exudate, but the value of such treatment in preventing infection is yet to be proved. Prevention of injuries, or protection of injuries that do occur, is necessary. This applies especially to injuries made by harvest shakers. Gardner and Kado (1) suggest that if few trees are infected in the orchard they should be harvested last to minimize risk of shaker-spread. Varieties other than Hartley should be considered for new orchards.

References

1. Gardner, J. M., and C. I. Kado. 1972. Deep bark canker. Diamond Walnut News 54: 2 p.
2. _____ 1973. Evidence for systemic movement of *Erwinia rubrifaciens* in Persian walnuts by the use of double-antibiotic markers. Phytopathology 63:1085-86.
3. Schaad, N. W., and E. E. Wilson. 1970. Structure and seasonal development of secondary phloem of Juglans regia. Canadian J. Botany 48:1049-53.
4. _____ 1970. Pathological anatomy of the bacterial phloem canker disease of *Juglans regia*. Canadian J. Botany 48:1055-60.
5. _____ 1970. Survival of *Erwinia rubrifaciens* in soil. Phytopathology 60:557-58.
6. _____ 1971. Bacterial phloem canker of Persian walnut. Development and control features. California Agric. 25:4-7.
7. _____ 1971. The ecology of *Erwinia rubrifaciens* and the development of phloem canker of Persian walnut. Ann. Appl. Biol. 69:125-36.
8. _____ 1971. Bacterial phloem canker of Persian walnut. California Agriculture 25(4):4-7.
9. Schaad, N. W., M. G. Heskett, J. M. Gardner, and C. I. Kado. 1973. Influence of inoculum dosage, time after wounding, and season on infection of Persian walnut trees by *Erwinia rubrifaciens*. Phytopathology 63:327-29.
10. Wilson, E. E., M. P. Starr, and J. A. Berger. 1957. Bark canker a bacterial disease of Persian walnut trees. Phytopathology 47:669-73.
11. Wilson, E. E., F. M. Zeitoun, and D. L. Fredrickson. 1967. Bacterial phloem canker, a new disease of Persian walnut trees. Phytopathology 57:618-21.
12. Zeitoun, F. M., and E. E. Wilson. 1966. Serological comparisons of *Erwinia nigrifluens* with certain other Erwinia species. Phytopathology 56:1381-85.
13. _____ 1969. The relation of bacteriophage to the walnut-tree pathogens *Erwinia nigrifluens* and *Erwinia rubrifaciens*. Phytopathology 59:756-61.

FUNGAL DISEASES OF ENGLISH WALNUT

Armillaria Root Rot of English Walnut
Armillaria mellea (Vahl.) Quel.

This disease, a general discussion of which appears in section III of this publication, is an example of disease effectively controlled by using resistant rootstocks. English walnut on its own rootstock cannot survive in *Armillaria*-infested soil, but on resistant northern California black walnut rootstock the trees can be planted in infested areas where other tree fruit could not survive.

Blotch or Anthracnose of English Walnut
Gnomonia leptostyla (Fr.) Ces. and DeN.

This disease affects eastern black walnut (*Juglans nigra),* Hind's or northern California black walnut

(*J. hindsii*), southern California black walnut (*J. californica*), English walnut (*J. regia*), and butternut (*J. cinerea*) of the eastern U.S. It is rarely of importance in English walnut orchards of the Pacific Coast states.

Symptoms. Circular reddish-brown to grayish-brown spots with grayish centers and 1/16 to 3/4 inch in diameter develop on leaves. Oval or irregularly circular, sunken, light grayish-brown spots with dark-brown margins develop on green shoots. On the nuts the disease is characterized by circular depressed necrotic lesions in the hull. If infection occurs early in the season the infected nuts may drop or, if they remain on the tree, become malformed. Reduction in yield is the most serious aspect of this disease.

Causal organism. The causal organism is the fungus *Gnomonia leptostyla* (Fr.) Ces. and DeN.; the imperfect is *Marssonina juglandis* (Lib.) Magn.

Disease development. The fungus overwinters in infected leaves and nuts on the ground and in cankers on twigs infected the previous year. The ascigerous stage is produced on these parts. In spring, the ascospores ejected from the perithecia are carried by air currents to the new growth where they produce the initial infection of the season. Conidia produced in acervuli on old twigs lesions may also be primary inoculum. Conidia produced in old and new lesions constitute the principal inoculum for summer infection.

Control. Control measures are rarely necessary for this disease in the U.S. In France, where walnut blotch sometimes causes severe leaf and fruit infection of both the wild and cultivated walnuts, spraying with Bordeaux mixture effectively reduced the amount of infection (1). Rankin (4) reported reduction of the disease on eastern black walnut by three treatments with Bordeaux given as follows: a) when leaves are unfolding, b) when leaves have reached mature size, and c) about 2 weeks after second application.

References

1. Gard, M. 1928. Developpment des Maladies Cryptogamique sur les Noyers en 1926. Annales des Epiphyties 14:152-62.
2. Hammond, J. B. 1931. Some diseases in walnuts. Ann. Rept. East Malling Research Sta. 1928, 1929, and 1930. Supplement II. p. 143-49.
3. Miller, P. W., C. E. Schuster, and R. E. Stephenson. 1945. Diseases of the walnuts in the Pacific Northwest and their control. Ore. Agr. Exp. Sta. Bul. 435:1-42. (reprinted 1947).
4. Rankin, W. H. 1932. Spraying for leaf diseases of shade trees. Proc. Eighth Ann. Meeting Nat. Shade Tree Conf. pp. 64-69.

Branch Wilt of English Walnut
Hendersonula toruloidea Nattrass

The fungus causing branch wilt and limb wilt is found on English (Persian) walnut (*Juglans regia*), lemon (*Citrus limonia*), grapefruit (*C. grandis*), orange (*C. sinensis*), European chestnut (*Castanea sativa*), fig (*ficus carica*), almond (*Prunus amygdalus*), and poplar (*Populus* sp.). It has also been found on dead branches of the black walnut (*Juglans hindsii*). In Egypt, Nattrass (4) isolated the causal fungus from apple, apricot, and peach trees thought to have been injured by excessive soil moisture. The fungus was first isolated in California by Fawcett (3).

In California the disease has not been found on walnut in coastal areas, but is widely distributed throughout the Sacramento and San Joaquin valleys and in interior districts of southern California (14). Branch wilt is a major walnut disease in Tulare County, but it has been of secondary importance in other localities.

Symptoms. During July and August the leaves on certain branches wither, turn deep brown, and dry up, but remain attached to the twigs. The symptoms which conclusively identify branch wilt occur in the branches: the outer layer of bark (periderm) becomes loosened in certain areas and the underlying cortex is covered by a black powdery material composed of numerous black one-celled spores (arthrospores) of the causal fungus. The cortex underlying the spore mass is brown, and the wood is dark-gray to black (14) (fig. 53). Once established in a branch, the fungus may spread to other branches and eventually to the trunk.

The causal organism. The conidial, or more specifically, the arthrospore stage was described as *Exosporinia fawcetti* (14) but a few years later a pycnidial stage was found (15) which proved to be identical with *Hendersonula toruloidea* Nattrass (6). Until such time as a perithecial stage is found the latter is the correct binomial, though it is probable that this fungus was first described as *Torula dimidiata* Penzig (10), an incorrect generic classification.

Arthrospores (= conidia) are produced by the progressive segmentation of closely packed hyphae arising from a slight hypostroma. The structure, therefore, is a sporodochium. Pycnidia are produced in a stroma, which Nattrass (6) believed developed from the conidium-bearing hyphae. One to six pycnidia with long necks are partially immersed in the stroma. The pycnospores (5.3 × 14.6 μm in width and length) which are produced on short stalks arising from the base of the pycnidium are one-celled and hyaline as long as they remain in the pycnidium, but a few days after being extruded from the pycnidia they become three-celled and the central cell turns dark brown.

Disease development. The fungus undergoes a period of inactivity as mycelia and arthrospores in and on infected branches. These spores constitute the chief inoculum for infection, pycnidiospore development being comparatively rare. Arthrospores are produced in dense layers beneath the periderm of infected branches. They are capable of withstanding hot dry weather for long periods. Inasmuch as arthrospores are only 4.6 to 7.3 μm in diameter, and are produced in powdery masses, they are suited to wind dissemination but may also be washed about by rain. Sunburn cracks and mechanical injuries are common avenues for entry of the fungus into the branch; the fungus is not known to penetrate uninjured bark. Inoculation of the cracks or cuts in branches probably occurs during the winter, but infection does not occur until spring or early summer. The most active extension of the fungus through the branches occurs during mid-summer. The incubation period is greatly affected by temperature. Inoculations produced large cankers in 10 to 15 days during the summer, whereas inoculations in winter or early spring did not produce cankers for several months. High temperatures can cause sunburning which allows entry of the fungus—the absence of serious branch wilt in coastal areas is believed to be due to the lower summer temperatures. Temperatures below 25 °C are less favorable to the fungus than are temperatures between 25 and 35 °C, the optimum being somewhere between 30 and 33 °C. Vigor of the tree has a marked influence on susceptibility to the disease. Unfavorable soil fertility, soil moisture, and presence of root or crown diseases which lower the tree's vigor also increase its susceptibility.

The pathological histology of the disease has not been thoroughly studied but it is known that the mycelium of the fungus invades most elements of the xylem, causing formation of tyloses and a dark gummy substance. Mycelia also occur throughout the ray cells and most elements of the phloem and cortex.

Control. Franquette, Mayette, Eureka and Meyland are most susceptible. Payne is somewhat less susceptible, and Concord apparently is fairly resistant (the latter, however, is not well adapted to Central Valley conditions). Cultural practices beneficial to the trees, and adequate irrigation and fertilization, help to reduce the severity of the disease.

Removal and destruction of affected branches are necessary procedures. One or two applications of Bordeaux mixture in winter will reduce infection (16), although spraying walnut trees is expensive.

References

1. Ashworth, L. J. 1954. Variation in the walnut branch wilt fungus, *Hendersonula toruloidea.* Unpublished, Dept. Plant Pathology, University of California, Davis.
2. Bates, G. R. 1937. Disease of citrus fruits in southern Rhodesia. Mazoe Citrus Exp. Sta. Ann. Rept. Publ. 6(1936):173-208.
3. Calavan, E. C., and J. M. Wallace. 1948. *Exosporina* branch blight of grapefruit in southern California. Phytopathology 38:913. (Abstr.)
4. English, H., J. R. Davis, and J. E. DeVay. 1975. Relationship of *Botryosphaeria dothidea* and *Hendersonula toruloidea* to canker disease of almond. Phytopathology 65:115-22.
5. Fawcett, H. S. 1936. Citrus diseases and their control. McGraw-Hill, New York. 656 pp. (see pages 218 and 222).
6. Nattrass, R. M. 1933. A new species of *Hendersonula (H. toruloidea)* on deciduous trees in Egypt. Brit. Mycol. Soc. Trans. 18:189-98.
7. Ogawa, J. M. 1954. The occurrence of *Hendersonula toruloidea* Nattrass on *Populus* species in California. Plant Dis. Rep. 38:238.
8. Paxton, J. D., and E. E. Wilson. 1965. Anatomical and physiological aspects of branch wilt disease of Persian walnut. Phytopathology 55:21-26.
9. Paxton, J. D., and E. E. Wilson, and J. R. Davis. 1964. Branch wilt of fig caused by *Hendersonula toruloidea.* Plant Disease Rep. 48:142.
10. Penzig, O. 1887. Studi botanici sugli agrumi e sulli piante affini. Memoria Premiata dal R. Minister, Dell' Agricultura. Tipografia Eredi Botta, Rome, Italy. 590 pp.
11. Sommer, N. F. 1955. Infection of the Persian walnut tree by *Hendersonula toruloidea* Nattrass. Ph.D. dissertation. Department of Plant Pathology, University of California, Davis. 82 pp.
12. Warner, R. M. 1952. Some observations of branch wilt on figs. Proc. Sixth Ann. Res. Conf., Calif. Fig. Inst., Fresno.
13. Wilson, E. E. 1945. A wilt disease of Persian walnuts in California. Plant Dis. Rep. 29:614-15.
14. _____ 1947. The branch wilt of Persian walnut trees and its cause. Hilgardia 17:413-36.
15. _____ 1949. The pycnidial stage of the walnut branch wilt fungus, *Exosporina fawcetti.* Phytopathology 39:340-46.
16. _____ 1950. Studies on control of walnut branch wilt. Diamond Walnut News. 32 (No. 4).

Downy Leaf Spot of English Walnut
Microstroma juglandis (Bereng.) Sacc.

This disease is of minor importance in the walnut-growing areas of the Pacific Coast.

Symptoms. White or pale-yellow downy spots develop on the underside of leaves. On fruit, lesions (fig. 54) are roughly circular with a downy texture and are extended by increase in fruit size until they are 1 inch or more in diameter; the downy mat of fungus is commonly confined to the periphery of such lesions. Surface of the hull may be slightly indented at the periphery of the lesion, but the fruit is not otherwise malformed.

Causal fungus. *Microstroma juglandis* (Bereng.) Sacc. Pires (3) believed this fungus to be a Basidiomycete, but Wolf (4) and Karakulin (1) placed it in Melanconiaceae of the Fungi Imperfecti. *M. juglandis* var. *robustrum* is said to cause a disease of pecan catkins.

Little is known about the life history of the fungus or the development of the disease. It is more common in wet years and in orchards where there is poor air circulation.

Control. Control of downy leaf spot is seldom necessary. The disease has not occurred in orchards regularly sprayed with Bordeaux mixture for control of bacterial blight.

References

1. Karakulin, B. P. 1923. On the question of the systematic position of fungi belonging to the type of *Exobasidiopsis* (in Greek). Not. Syst. ex Inst. Cryt. Horti. Bot. Petropol. 2(7):101-08.
2. Miller, P. W., C. E. Schuster, and R. E. Stephenson. 1945. Diseases of the walnuts in the Pacific Northwest and their control. Ore. Agr. Exp. Sta. Bull. 435:1-42 (reprinted 1947).
3. Pires, V. A. 1928. Concerning the morphology of *Microstroma* and the taxonomic position of the genus. Amer. J. Botany 15:132-40.
4. Wolf, F. A. 1927. The morphology and systematic position of the fungus, *Microstroma juglandis* (Bereng.) Sacc. J. Elisha Mitchell Scient. Soc. 43:97-99.

Melaxuma Canker and Twig Blight of English Walnut
Dothiorella gregaria Sacc.

This disease occurred commonly throughout California in 1915 but caused extensive damage only in a relatively few orchards (1); it has not been identifiable in recent years. Where outbreaks occur, however, large branches of the walnut tree may succumb or numerous small terminal branches may be killed. The symptoms which develop in tree crotches, resemble those of the phloem canker caused by *Erwinia* and the twig dieback phase caused by *Hendersonula*.

Symptoms. The most conspicuous aspect of the disease, and one which has given it the name of melaxuma, is the exudation of a dark watery material from the surface of cankers located at the crotches of large limbs. The bark of such cankers is moist and dark-brown to black and underlying sapwood is also dark. Occasionally, the disease develops on the outermost branches and is first noticeable in midsummer when the leaves on such branches suddenly wither. This phase of the disease resembles the branch wilt disease caused by *Hendersonula toruloidea*. However, melaxuma twig blight progresses more slowly than branch wilt and seldom extends downward into large branches from its location in the small branches.

The causal organism. The fungus *Dothiorella gregaria* Sacc. was shown by Fawcett (1) to be the cause of the disease. He obtained it both from the cankers on large limbs and from the small blighted twigs. On the latter, the fungus often fruits abundantly, producing subcutaneous pycnidia either singly or in groups on a basal stroma. The spores are oblong-fusoid, 20 to 26 × 5 to 7 μm in dimension, and nonseptate until germinating at which time they produce a single septum. The fungus is said to be the pycnidial stage of *Physalospora gregaria* Sacc. (2).

The same fungus occurs on other hosts, particularly members of *Cornus, Populus,* and *Salix.* Fawcett (1) found it on the arroyo willow, *Salix lasiolepis,* in Santa Barbara County, California.

Disease development. Cankers commonly occur at the crotches of large limbs, indicating that such places are particularly favorable for infection or for growth of the fungus after infection. Other probable infection sites are injuries of various sorts, including those caused by harvesting tools and cracks produced by wind and other natural agencies.

Though the height of disease activity, as judged by enlargement of cankers and wilting of leaves on affected branches, occurs in summer, infection probably occurs in winter or not later than spring.

Control. Removal of wilted branches and excision of a canker on larger limbs are beneficial measures (1, 3). Although fungicides might prove beneficial, a spray program for the disease has not been developed.

Trees in low vigor are more prone to serious infection than those high in vigor. Experience in some area indicates that a lack of soil moisture may predispose the tree to infection.

References

1. Fawcett, H. S. 1915. *Melaxuma* of the walnut, *"Juglans regia."* Calif. Agr. Exp. Sta. Bul. 261:133-48 (out of print).
2. Grove, W. B. 1935. British stem- and leaf-fungi. Vol. 1, p. 240. Cambridge University Press, London.
3. Smith, R. E. 1941. Diseases of fruits and nuts. Calif. Agr. Exp. Sta. Circ. 120:33 (out of print).

Phytophthora Crown and Root Rot of English Walnut
Phytophthora species

The organisms causing crown and root rots have been identified as *Phytophthora cactorum, P. cinnamoni* and other unidentified *Phytophthoras.* The disease has been serious in years having heavy rainfalls in winter and early spring. The characteristic symptom is the gradual decline of the trees. Review of literature indicates that *J. regia* rootstock is more resistant to *P. cactorum* than are the black walnut rootstocks, but preliminary data in recent studies by Mircetich *et al.* (1) show no significant difference in severity between 6-month-old *J. regia, J. hindsii* and paradox hybrid seedlings, and *P. cactorum* and *Phytophthora* sp. (although the first three rootstocks were highly susceptible to *P. cinnamoni*). Furthermore, *P. cinnamoni* produced larger cankers than did *P. cactorum* or *Phytophthora* sp. on 3-year-old *J. regia* rootstocks. These results suggest that relative resistance of walnut rootstocks to *Phytophthora* spp. may be influenced by age or physiological state or both, of rootstocks during the growing periods.

Details concerning this disease are discussed in section III of this publication.

Reference

1. Mircetich, S. M., W. J. Moller, D. E. Ramos, M. E. Matheron, and W. R. Schreader. 1976. Phytophthora root and crown rot of walnut trees. Abstr. Proc. Eighth Annual Walnut Research Conf., Univ. of Calif., Davis, January 27-28, 21 pp.

Ring Spot of English Walnut
Ascochyta juglandis Boltsh.

This disease is of minor importance in the Pacific Northwest and has not been reported from California.

Symptoms. Irregular circular brown spots 1/8 to 1/2 inch in diameter develop on the leaves. Necrosis of the tissue extends from the upper to lower epidermis of the leaf blade. On the upper side of the leaf, the surface of the spot is somewhat depressed in the center and raised at the margins; the spot is light-brown at first, and later turns ash-gray. Concentric ridges occur in the center of the spots, and scattered among them are the dark pycnidia of the causal fungus.

Causal organism. *Ascochyta juglandis* Boltsh., an imperfect fungus producing globose semi-immersed pycnidia 80 to 120 μm in diameter. Pycnidiospores are 2-celled, oblong, 10 to 13 by 4 to 5 μm and often restricted at the septum.

Little is known about the life cycle of this fungus. Apparently it overwinters on old leaves on the ground and spreads from there to new leaves in spring.

Control. As this disease seldom occurs in trees regularly sprayed for walnut blight, Miller, Schuster, and Stephenson (1) believed that a spray program similar to that for blight will effectively prevent it.

Reference

1. Miller, P. W., C. E. Schuster, and R. E. Stephenson. 1945. Diseases of the walnuts in the Pacific Northwest and their control. Ore. Agr. Exp. Sta. Bul. 435:1-42 (reprinted 1947).

NONPARASITIC DISEASES OF ENGLISH WALNUT

Black Line or Girdle of English Walnut
Causal Agent—Unknown

The disorder known as "black line" or "girdle" of walnut trees causes the decline and death of many trees in Oregon and California. The disease is quite common in some places but rare or absent in others. For example, it is said to affect about 9 percent of the walnut trees in parts of the Willamette Valley of central Oregon, and it is responsible for most of the decline and death occurring in that region (2, 5). In California, the disorder is most prevalent in walnut-growing districts around San Francisco Bay and has recently been detected in a number of orchards in the central valley, including Yolo, Sacramento, San Joaquin, Stanislaus and Merced counties. In all locations, only English walnut growing on Hind's black walnut (*J. hindsii*) rootstock, Paradox hybrid, or on rootstock of hybrids between *J. hindsii* and other black walnuts is affected.

Symptoms. The first outward sign of the disorder (fig. 55A) is the gradual decline in vigor of the tree, accompanied by early leaf fall in autumn from some or all branches. Meanwhile, water sprouts are frequently produced in unusual profusion from the understock. Death of the top part of the tree usually occurs 2 to 5 years after the first symptoms appear.

The decline and death of the tree occurs coincidentally with development of a dark-brown to black layer of tissue cork-like in consistency and located at the junction between the scion and the understock —it is 1/8 to 1/4 inch thick and variable in length, depending on the stage of disease development. In early stages, the layer may be only a few inches long, in late stages it extends completely around the trunk. It also extends completely through the bark and into the sapwood, causing a break in the continuity between xylem and phloem tissues of the scion above and the corresponding tissues of the understock below (fig. 55B).

Cause. The cause remains unknown, but apparently no bacterial or fungus organism is involved. Some investigators suggest that since it occurs only when English walnut is budded onto black walnut or Paradox hybrid rootstock, it may be an incompatibility (3). Such a theory seems to be untenable, however, because thousands of English walnut trees growing on black walnut rootstock never develop the disorder (1). Another view is that the disorder results from some unfavorable environmental condition, probably some chemical feature of the soil (1). Soils on which the disorder occurs most commonly in California are sufficiently high in boron to induce leaf injury in walnut trees, although black line is absent in other California soils equally high in boron. The possibility of the cause as being a virus is under investigation.

Development of the disorder. Walnut trees seldom develop black line until they are 10 years old or older. Not uncommonly, trees which have grown normally for 20 years will suddenly develop the disorder and die within a few years. English walnut scions grafted onto water sprouts arising from the black walnut rootstock of such trees may, however, develop the disorder in 4 or 5 years.

Control. No satisfactory control is known. Bridge grafting, inarching, and other means of establishing a new root system for the tree have been tried (3, 6, 7). Complete elimination of black line could be effected by propagating the trees on English walnut rootstock, but as English rootstock is highly susceptible to *Armillaria* root rot these trees could be grown only on soil free of *Armillaria mellea*. This procedure is being followed in some areas because the disorder is considered a greater killer than *Armillaria*.

References

1. Davey, A. E. 1946. Walnut girdle disease (black line). Diamond Walnut News. July, 1946. p. 8-9. (Official publication of the Calif. Walnut Growers Assoc.).
2. Miller, P. W. 1942. A report of progress on studies of the cause of the decline and death of walnuts in Oregon. Ore. State Hort. Soc. Rept. 1941:124-26.
3. Miller, P. W., C. E. Schuster, and R. E. Stephenson. 1945. Diseases of the walnuts in the Pacific Northwest and their control. Ore. Agr. Exp. Sta., Bul. 435:1-42. (reprinted 1947).
4. Rawlings, C. O. 1949. Some rootstock problems relative to walnut girdle and crown rot. Oregon State Hort. Soc. Proc. 41:131-35.
5. Rawlings, C. O., J. H. Painter, and P. W. Miller. 1950. Importance of black line in certain Oregon walnut orchards. Oregon State Hort. Soc. Report 1950:150-51.
6. Serr, E. F. 1953. Bridge grafting, possible method of preventing death of trees from "black line." Diamond Walnut News. March. P. 8.
7. _____ 1953. Grafting in black walnut sprouts, another method of saving "black line" trees. Diamond Walnut News. May. P. 12.

Shell Perforation of English Walnut
Cause—unknown

This malformation consists of circular or irregular-shaped holes extending through the shell and occurring any place in the shell but usually near the apex. Such nuts are not marketable as such but must be cracked and sold as "meats."

Some workers have attributed the perforations to feeding by the walnut aphid, *Chromaphis juglandicola* Kalt, but the insect is not the only cause of the disorder. Trees of certain cultivars are more prone to produce perforated nuts than are those of other cultivars. Trees low in vigor are said to have more perforated nuts than do highly vigorous trees.

Little is known about the prevention. Top-working trees which produce abnormal numbers of perforated nuts with a cultivar such as Franquette is one way of eliminating it.

Reference

1. Miller, P. W., C. E. Schuster, and R. E. Stephenson. 1945. Diseases of the walnuts in the Pacific Northwest and their control. Ore. Agr. Exp. Sta. Bul. 435:1-42. (Reprinted 1947).

V. THE OLIVE AND ITS DISEASES

The Olive

The family Oleaceae, to which the edible olive, *Olea europea* L., contains the following genera: *Fraxinus,* ash; *Syringa,* lilac; *Lingustrum,* privet; *Forsythia,* forsythia; *Jasminum,* jasmine; and *Foresteria,* California wild olive.

Other species of *Olea* are: *O. ferruginosa, O. verrucosa,* and *O. chrysophylla.* The fruit of these species, however, is not edible.

The olive originated in southwestern Asia, probably Syria, many centuries ago and was gradually introduced into all the countries surrounding the Mediterranean Sea. Today about 99 percent of the world supply of olives is produced in Spain, Italy, Greece, Portugal, Turkey, Tunisia, France, French Morocco, Algeria, Syria, Yugoslavia, Jordan, Cyprus, Israel, Libya, and Egypt. The remainder is produced in the U.S., Argentina, Chile, Peru, Mexico, the Union of South Africa, Australia, and Japan.

Olives were introduced into California about 1769 when seeds were brought to Mission San Diego from Mexico by Father Junipero Serra and Don Jose de Galvez. After 1850 the number of trees increased rapidly until by 1910 they numbered almost a million. Between 1928 and 1950, acreage dropped from 29,000 to 26,826, but between 1950 and 1957 it increased again to 31,000 acres; by 1977 it had once more dropped, this time to a total of 24,944 acres.

Presently, 84 percent of the commercial plantings are located in the San Joaquin and Sacramento valleys. Although olives were planted extensively in the coastal areas of California, they were not as successful there as in the interior valleys.

Principal varieties grown in California are Mission (probably a seedling of the Spanish variety, Cornicabra), Manzanillo, Sevillano, Ascolano, and Barouni. Most of the olive oil produced in the state comes from fruit of the first two varieties; the fruit of the other three varieties is used almost exclusively for pickling.

Attempts to use other species of Olea as rootstocks for *O. europea* have generally proved unsuccessful. Except for Sevillano grafted on *O. chrysophylla,* there is excessive overgrowth at the union and the trees develop large numbers of abortive shotberries or excessive numbers of yellow leaves, followed by death of the tree.

The method of propagation in certain olive-growing countries is to saw off swellings (souchets), which are common on the trunks of certain varieties, and then plant them. Such swellings contains dormant buds which grow when the souchet is planted. All but one or two are allowed to grow.

Similar methods of propagation have sometimes been employed in this country. One involves the planting of large pieces of green wood (truncheons) horizontally 3 to 6 inches deep in the soil. From these arise shoots which become rooted and develop into trees. Another is the planting of the enlargements (ovuli) from the trunks of growing trees.

More common methods of propagation are a) grafting of seedlings with scions of the desired horticultural variety, b) self-rooting of 1 to 2-year-old terminal growth with leaves, and c) self-rooting of hardwood cuttings of branches several years old and 1 to 3 inches in diameter.

Where it is desirable to change the variety of mature olive trees, this can be done by grafting scions of the desired variety into the primary (scaffold) branches of the tree. This should be done between early March and late April.

Reference

1. Hartmann, H. J. 1953. Olive production in California. Calif. Agr. Expt. Sta. and Ext. Ser. Man. 7, 55 pp. (Out of print).

BACTERIAL DISEASES OF OLIVE

Olive knot
Pseudomonas savastanoi (Smith) Stevens

The disease "olive knot" (or "olive tubercle") has been known since ancient times. It was spread around the world with the olive host and now occurs in all olive-producing regions. It probably was not introduced into California by the Spanish settlers because the first olives grown there were produced from seeds. Between 1850 and 1900, however, the vegetative parts of many of the Spanish and Italian cultivars were brought into the state and it was probably during this time that olive knot was introduced. It was present in California in 1898 according to Bioletti.

Studies on the cause of olive knot were reported in 1886 by Archangeli, who described the disease thoroughly and who gave the name *Bacterium oleae* to an organism which he, however, did not consider to be the causal agent. Between 1887 and 1889, Savastano proved that the disease was caused by a bacterium, and this was soon confirmed by Cavara. Savastano called the organism *Bacillus oleae-tuberculosis* but neither he nor Cavara described it adequately. The bacterium, which later became known as *Bacillus oleae* (Arch.) Trevisan, was described by Berlese (1905) as being a yellow organism in culture. In 1908, Smith (10) published results of a careful study of the cause of olive knot, and he gave the name *Bacterium savastanoi* to the bacterium which he found to be the causal agent (11).

The disease reduces the production of the olive crop by defoliation and killing the twigs and branches. Recent studies indicate that fruit from diseased trees contain compounds which impart bitter, salty, sour or rancid tastes (8).

If branches become infected in late winter, water-soaked lysigenous cavities 2 to 5 mm in length often develop. The cells of the host are collapsed in such cavities and bacterial masses occur through the tissue. When the host starts growth a knot (fig. 56A) develops around this cavity, proliferation of the tissue occurring at its periphery. Hypertrophy and hyperplasia of cells occur. Cells nearest the center of the knot differentiate into xylem; those near the periphery differentiate into parenchyma and phloem. The elements of such tissues are arranged in a disorderly manner. The bacteria are found in sutures formed by folding of the proliferating tissues. Smith (11) claimed that metastasis (development of tubercles at a distance from the point of inoculation) occurred. There is evidence that secondary knots may sometimes develop 1/2 to 1 inch from the point of the primary infection when the lysigenous cavities extend to this distance, but seldom if ever are knots produced at a greater distance from the infection court.

The causal organism. Formerly known as *Bacterium savastanoi* E. F. Smith, and *Phytomonas savastanoi*, it is now classified as *Pseudomonas savastanoi* (Smith) Stevens. A similar organism on Fraxinus is known as *Pseudomonas savastanoi* var. *fraxini* (Brown) Dowson. The organism producing tumors on oleander *(Nerium oleander)* similar to those on olive was found by C. O. Smith (9), Adams and Pugsley (1), and Pinckard (6) to be similar in morphological and physiological characters to the olive pathogen. These workers and others, however, reported that while the oleander pathogen readily produced tumors on olive the olive pathogen would not infect the oleander. Smith (9) suggested the oleander pathogen be called *Phytomonas (= Pseudomonas) savastanoi* var. *nerii*. Bergey's Manual of Determinative Bacteriology, 1957 edition, nevertheless listed this organism as *Pseudomonas tonelliana* (Ferr.) Burk. Dowson (3) followed C. O. Smith in calling the organism *P. savastanoi* var. *nerii*. In 1963, Wilson and Magie (13) reported that while certain isolates of *P. savastanoi* from olive did not infect the oleander, others produced tumors on this host similar to those produced by the oleander pathogen. Furthermore, cultural, physiological, bacteriophage relations, and serological reactions were similar for the bacteria from the two hosts.

Domenico (2) later reported evidence that under natural conditions the olive pathogen would spread to and infect the oleander, but the frequency of infection was low. Low frequency of infection was in character with results of artificial inoculation, where not over 20 percent of the isolates from olive infected the oleander. Later unpublished evidence indicated that while the pathogen from oleander can utilize sucrose as a carbon source, the pathogen from olive cannot, because it lacks the ability to produce the enzyme sucrase (invertase). There still remains the unanswered questions of whether the low pathogenic affinity for the oleander exhibited by isolates of the bacterium from olive and their inability to produce sucrase are stable characters. Despite the differences so far found there seems to be little justification for regarding the oleander pathogen as a distinct species. A biotype or strain distinction would suffice.

P. savastanoi is a gram-negative motile rod (0.4-0.8 × 1.2-3.3 μm) with 1 to 4 polar flagella. Colonies are white, smooth with wavy or entire margins. It produces acid but no gas from glucose, galactose, and certain other carbon sources. Starch is hydrolyzed. It produced a fluorescent pigment on certain media.

Disease development. *Pseudomonas savastanoi* survives from one season to the next in the knots where it is produced in large numbers at all times of the year. It exudes to the surface during rains and is readily washed about (5). If not exposed to direct sunlight, bacteria in the ooze may resist desiccation for several hours or even days (11). There is some evidence that the bacteria are windborne, for short distances at least, probably in water droplets (11). Birds have been suspected of carrying the bacteria on their feet. In Italy, the olive fly *(Dacus olea)* is said to spread the bacteria. This insect is not found in California.

There is some evidence (unpublished) that the pathogen survives only a matter of days in the soil.

Scars formed by abscission of leaves are the most common avenues for entry of the bacteria into the twigs (5) (fig. 56B). Blossom scars may become infected if rains occur at the end of the blossoming period. Other infection courts are pruning wounds or other injuries such as hail and frost and cracks made by shoots as these emerge from the branch. Because of the profuse production of water shoots, varieties such as Sevillano, Nevadillo, and Ascolano are prone to branch and trunk infection. Severe multiple infection of branches occurred in 1932 and again in 1950 through bark cracks caused by freezing injury.

Natural infection occurs during our rainy season from late October to early June, but knots do not develop until tree growth starts in spring. Knot development is rapid from May through June. If infection occurs in the fall, the time between infection and the first visible evidence of the knot is several months, but is only 10 to 14 days when infection occurs in spring. The tree must be growing before the knot will develop. Systemic invasion was uncommon in olive knot but common in oleander (15).

The pathogen can grow and reproduce at a wide range of temperatures, 23° to 24°C being the optimum. The development of water-soaked areas in branches following inoculation in winter indicates that the bacteria are capable of producing infection at fairly low temperatures (5° to 10°C). Temperatures below the maximum for growth (32°C) are therefore not a limiting factor in infection. Moisture, however, is a limiting factor—infection rarely if ever occurs during the dry season. Rains followed by periods of high humidity are favorable to infection of such natural courts as leaf and blossom scars.

Soil fertility and soil moisture may indirectly affect the susceptibility of the host to olive knot. Anything which causes the trees to lose leaves will increase the likelihood of infection.

Control. Control results from reducing the sources of inoculum by removing the knots. This may involve cutting off much of the branch system of badly infected trees. The work should be done in midsummer to avoid infection of cuts. Sufficient irrigation and fertilization to prevent the unseasonal dropping of leaves will aid in reducing the amount of infection. Protection against frost damage, if practical, is also helpful.

Chemicals such as phenol derivatives and kerosene painted over the knots kill the bacteria therein. It is difficult, however, to destroy the bacteria in the bark at the base of the knot without seriously injuring the branch. For this reason the Elgetol-methanol mixture which is effective against crown gall is not successful against olive knot. Schroth and Hildebrand (7) provided the first successful chemotherapeutic treatment to selectively destroy knot tissue: the chemical used was a paraffin oil + water emulsion containing 1,2,3,4-xylenol and m-cresol, and the proprietary product is called "Gallex."

Bordeaux mixture (10-10-100) has prevented olive knot when applied to the infection courts (leaf scars, etc.), but adequate protection can be obtained only by repeated applications because leaf fall, although normally occurring in greatest amounts in spring, may produce infectible leaf scars at almost any time in winter. Copper injury may occur in areas of low rainfall.

References

1. Adams, D. B., and A. J. Pugsley. 1934. A bacterial canker disease of oleander. J. Dept. Agr. Victoria, Australia 32:309-11.
2. Domenico, J. 1969. Relative infectivity of *Pseudomonas savastanoi* from olive and oleander. Phytopathology 59:11.
3. Dowson, W. J. 1949. Manual of bacterial plant diseases. Adam and Charles Black, London, 183 pp.
4. Hewitt, W. B. 1939. Leaf-scar infection in relation to the olive knot disease. Hilgardia 12:41-66.
5. Horne, W. J., W. B. Parker, and L. L. Daines. 1912. The method of spread of the olive knot disease. Phytopathology 2:101-05.
6. Pinckard, J. A. 1935. Physiological studies of several pathogenic bacteria that induce cell stimulation in plants. J. Agr. Research 50:933-52.
7. Schroth, M. N., and D. C. Hildebrand. 1958. A chemotherapeutic treatment for selectively eradicating crown gall and olive knot neoplasms. Phytopathology 58:848-54.
8. Schroth, M. N., D. C. Hildebrand, and H. J. O'Reilly. 1968. Off-flavor of olives from trees with olive knot tumors. Phytopathology 53:524-25.
9. Smith, C. O. 1928. Oleander bacteriosis in California. Phytopathology 18:503-08.

10. Smith, E. F. 1908. Recent studies of the olive-tubercle organism. USDA Bur. of Pl. Ind. Bul. 131 (Pt. IV):25-42.

11. _____ 1920. Bacterial diseases of plants. W. B. Saunders, Philadelphia. p. 389-412.

12. Wilson, E. E. 1935. The olive knot disease: its inception, development and control. Hilgardia 9:233-64.

13. _____ 1963. Physiological, serological, and pathological evidence that *Pseudomonas tonelliana* is identical with *Pseudomonas savastanoi*. Phytopathology 53:653-59.
Wilson, E. E., and A. Magie. 1963. Physiological, serological, and pathological evidence that *Pseudomonas tonnelliana* is identical with *Pseudomonas savastanoi*. Phytopathology 53:653-659.

14. _____ 1964. Systemic invasion of the host plant by the tumor-inducing bacterium, *Pseudomonas savastanoi*. Phytopathology 54:576-79.

FUNGAL DISEASES OF THE OLIVE

Armillaria Root Rot of Olive
Armillaria mellea (Vahl.) Quel.

Armillaria mellea occasionally attacks the olive tree and in time kills it. The symptoms of the disease are similar to those on stone-fruit trees. White to yellowish fan-shaped mycelial mats are present between the bark and wood of the affected roots, and dark brown to black rhizomorphs are present on the surface. Early recognition of the disease and removal of infected roots before the fungus girdles the crown may enable one to prolong the life of the tree (see section III for further discussion).

Cercospora Leaf and Fruit Spot of Olive
Cercospora cladosporoides Sacc.

A disease affecting leaves and fruit of olive was reported by Hansen and Rawlins (2) in 1944 but it has not been been reported from California since.

Indistinct dark areas occur on the lower surfaces of affected leaves, which may fall. The conidial stage of the causal fungus is found on these spots. Fruit which remains on the tree during winter develops dark circular spots. Uninfected areas of fruit may remain green instead of turning black as does normal fruit. Mycelia of the fungus is present between fruit cells but seldom enter them. Tufts of conidia are produced on the surfaces of the lesions.

The causal fungus is said to have been described and named *Cercospora cladosporoides* Sacc. by Govi (1) in 1952.

References

1. Govi, G. 1952. La Cercosporiosi o "piombatura" dell'olivo. Annali Sperimentazione Agraria 6:69-80.

2. Hansen, H. H., and T. E. Rawlins. 1944. Cercospora fruit and leaf spot of olive. Phytopathology 34:257-59.

Cycloconium Leaf Spot of Olive
Cycloconium oleaginum Castagne = *Spilocaea oleaginea* (Cast.) Hughes

This disease, also called "leaf spot," "bird's eye spot," and "peacock spot" is well known in all Mediterranean olive-growing countries, where it has received the attention of plant pathologists since the middle of the last century. In 1845, Castagne (4) described the disease in France and named the causal fungus *Cycloconium oleaginum*. In 1891, Boyer (2) in France published results of a careful study on the disease together with a detailed description of the causal fungus. In 1899 Brizi (3) investigated the morphology and life history of *C. oleaginum* and illustrated the changes which it produces in the olive leaf. Brizi was apparently the first to show that the disease could be prevented by spraying with Bordeaux mixture. In the early part of the present century, Ducomet (5) and Petri (9) made further studies of the relation of the fungus to the leaf tissue, and Tobler and Rossi-Ferrini (10) investigated its control with Bordeaux mixture.

Cycloconium leaf spot has been known in California since 1899 (1), but according to all earlier reports it seldom caused much damage. Outbreaks between 1941 and 1949, however, reduced the productivity of some trees as much as 20 percent. Yearly losses of 9 to 15 percent of the leaves followed by death of 10 to 20 percent of the fruiting twigs occurred in some orchards.

Symptoms. Although the disease lesions (fig. 57) most often occur on the leaf blade, they are sometimes found on the leaf petiole, the fruit, and the fruit stem. They are at first inconspicuous, superficial, sooty blotches, but later develop into muddy green to almost black circular spots 2 to 10 mm in diameter. A faint yellow halo sometimes occurs in the leaf tissue at the periphery of the spot. When the lesions are numerous the leaf becomes yellow and soon falls. The dark green to black spots on the yellow background of the infected leaf blades are thought by some to resemble the spots on a peacock's tail, hence the name peacock spot (1).

Lesions are notably more abundant on leaves in the lower part of the tree; many of the twigs in these parts are completely defoliated. Defoliated twigs die in large numbers during the summer.

Causal organism. The causal fungus of olive leaf spot was originally named *Cycloconium elaeaginum* by Castagne (4) in 1845 and was found in material collected near Marseilles, France. Boyer (2) described the fungus much more completely in 1891 and introduced the Latinized spelling, *oleaginum*. The mycelium, composed of hyaline, septate, much-branched, radiating hyphae, is immersed in the outer-most layer of the two-cell-thick leaf epidermis. This layer of epidermal cells is embedded in cutin and other fatty materials (7). Slender hyphal branches from the mycelium penetrate upward through the leaf cuticle and end in globose to flask-shaped light-brown conidiophores from which arise singly the obclavate to pyriform, two-celled, light-brown conidia (14 to 27 μm long and 9 to 15 μm broad) on short protrusions. Several protrusions or necks may occur on conidiophores that have borne a succession of conidia.

In 1953, Hughes (6) suggested that this fungus properly belonged in the genus *Spilocaea* which Fries erected in 1819 on the type species *S. pomi*. If his view is accepted, the name would become *Spilocaea oleaginea* (Cast.) Hughes.

In the living leaf the fungus seldom penetrates the lower layer of epidermal cells. After the leaf falls from the tree and dies, however, the fungus grows into palisade and mesophyll cells and at times forms dense masses of stromatic tissue. The fungus produces similar masses of stromatic tissue in culture (7, 12). Though Petri (9) suggested that such structures are sporocarps arrested in a primary stage of development, none has been found to develop to maturity.

Hosts. The edible olive, *Olea europea,* is the principal host of the fungus. Species of *Phillyrea* in Mediterranean countries are attacked by a fungus which has been designated *Cycloconium oleaginum* var. *phillyrea* (Desm.) Nic. and Agg.

Olive cultivars differ widely in susceptibility to infection. In California, Mission is severely infected, Manzanillo occasionally, while other important cultivars (Sevillano, Barouni, Ascolano, and Nevadillo Blanco) are seldom seriously infected.

Disease development. The fungus survives unfavorable periods, such as the hot dry summers of interior California, in the affected leaves on the tree. Although newly formed lesions sporulate freely during the spring months, few spores are produced during the summer months. In October or November the margins of the lesions extend laterally into adjacent leaf tissue, and a new crop of conidia develops there. These are the principle if not the only inoculum for infection. They are spread about the tree, mostly in a downward direction, by rain; lateral spread is notably limited. They are apparently not readily detached from the conidiophores by air currents, and thus are not readily air-borne. What lateral dissemination does occur probably results from wind carrying of spore-laden droplets of rain water.

Under California conditions a few new lesions may develop in autumn, but the greatest disease development occurs in spring. Very little is known about the role which moisture plays in the initiation of infection. The occurrence of infection in fall, winter and spring, however, is associated with periods of rainfall, the disease does not develop during rainless periods. Moreover, the conidia germinate only in the presence of water. Temperature is an important but not a limiting factor in the development of the fungus. High temperatures appear to restrict spore germination and mycelial growth more than does low temperatures. Though both processes occur quite readily at 8.9°C the optimum temperature is near 21.1°C. There is evidence that infection occurs during the coldest part of the California winters, but the lesions do not develop to a visible stage until spring. Lesions resulting from infection in spring become visible in a few weeks. The major effect of temperature, therefore, is seen in the rapidity with which infection occurs and symptoms develop.

Control. Elimination of Mission cultivar from an orchard would largely solve the leaf spot problem in California, but this could hardly be done because Mission is very important in oil-production and pickling.

Control by fungicides has been demonstrated (8, 10, 12). Bordeaux mixture 10-10-100, or lime-sulfur 3 percent applied in early autumn before the winter rains begin prevented infection effectively. Lime-sulfur, in addition to its protective value, exhibited distinct eradicatory action against the fungus in the leaf (11). To avoid copper injury, a 5-10-100 Bordeaux mixture or the equivalent of fixed copper can be used.

References

1. Bioletti, F. T., and Geo. E. Colby. 1899. Olives. Calif. Agr. Exp. Sta. Bul. 123:1-34.
2. Boyer, G. 1891. Recherches sur les maladies del'olivier. Le *Cycloconium oleaginum*. J. de Bot. 5:434-40.
3. Brizi, U. 1899. Bird's eye of olives (Translated title). Staz. Sper. Agr. Italy. 32:329-98.
4. Castagne, L. 1845. Catalogue des plantes qui Croissent. Naturallement aux environs des Marseilles, p. 200. Reviewed by Boyer (2).

5. Ducomet, V. 1907. Recherches sur le develop-ment de quelques champignons parasites a thalle subcuticulaire. Ann. Ecol. Nat. Agr. Rennes. 1907: 380-91.

6. Hughes, S. J. 1953. Some foliicolous Hypho-mycetes. Canad. J. Botany 31(5):560-576.

7. Miller, H. N. 1949. Development of the leaf spot fungus in olive leaf. Phytopathology 39: 403-10.

8. Papo, S., and J. Peleg. 1952. Trials in control of the olive leaf spot, caused by the fungus *Cyclo-conium oleaginum*. State of Israel, Div. of Pl. Protec. Bul. 34, 16 p.

9. Petri, L. 1913. Studie sulle malattie dell olive, III. Alcune richerche sulla biologia del *Cyclo-conium oleaginum* Cast. R. Staz. Patol. Veg. Roma Mem., 136 pp.

10. Tobler, O., and U. Rossi-Ferrini. 1906-07. The use of Bordeaux mixture for the control of *Cyclo-conium* on the olive. (Translated title). R. Acad. Econ. Agr. dei Georg. Frienze Atti (Series 3) 5:326-37.

11. Wilson, E. E. 1950. The protective and eradica-tive actions of lime-sulfur and puratized in con-trolling a fungus leaf-spot disease of olive. Phyto-pathology 40:32 (Abstr.).

12. Wilson, E. E., and H. N. Miller. 1949. Olive leaf spot and its control with fungicides. Hilgardia 19:1-24.

Polyporous Trunk and Root Infection of Olive
Polyporous oleaea n. sp.

A brief account of *Polyporus* infecting olive trees at Berkeley was given by Bonar (1) in 1964. The disease, which involves the crown and primary roots of the tree, is said to be produced by *Polyporus oleaea* which was described as a new species by Pan-izzi (2) in 1886.

Pilei of the fungus are creameous at first but later change to bright pink; they develop on the trunk near the ground.

References

1. Bonar, L. 1964. *Polyporus oleaea* on olive in Cali-fornia. Plant Dis. Rep. 48:70.

2. Panizzi, F. 1886. Nuova specie *Polyporus scoperta* e descritta. N. Giorn. Bot. Ital. 8:65-66.

Verticillium Wilt of Olive
Verticillium dahliae Kleb.

This disease, a general discussion of which appears in section III of this publication, has become of eco-nomic importance on olive (particularly in the San Joaquin Valley) with the introduction of a more pathogenic strain of the fungus.

External symptoms are similar to those in stone-fruit trees (fig. 58). The leaves on one or more branches suddenly wilt during the summer. Discoloration of the sapwood, which occur extensively in apricot and almond, does not occur in olive. Death of mature trees with *Verticillium* infection is probably more common in the olive than in the stone fruits.

A recent, apparently successful, attempt to obtain resistance of olive to *Verticillium* was that of grafting the susceptible Seveillano onto roots of *Oblonga*, which was developed as a seedling some 30 years ago (1).

Reference

1. Hartmann, H., W. C. Schnathorst, and John Whistler. 1971. *Oblonga*, a clonal olive root-stock resistant to Verticillium wilt. Calif. Agr. 25:13-15.

NONPARASITIC DISEASES OF OLIVE

Shotberry of Olive

Fruit small in size and almost spherical in shape develop in the fruit clusters (fig. 59). Sevillano and Manzanillo exhibit the disorder most commonly. Affected fruit does not develop seed, so it seems likely that the disorder is a delayed form of pistil abortion. Presumably, the pistil develops sufficiently to stimulate the fruit to considerable growth before it aborts.

Soft Nose of Olive

Soft nose or blue nose is a disorder of minor import-ance affecting fruit of the Sevillano variety (fig. 60). As the fruit begin to ripen a large area at the stylar end turns blue. Later the flesh in this area turns dark and shrivels, and becomes unfit for pickling. Cause of the disorder is unknown. Apparently it is nonparasitic and may be associated with water stress or heavy nitrogen fertilization. It is more severe on young trees than on older ones.

Split-Pit of Olive

Split-pit is largely a problem on Sevillano and is seri-ous only in some years. Fruit are bluntly flattened and the pits are split along the suture. The cause is not known but is suspected to be environmental; some workers believe that heavy irrigation of dry soil may induce it.

Reference

1. Hartman, H. T. 1953. Olive production in Cali-fornia. California Agr. Exp. Sta. Serv. Manual 7. 59 pp.

VI. THE FIG AND ITS DISEASES

The Fig (*Ficus carica* L.)

The fig is a native of southwestern Asia, and probably was first cultivated in Arabia and neighboring countries. It is now grown in all Mediterranean countries, southern Iran, southern Russia, Afghanistan, India, China, Japan, Australia, and the Union of South Africa.

Fig trees were introduced into the Western Hemisphere about 1520 when they were brought to the West Indies from Europe. Today they are grown commercially in Chile, Mexico, Argentina, and the U.S. The principal fig-producing states are California, Texas, Alabama, Georgia, Louisiana, Mississippi, and North Carolina.

Although the fig was brought into California by Franciscan missionaries about 1769, commercial production of some of the cultivars did not begin until the middle of the 19th century. Later new cultivars from the eastern U.S. and Spain were planted, and the practice of introducing the better European cultivars continued to the end of the 19th century.

Today, California has about 14,730 bearing acres of figs, 93 percent of the acreage being located in four San Joaquin Valley counties. The most important cultivars are Calimyrna (California Smyrna, or Lob Injir), Adriatic (White Adriatic, Verdone, Nebian, or Grosse Verti), Kadota (Dottato, White Pacific, or White Endrich), and Mission (Black Mission).

Figs are propagated by means of rooted cuttings. Sections of branches 9 to 12 inches long and 1/2 to 3/4 inches in diameter placed in moist soil will produce roots readily. The roots are grown for 1 year in the nursery before being field planted.

An understanding of diseases of fig fruit requires knowledge of the structural peculiarities of the fruit and the role played by the fig wasp, *Blastophaga psenes* L., in the development of the fruit of certain cultivars. The structure popularly regarded as fruit is known to horticulturists as a "synconium." This is a hollow receptacle with an apical orifice or "eye." In an immature synconium the eye is closed by overlapping bracts, but as fruit matures an opening 2 to 10 mm in diameter is formed by loosening of the bracts. The true fruit are borne on the inner wall of the synconium and, when mature, each consists of a stalk, the remains of the flower perianth, some parenchymatous tissue of the outer ovary wall, and one seed.

Ficus carica consists of two botanically different groups, the caprifig and the edible fig. In addition to edibility, the two groups differ with respect to the kinds of flowers present in the synconium. The caprifig synconium produces short-stiled pistillate flowers over a greater part of the inner wall and staminate flowers around the eye. For the most part, synconia of the caprifig are inedible. Trees of this group are necessary to the production of the edible fruit of certain fig cultivars because their synconia are the habitat for the wasp, *B. psenes* L., whose activity results in the pollination (caprification) of the female flowers of the edible fig. Edible figs are of three types: Smyrna, San Pedro, and common (self-pollinated). Synconia of the Smyrna type produce only long-stiled pistillate flowers, which require caprification before the synconia will develop to maturity. Synconia of the San Pedro type are of two kinds: those of the first crop, which contain only long-stiled pistillate flowers; and those of the second crop, which are borne on wood of the current season. These contain long-stiled pistillate flowers, but require pollination before the synconia will develop to maturity. Fruit of all cultivars of the common type develop to maturity without pollination, and caprification by the fig wasp is not necessary to production of a crop.

Development of two distinct crops of fruit—the first on the wood of the previous season and the second on wood of the current season—is common among certain cultivars of all types, including the caprifig. In California the first crop of edible figs (known as the "breba" crop), matures from May to June; the second crop matures from August to October. Certain cultivars of edible figs sometimes produce a third crop, which matures some weeks after this second crop; this crop is borne on wood of the current season and thus is nothing more than an extension of the second crop. The caprifig commonly develops three more or less distinct crops in the interior valleys of California. Because all three crops are associated with development of the wasp, they have been given names: the spring crop, developing in March or April and remaining on the tree until June, is called the "profichi"; the summer crop, developing in July and remaining on the tree until November, is called the "mammoni"; the winter crop, developing in November and remaining on the tree throughout the winter, is called the "mamme."

B. psenes passes the winter as larvae in parasitized pistillate flowers of the mamme synconia. It goes into the pupal stage in early spring and emerges as a winged adult at the time the profichi crop is developing. The female, previously fertilized by the male while still in the "inhabited" flowers of the mamme synconium, enters a profichi synconium through the orifice and deposits her eggs in the pistillate flowers. These eggs hatch about June, and the fertilized adult female emerges sometime later and lays her eggs in the pistillate flowers. These eggs hatch about June, and the fertilized adult female emerges some-eggs in a synconium of the mammoni crop. The new population of fertilized females emerge from the mammoni synconia in late summer and enter the mamme synconia, where they lay their eggs, thereby completing the yearly cycle.

Caprifigs formerly were planted in rows or in groups among trees of the edible Smyrna type, but after it was found that the insect transmitted spores of the endosepsis fungus *Fusarium moniliforme* from the caprifig to the edible fig, many orchardists removed the caprifig trees from the orchards and grew them in separate plantings. The practice of caprification as now followed is to pick the fruit of the profichi crop (the only crop with viable pollen) just before the male wasps begin to emerge and the staminate flowers are beginning to shed pollen. The fruit are placed in wire baskets and the baskets are hung in the trees of the edible varieties. As the female wasp emerges from the profichi fruit her body becomes dusted with pollen. She immediately enters a synconium of the edible fig and attempts to lay her eggs in the flower ovaries by inserting her ovipositor down the stilar canal. She is unable to do so, owing to the long stiles possessed by flowers of the edible sorts. In her vain attempt at oviposition, however, pollen from her body is deposited on the stigmas of the florets, thereby completing the process of caprification.

References

1. Condit, Ira J. 1947. The fig. Chronica Botanica Co., Waltham, Mass. 206 pp.
2. Eisen, Gustav. 1896. Biological studies on figs, caprifigs, and caprification. Proc. California Acad. Sci. II, 5:897-1003.

BACTERIAL DISEASES OF FIG

Bacterial Canker of Fig
Phytomonas fici (Cavara) Magrou

A bacterial canker of fig, originally described in Italy, was reported as occurring in California on the white Adriatic fig by Hansen (1) in 1948.

In Italy, the disease is said to cause dark lesions on leaves and elongated lesions on the new shoots, followed by wilting of these parts. In California, the disease is characterized by the development of roughly circular necrotic areas in inner bark of older limbs. A slight cracking of the outer bark is the only external evidence of the cankers (1, 3).

It is said (2) that the causal organism was named *Bacterium fici* by Cavara in Italy, where it causes a leaf spot and shoot wilt of *Ficus carica*. Although only a meager description of this organism exists. Magrou transferred it to the genus *Phytomonas* in 1937.

References

1. Hansen, H. N. 1948. A canker disease of figs. Phytopathology 38:914-15. (Abstr.).
2. Petri, L. 1906. Investigations on the bacteriosis of figs. Atti R. Acad Lincei, Rend. Cl. Sci. Fis., Mat. e Nat. 5 ser. 15, II, No. 10. pp. 644-51.
3. Pilgrim, A. J. 1950. Bacterial canker of Adriatics. Proc. Fourth Ann. Research Conf. California Fig. Inst. pp. 32-33.

FUNGAL DISEASES OF FIG

Branch Wilt of Fig
Hendersonula toruloidea Nattrass

Branch wilt, produced by the fungus *Hendersonula toruloidea* Nattrass, has been found on Kadota fig trees in the San Joaquin Valley of California (1, 2, 2). It has not, however, become of great importance to the fig industry.

See description of the disease and the fungus under "Branch wilt of English walnut."

References

1. Paxton, J. D., E. E. Wilson, and J. R. Davis. 1964. Branch wilt disease of fig caused by *Hendersonula toruloidea*. Plant Dis. Rep. 48:142.
2. Warner, R. M. 1952. Some observations on branch wilt in figs. Proc. Sixth Ann. Res. Conf., California Fig Inst., 24-25.
3. Wilson, E. E. 1952. Factors affecting the branch wilt disease in walnuts. Proc. Sixth Ann. Res. Conf., California Fig Inst., p. 21-23.

Endosepsis of Fig
Fusarium moniliforme Sheldon var. *fici* n. var.

Endosepsis ("internal rot") also called "pink rot," "brown rot," "soft rot," and "eye-end rot" was described and named by Caldis (1, 2) in 1925 and 1927. It occurs wherever figs are grown in California but has not been reported from other parts of the U.S. or from other countries (2, 5). Before control measures were developed, 30 to 50 percent of the crop in many California orchards was often lost to this disease.

Symptoms. The first observable symptoms of endosepsis are found in the cavity of the fruit as it begins to ripen (fig. 61). Brown streaks develop along the normally white stalks of the female florets. Later, as the number of infected florets increase, the diseased areas are clearly visible as yellowish-brown spots. At this time no external symptom is visible but as the fruit ripens, indefinite water-soaked spots appear on the skin. The spots, which are usually most numerous around the eye (orifice) or along the neck of the fruit, gradually develop a bright pink, brown, or purplish color. At this time the fruit may split across the eye end and a drop of amber gum-like substance appears in the eye. Infected fruit are insipid in taste and lack the characteristic sweetness and flavor of normal figs.

Types and cultivars of figs affected. Endosepsis occurs both in the caprifig and the edible sorts. Although it sometimes develops in the fruits of the common type when these fruits are entered by the Blastophaga, it is an economic problem only in fruit of the Smyrna type which are caprified by the wasp.

Causal organism. Although Caldis (2) identified the causal fungus as *Fusarium moniliforme* Sheldon var. *fici* n. var., any clone of *F. moniliforme* apparently can cause endosepsis. The clone described by Caldis produced macroconidia that are sickle-shaped, attenuate, subpedicellate, 3- 5-septate, 20 to 52

µm long and 2 to 5 µm broad. Microconidia are produced in false beads or in chains, on white to dark maroon aerial hyphae and are ovoid-fusoid 5 to 11 µm long and 2 to 3 µm broad.

Development of the disease. The fungus survives from one year to the next in the mamme or winter fruit of the caprifig. Conidia of the fungus are introduced into these fruits in the fall by the female wasps when they enter them to lay eggs. The fungus is in turn transferred to successive caprifig crops (profichi, mammoni) during the summer; its introduction into edible cultivars occurs when the wasp emerges from infected caprifigs and enters the fruit of those cultivars. Caldis (2) showed that female wasps emerging from diseased caprifigs bear conidia of *F. moniliforme* on their bodies, and proved that fruit which had not been entered by the wasp were free of the fungus. He also showed that endosepsis in parthenocarpic varieties (common type) occurred only after wasps contaminated with spores of *F. moniliforme* enter the fruit.

The female wasp enters the fruit of the edible fig when these structures are still green, and after vainly trying to lay her eggs in the florets she dies. Although the fungus develops saprophytically on the dead body of the wasp, it is unable to invade the fig tissue until the fruit begins to ripen. Subsequent development of the disease is usually rapid, depending on weather conditions. If, however, the weather hastens ripening (thus producing a rapid increase in sugar concentration) development of the fungus may be checked and the fruit will dry without appreciable loss in quality.

Control. Once it became known that the caprifig harbored the fungus from one year to the next, efforts were directed towards cleaning up this source of inoculum. Caprifig trees were removed from the plantings of edible figs and separate plantings were established. The trees are maintained in good growing condition by proper fertilization and irrigation, and are sprayed with whitewash occasionally to destroy lichens which might harbor insects. Moldy fruit or fruit injured by frost are removed from the trees.

About the end of March, before the wasps begin to emerge from caprifigs (mamme), the figs are picked and given a chemical treatment designed to kill or suppress the fungus inside them (3, 4). The treatment involves making an X-shaped cut in the end of each mamme (winter crop to open them). They have been dipped in solution containing benomyl 50 percent (Benlate 50W) at a rate of 1/4 to 1/8 pounds to 25 gallons. Treatment is repeated after 4 or 5 days.

Any figs with water-soaked or rotten spots are removed, and treated figs are then hung back on trees of the Caprifig when the profichi crop is receptive (to the insect). Such treatments reduce contamination of emerging wasps by the causal fungus, thus reducing the incidence of endosepsis in profichi fruit. The profichi fruit are then collected and hung in trees of the edible fig.

References

1. Caldis, P. D. 1925. A rot of the Smyrna fig in California. Science 62:161-62.
2. _____ 1927. Etiology and transmission of endosepsis in the fruit of the fig. Hilgardia 2:287-328.
3. Hansen, H. N. 1927. Control of internal rot of caprified figs. Phytopathology 17:199-200.
4. _____ 1928. Endosepsis and its control in caprifigs. Phytopathology 18:931-38.
5. Smith, R. E. and H. N. Hansen. 1931. Fruit spoilage diseases of the fig. California Univ. Agr. Exp. Sta. Bul. No. 506, 85 pp (out of print).

Phomopsis Canker of Fig
Phomopsis cinerascens Trav.

Phomopsis canker (also called "fig canker") affects all commercial fig cultivars in California. Kadota is most seriously affected because of certain pruning practices. Calimyrna is damaged to some extent, but Mission and Adriatic are rarely attacked.

The disease was first reported from Italy in 1876. It was observed in southern France in 1912, a few years later in England, and in more recent years in North and South Africa, Denmark, the southern coast of Crimea, and Brazil. The first published report from the U.S. was by Smith (16) in California in 1941. Hansen (9) indicated, however, that the disease was observed in California on trees of the Adriatic cultivar as early as 1918, and that it was epidemic in a Kadota orchard just south of Stockton in 1936 (11). More recently, the disease became prevalent in Kadota plantings in Merced County, California (1).

Kadota trees, which are pruned annually, may have as many as 100 cankers that eventually girdle branches (4). The most important cause of loss is from reduction in fruiting wood.

Symptoms. Localized dead area in bark and wood develop at pruning wounds (fig. 62) or at injuries caused by some other agency such as frost (1). Cankers are extremely difficult to see the year that infection occurs because there is very little discoloration of the outer bark. In succeeding years, however, the bark in the older portions of the cankers becomes bleached, cracked, and somewhat sunken, and upon close examination the minute black fruiting bodies of the causal fungus can be seen in the outer bark layers. Yearly elongation of cankers is evidenced by distinct zonations with the outermost zone sporulating most profusely. The cankers become more or less elliptical in shape because they extend more rapidly longitudinally than transversely. Branches are eventually girdled, and the withered brown foliage remains hanging on these dead branches during the summer. New shoots and foliage which develop on partially girdled branches are markedly dwarfed. Cankers occasionally are found around buds, suggesting infection through leaf scars (1).

Causal organism. The causal fungus is *Phomopsis cinerascens* Trav. (8). Synonyms are *Phoma cinerescens* Sacc. (15) and *Phoma ficus* Cast. (16). The perfect stage of this fungus has been reported to be *Diaporthe cinerascens* Sacc. (8).

Pycnidia are gregarious, immersed in the bark, globose-depressed, 250 to 500 μm in diameter, blackish, at length emerging by the ostiole. A-spores are elliptic-fusoid, 6 to 9 $\times$ 2 to 2.5 μm, somewhat obtuse at one or both ends, and often biguttulate, sometimes exuding as a pallid globule; sporophores are crowded, filiform-subulate, 15 to 20 $\times$ 1.5 to 2 μm, nearly straight, and faintly colored at base; B-spores are filiform, 20 to 25 $\times$ 1 μm, mostly hooked, on short pedicels, with occasional A-spores intermixed (8).

Disease development. The fungus survives from one year to the next in cankers on the trees, or on infected branches cut from the tree and left in the orchards (9).

Pycnidiospores are first produced on the cankers during wet spells the winter after infection (1, 12). Splashing rains are probably the chief means of pycnidiospore dispersal, but pruning tools undoubtedly also play a part in disseminating the spores from one cut to another and from one tree to another (9). Insects (bark beetles) and birds may also be factors in spreading the spores. Spores are produced in a sticky mass which becomes firm and adherent when dry, so it is doubtful that wind plays an appreciable part in their dissemination (1, 12).

New pruning cuts are susceptible given proper moisture and temperature and the fungus can infect them. Inoculation tests have shown that Kadota trees are practically immune to infection from the first of April through the growing season, but from around November 1 until at least February they are

174

highly susceptible (1, 2). The fungus advances most rapidly on the upper side of the branch.

Wounds and bark killed by frost and sunburn are the chief areas of infection (1, 10, 12). Leaf scar infections are of minor importance (1).

External symptoms on pruned stubs appear a year after infection, although internal symptoms are seen much earlier. Artificial inoculations of the bark during the dormant season produce visible cankers within a few months.

In culture, growth of the fungus is most rapid at 25 °C. Growth is relatively slow at 4.4 ° and at 30.0 °C or above.

Failure of rapid canker extension between April and October is apparently due to active growth of the host.

Control. Pruning late in the dormant season (late March to early April) has usually resulted in a marked reduction in disease, but is often undesirable from the standpoint of orchard management because it delays fruit maturity (4, 5). Removing cankered branches and chiseling away smaller cankers late in the dormant season is beneficial. Trees with many large cankers on the scaffold branches should be cut off just above the ground and new trees developed from the stumps (2, 10). Pruning tools used in these operations should be sterilized with 5.25 percent sodium hypochlorite diluted 1:9 with water (13).

Cultural practices should be designed to keep the trees vigorous, because such trees appear to be least susceptible to the disease.

Branches and twigs cut from diseased trees should be removed from the orchards and burned (9).

Studies by English (1, 3, 4, 6) from 1950 to 1959 indicated that fungicides at economically feasible concentrations did not provide satisfactory control.

A single organic mercury spray applied within 24 to 48 hours after pruning of Kadota trees provided better control than did any other spray material (4, 7). Plastic caps gave effective control, but an elastic film applied as a liquid did not afford protection (6). Mercury fungicide prevented sporulation in some years (3).

No control was afforded by the tree seals, by sodium pentachlorophenoxide, liquid lime sulfur, sodium dinitro-ortho-cresolate (Elgetol), dodecylguanidine acetate (Cyprex), or polyethylene thiuram sulfide (Thioneb). Bordeaux mixture spray recommended by Hansen (9) also proved to be ineffective (4).

References

1. English, H. 1951. Phomopsis canker: A progress report. Proc. Fifth Ann. Res. Conf. California Fig Inst., pp. 45-48.
2. _____ 1952. Phomopsis canker of figs. Phytopathology 42:513. (Abstr.)
3. _____ 1952. Pruning and spraying experiment for Phomopsis canker. Proc. Sixth Ann. Res. Conf. California Fig Inst., pp. 16-19.
4. _____ 1953. Further work on the control of Phomopsis canker. Proc. Seventh Ann. Res. Conf. California Fig Inst., pp. 12-15.
5. _____ 1958. Physical and chemical methods of reducing Phomopsis canker infection in Kadota fig trees. Phytopathology 48:392. (Abstr.)
6. _____ 1960. Experiments on the control of Phomopsis canker in Kadota fig trees. Proc. Fourteenth Ann. Res. Conf. California Fig Inst., pp. 13-15.
7. Gilmer, R. 1957. Phomopsis canker on Kadota figs. Proc. Eleventh Ann. Res. Conf. California Fig Inst., pp. 26-28.
8. Grove, W. B. 1935. *In:* British Stem-and-Leaf Fungi. Vol. 1:186-87. Cambridge Univ. Press.
9. Hansen, H. N. 1949. Phomopsis canker of fig. California Agri. 3(11):13-14.
10. _____ 1949. Control and cure of Phomopsis canker of fig. California Fruit and Grape Grower 3(9):7.
11. _____ 1949. Canker diseases in figs. Proc. Third Ann. Res. Conf. California Fig. Inst. pp. 18-19.
12. Livshits, I. Z., and L. I. Pupysheva. 1949. Fig canker and measures of its control. Sad i Ogorod (3):25-27.
13. Pilgrim, A. J. 1959. Phomopsis canker of Kadotas. Proc. Fourth Ann. Res. Conf. California Fig. Inst. Pp. 30-32.
14. Saccardo, P. A. 1884. Sylloge fungorum 3:96.
15. _____ 1895. Sylloge fungorum 11:486.
16. Smith, R. E. 1941. Diseases of fruits and nuts. Calif. Univ. Agr. Exp. Sta. Circ. No. 120. 168 pp. (out of print).
17. Warner, R. M. 1952. Injection of fig trees for Phomopsis canker. Proc. Sixth Ann. Res. Conf. California Fig Inst. Pp. 20-21.

Smut and Mold of Fig
Aspergillus niger van Tiegh.
Other Fungus Species

"Fig smut," an unfortunate choice of a name, is caused chiefly by *Aspergillus niger* van Tiegh. The name "mold" refers to a number of internal rots other than endosepsis caused by such common saprophytes as *Botrytis, Hormodendron, Penicillium,* and *Rhizopus* (3, 4, 5). Both are troublesome in the principal fig-growing districts of California. These fungi, which occur both in edible fig and the caprifig, probably occur worldwide but foreign literature is vague on this point. Edgerton (1) reported a soft rot caused by *Rhizopus stolonifer* to be common in Louisiana.

Symptoms. Smut is distinguishable by the presence of black powdery masses of spores of *A. niger* in the pulp of the fruit cavity (fig. 63). With mold, the pulp is discolored dirty gray, greenish or yellowish.

Disease development. The fungi are present in the soil and decaying organic matter. They are also present in affected caprifigs. Phillips, Smith, and Smith (4) blamed the vinegar fly, *Drosophila ampelophila,* and the dried-fruit beetle, *Carpophilus hemipterus* for carrying the spores into the cavities of the edible fig. According to Hansen (2) and Hansen and Davey (3), thrips and predaceous mites carry spores of organisms capable of producing spoilage. These small insects enter the green fig long before the scales around the orifice of the fruit loosen sufficiently to permit entry of larger insects. The time at which the interior of the fig fruit becomes contaminated by fungus spores corresponds closely with the time of infestation by thrips and mites.

Aspergillus niger and *Botrytis cinerea* may attack fig fruit through external injuries. Subsequent spread of the mold may occur when fruit are in contact.

Control. Reduction of the insect population in fig orchards is helpful in preventing smut and mold. It is advisable to practice clean cultivation to destroy the weed hosts of the thrips and mites, and to remove fallen figs from the ground to eliminate these sources of fungi, the fruit fly, and the dried-fruit beetle. Insecticidal sprays are being evaluated.

References

1. Edgerton, C. W. 1911. Diseases of the fig tree and fruit. Louisiana Agr. Exp. Sta. Bul. No. 126. 20 pp.
2. Hansen, H. N. 1929. Thrips as carriers of fig-decaying organisms. Science 69:356-57.
3. Hansen, H. N., and A. E. Davey. 1932. Transmission of smut and molds of fig. Phytopathology 22:247-52.
4. Phillips, E. H., R. E. Smith, and E. H. Smith. 1925. Fig. smut. California Univ. Agr. Exp. Sta. Bul. No. 387, 38 pp.
5. Smith, R. E. 1941. Diseases of fruit and nuts. California Univ. Agr. Exp. Sta. Circ. No. 120 (out of print).
6. Smith, R. E., and H. N. Hansen. 1931. Fruit spoilage diseases of figs. California Univ. Agr. Exp. Sta. Bul. No. 506.

Souring of Fig

Souring or fermentation of the flesh of the fig fruit, a widespread disease of long standing (1, 2, 3), occurs in all three types of figs. It is caused by different types of yeasts.

Symptoms. Symptoms are noticeable (fig. 64) only when the fruit begins to ripen and the "eye" is open. The inner flesh (pulp) of the fruit first develops a pink color, later becoming water-soaked. A pink exudate exudes from the eye. Gas bubbles, detectable in the pulp, give off a strong alcohol smell. In late stages of the disease a scum of the yeast organism collects in the watery pulp. The fig fruit loses its firmness and later dries up on the twig.

Disease development. The dried fruit beetle *(Carpophilus hermipterus)* and vinegar fly *(Drosophila melanogaster)* are responsible for disseminating the yeast cells from fruit to fruit. These insects are attracted to fermenting fruit and since they are small enough to enter the eye of the fruit after the eye scales are shed, they can transmit the yeast to the interior of the fruit.

Control. Little can be done to control the disease.

References

1. Caldis, P. D. 1930. Souring of figs by yeasts and the transmission of the disease by insects. J. Agr. Research 40:1031-51.
2. Haring, C. M. 1922. Splitting and souring of Smyrna figs. California Univ. Agr. Exp. Sta. Ann. Rept. 1920-21:80-81.
3. Howard, L. O. 1901. Smyrna fig culture in the United States. U.S. Dept. Agr. Yearbook 1900: 79-106.

Surface Mold and Alternaria Rot of Fig
Cladosporium herbarum (Pers.) Lindt.
Alternaria alternata (Fr.) Keissl.

"Surface mold" and "Alternaria rot" are good descriptive terms for the fruit infections by *Cladosporium* and *Alternaria,* respectively. Other terms used are spotting, smudge, mildew and black spot (2, 4, 7). In the handbook published in 1971 (9), the use of the name Cladosporium spot is confusing because the term spot has been used to describe fruit infections caused by *Alternaria*.

All fig cultivars are susceptible to both pathogens but the disease is most severe on Kadota. In California, the moldy condition on Kadota fruit was first brought to the attention of researchers in the fall of 1951 with hopes of developing control measures (3). Losses of fruit are directly related to climate during fruit harvest in August and September—rains at this time not only cause moldy fruit but severe splitting of fruit.

Symptoms and pathogens. The surface mold, caused by *Cladosporium herbarum* (Pers.) Lindt. (2) develops on both immature and mature fruit and is largely restricted to the upper and outer surface of the fruit (4). The disease first appears as dark olive-green specks, and as the lesions enlarge they become slightly depressed and turn to a yellowish-olive colored smudge. Conidiophores arise in tufts, erect or nearly so, from nodular masses of cells embedded in the epidermis; they are septate and brownish-olive in color and are 3 to 4.8 μm in diameter. The catenulate conidia range from cylindrical to elliptical, ovoid, subfusiform or subglobose and may become one or more septate. Conidia measure 3 to 7.2 μm in length by 2 to 5.6 μm in width, and are at first hyaline to pale greenish-yellow and finally olivaceous.

Alternaria rot is first evident as water-soaked areas which soon become slightly depressed and dark as olivaceous-colored spores are produced (fig. 65). The organism penetrates the skin and the mycelium is found in abundance several cells deep with scattered hyphae much deeper in the tissue. Conidiophores are 25 to 250 μm in length by 3 to 5 μm in diameter and sometimes moderately echinulate. Conidia are produced in long, sometimes branched chains. They are obclavate to pyriform and muriform; echinulate; at first pale to amber-yellow but later olivaceous to fuscous; usually with short beaks; they are longitudinally and transversely septate and measure 20 to 75 μm in length by 8 to 17 μm wide. Mature conidia finally become distorted, swollen, and septa are formed at various angles. The fungus belongs to the *Alternaria tenuis* group (2) and recently was classified as *A. alternata* (Fr.) Kiessl.

Development of the disease. These fungi are commonly found in nature affecting other crops, and on dying or dead tissue of various kinds. On figs, *Cladosporium* and *Alternaria* can be found independently or together on the fruit surface with *Cladosporium* usually predominating; the only active decay or rot is produced by *Alternaria* (3). *Cladosporium* is found almost entirely on low-vigor trees producing subnormal vegetative growth (4); *Alternaria* is found more often in trees having dense foliage (7). *Cladosporium* occurs on fruit at all stages of maturity, while *Alternaria* is serious only on ripe fruit (4). Because spores of both fungi require high humidity or free moisture for germination and infection, the disease in California does not develop until late August, becoming progressively worse in September. Water droplets are detrimental to production of appressoria by *Alternaria* spores, while relative humidities in the 90s favor both germination and infection (6).

Control. Reduction of field infection by *Cladosporium* was achieved by spray applications of zinc coposil and Dithane Z78 (zinc ethylene bis-dithiocarbamate) in the first week of September. *Alternaria* control was obtained with two or three applications of Dithane Z78 during the same period (4). Alternaria rot is also reduced by picking the fruit before it becomes over-ripe. On figs picked for immediate marketing, maneb and captan field sprays effectively reduced decay for at least 2 days at room temperature, after storage at 2 °C. Sanitation of the picking buckets and field boxes also influenced decay during storage. Fungicide dips are ineffective or phytotoxic (7). More recently Clorothalonil (Bravo 6F) sprays were shown to be effective in controlling Alternaria fruit rot (1). A modified atmosphere containing 23 percent or more carbon dioxide during storage and transit is as effective in controlling Alternaria rot as immediate storage at 0 °C (2).

References

1. Bewaji, O. and W. H. English. 1974. Personal communication.
2. Brooks, C., and L. P. McColloch. 1938. Spotting of figs on the market. J. Agr. Research 56: 473-88.
3. English, W. H. 1953. Sprays for reducing surface mold and rot of Kadota figs. Proc. Seventh Annual Research Conference of the California Fig Institute. Pp. 17-20.
4. _____ 1954. Further experiments on the control of surface mold and rot of Kadota figs. Proc. Eighth Annual Research Conference of the California Fig Institute. Pp. 16-20.
5. Harvey, J. M. 1957. The effect of handling practices and fungicide treatments on market decay losses in fresh figs. Proc. Eleventh Annual Research Conf. of the Calif. Fig. Institute. Pp. 23-26.
6. Koepsell, P. A. 1968. The etiology of *Geotrichum* and *Alternaria* molds and their effects on mechanical harvesting of tomato. Ph.D. dissertation. Univ. of California, Davis.

7. Smith, R. E., and H. N. Hansen. 1931. Fruit spoilage diseases of figs. University of California Agricultural Experiment Station Bul. 506:49-51 (out of print).
8. Smith, R. E. 1941. Diseases of fruits and nuts. California Agr. Ext. Service Circ. 120. P. 71 (out of print).
9. Smooth, J. J., L. G. Houck, and H. B. Johnson. 1971. Market diseases of citrus and other sub-tropical fruits. USDA Agricultural Handbook No. 398. Pp. 63-64, 65-66.

Whetzelinia and Botrytis Limb Blight
or Die-back of Fig

Whetzelinia sclerotiorum (Lib.) Korf and Dumont
Botrytis cinerea Pers. ex. Fr.

In 1919, Condit and Stevens (1) reported that a die-back of the new shoots of fig trees was common in California. It was thought that the shoots were first weakened by *Botrytis* and thus rendered more susceptible to sunburning and attack by other fungi. Shoot dieback following winter injury to fruits or branches can be caused by *Botrytis* (2, 3).

In 1931, Taubenhaus and Ezekiel (4) showed by inoculations that limb blight of the Magnolia culti-var of fig in Texas was caused by the fungus known as *Sclerotinia sclerotiorum* (Lib.) Massee or *Whetzelinia sclerotiorum* (Lib.) Korf and Dumont. The disease was characterized by a sudden wilting of the foliate of new shoots in the spring. The bark of affected branches was watersoaked and overrun by a thick white growth of the fungus. In later states of the disease, numerous sclerotia developed in and on affected portions of the limbs.

Stems affected with *Botrytis* or *Whetzelinia* and moldy "stick tight" figs should be removed (3).

References

1. Condit, I. J., and H. L. Stevens. 1919. "Die-back" of the fig in California. Fig and Olive J. 4:11-12.
2. English, H. 1962. Canker and dieback disorders of fig trees. Proc. Sixteenth Ann. Res. Conf. California Fig Inst. pp. 13-15.
3. Smith, R. E. 1941. Diseases of fruits and nuts. California Agric. Ext. Serv. Circ. 120. P. 71 (out of print).
4. Taubenhaus, J. J., and W. N. Ezekiel. 1931. A sclerotinia limb blight of figs. Phytopathology 21:1191-97.

VII. MINOR CROPS AND THEIR DISEASES

Chestnut and its Diseases

Chestnuts (*Castanea* spp.) belong in the family Fagaceae with beech and oak. Less than 50 acres are grown in California. The sweet and rich flavor of the nuts make them highly prized for roasting in the shell and for use in cooking.

Pathogens isolated from samples submitted for identification to the State Department of Food and Agriculture are *Armillaria mellea*, *Dematophora necatrix*, *Coryneum kunzei*, *Polyporous sulphureus*, *Agrobacterium tumefaciens*, and *Endothia parasitica* (6).

Chestnut blight, caused by *Endothia parasitica* (Murr.) P. J. & H. W. Anderson, is the most destructive in the eastern states and has reduced the U.S. chestnut culture to a position of minor importance. The disease was first discovered in New York in 1904 and within 30 years every stand of chestnut trees was infected or killed. No effective control measure is available. Although the American cultivars are highly susceptible, the edible Asiatic chestnuts (*C. japonica* and *C. mollissima*) are resistant. Details on this disease, which have been reported from California (14), are found in publications by Hepting (5).

Filbert and its Diseases

Filberts are a type of hazelnut (*Corylus* spp.) belonging to the birch family, *Betulaceae*. There are only about 8 acres in California. The major production areas in the U.S. are Oregon and Washington, where the most important cultivar is Barcellona. The first culture of *Corylus* species seems to have begun in Italy as early as 1671.

Fungus pathogens reported from California on filberts are *Armillaria mellea*, *Dothidea corylina*, *Physalospora obtusa*, and *Poria ferrea*. *Phyllactinia corylea* has been identified on submitted samples (6). The

dieback canker disease caused by *Apioporthe anomala* (Pk.) Hoehn [*Cryptosporella anomola* (Pk.) Sacc.] is a serious disease in the eastern U.S. (14) and recently was introduced into Washington and Oregon (3). The disease has not been reported from California (6).

Macadamia and its Diseases

The macadamia, *Macadamia* spp., is native to Queensland and New South Wales (Australia). The nut is more commonly called Queensland nut or Australian nut (3, 12). It is closely related to the silk-oak (Proteaceae) and requires a climate similar to that required for orange production. The macadamia is used exclusively as a dessert nut. Small commercial orchards are located in Hawaii and Australia. In California, about 138 acres are in production.

Phytophthora cinnamomi infections were observed on trunk wounds of *Macadamia integrifolia* seedlings and *M. tetraphylla* rootstock, but the roots of these seedlings are considered quite resistant (15). In Hawaii, two other *Phytophthora* species, *P. palmivora* and *P. nicotianae* var. parasitica, have been reported to infect the trees (8).

The most important disease in Hawaii is gray mold *(Botrytis cinerea)* which infects the racemes (7). In 1960, severe outbreaks followed prolonged rain and temperatures of 16 to 28 C.

Pecan and its Diseases

Pecan, *Carya illioensis* (Wang.) K. Koch., is native to the U.S. with production located primarily in the southern states from Oklahoma to Florida. California has about 725 acres in pecans with much of this in young trees.

Crown gall, *Agrobacterium tumefaciens*, is reported by Smith (12) to occur on pecan in California but trees were not extremely susceptible to the disease. Smith (12) also noted that pecan roots appear to be very resistant to *Armillaria mellea. Verticillium* sp. has been identified on submitted samples (6). The most important problem in California is little-leaf or rosette caused by zinc deficiency (4). Scab, caused by *Cladosporium effusum* (Wint.) Demaree, attacking leaves, shoots, and nuts, is the most important disease in the southern states but has not been reported in California (6).

Persimmon and its Diseases

Persimmon (*Diospyros* spp.) belongs in the family Ebenaceae. The most important species grown for its fruit is the Oriental persimmon or Kaki (*D. kaki* L.). The common American cultivar, *D. virginiana* L., was brought to California by the first American settlers (trees of this species were planted by General Bidwell on Rancho Chico and by 1889 were 30 to 40 feet tall). Until the Oriental or Japanese persimmon was introduced in 1870, however, there was little incentive for extensive planting. In the late 1870s the University of California Agricultural Experiment Station became interested in the fruit. The first large order of 3,000 trees, comprising many cultivars, was received in San Francisco in 1880.

The first cultivars grown in California were Hachiya, Tanenashi (seedless) and Yemon. Later came the Fuyu, which is non-astringent. Private importation ceased with the quarantine laws in 1919. In 1910 there were 3,274 bearing trees. By 1930 there were more than 98,000 trees in bearing and more than 96,000 non-bearing in southern California counties of San Bernardino, Los Angeles, Orange, and San Diego and the northern counties of Placer and Butte (2). In 1976, there were 599 acres of persimmon trees in the state.

The fruit is harvested for the fresh market, or for drying, from late September to early December. The most important cultivars, such as Hachiya, Tanenashi, and Fuyu, bear only pistillate flowers and therefore have strong tendency to set fruit parthenocarpically. To reduce astringency, the Hachiya is treated with ethylene or alcohol. In Japan, Hachiya are kept in cold rooms in an atmosphere of high carbon dioxide; fruit so stored will keep for several months and become non-astringent (4).

The pathogens reported from California on persimmons are *Agrobacterium tumefaciens, Phytophthora* sp., *Armillaria mellea* and *Botrytis cinerea* (11, 14). In 1933 the fungus pathogen, *Cephalosporium diospyri* Crandall was discovered on American persimmons in Tennessee. Since then the wilt disease it causes has spread in the southern states and as a result introduction of the American persimmon into California is prohibited (6). The Oriental persimmons, however, appear to be resistant to this fungus.

Pistachio and its Diseases

The pistachio nut tree, *Pistacia vera* L., belong in the family Anacardinaceae with the mango, the cashew nut, the sumac, the poison ivy, and the ornamental pepper tree. It is native to Asia and Asia Minor and was introduced into Mediterranean Europe during the Christian era, and thereafter into Tunisia, France, Australia and the U.S. In 1902, the U.S. Department of Agriculture Plant Introduction Station at Chico, California, began testing the suitability of pistachio cultivars and the Kerman was used to establish the first commercial orchards. There have been 27,233 acres of new plantings during the past 10 years, especially in the southern San Joaquin Valley (2).

No known serious diseases occur in Turkey or Iran, and trees have been known to attain trunk girths of 6 feet and remain productive for as long as 700 years. However, in California, orchards are threatened by Verticillium wilt (*Verticillium dahliae* Kleb.) with losses of 0.4 to 1.5 percent of the trees planted on virgin soils. In orchards planted in soil in which cotton had grown, losses have been as high as 12.5 percent.

Fumigating soils on which cotton had grown with a chloropicrin-methyl bromide mixture (2:1, w/w) has reduced *Verticillium* sclerotial counts to a trace, and has reduced losses of pistachio trees to that of tree loss on virgin soil. Resistant rootstocks have not been found.

Other pistachio diseases reported from California but not causing serious losses are Texas root rot (*Phymatotrichum omnivorum* (Shear) Dug.), and sapwood rots (*Pleurotus ostreatus* Jacq. ex. Fr. and *Schizophyllum commune* Fr.). *Armillaria mellea* and *Phytophthora parasitica* have been found on submitted samples (6).

Pomegranate and its Diseases

The pomegranate, *Punica granatum* L., native to the area currently known as Iran (Persia) and adjacent regions, is considered to be one of the oldest edible fruits known. It was introduced to California by the first Spanish settlers when Mission San Diego was founded in 1769. In 1859, there were 3,149 trees in California. According to the U.S. census for 1910 there were 1,771 bearing and 2,745 nonbearing trees in the state, and by 1930 the number of bearing acres had increased to 110,518. The bulk of the acreage was and is in Tulare and Fresno counties where in 1976 there were 2,089 acres. Fruit was shipped from the Sackett orchard on Putah Creek, Solano County, before 1889. Of the cultivars, Spanish Ruby was the early favorite, and Sweet Fruited was later tested. Wonderful has proven the best suited cultivar for California (2).

The crop requires a large amount of summer heat, yet can withstand low temperatures of -12.2 to $-9.4°C$. The fruit is usually harvested from mid-September to early November. Botanically a berry, the fruit has a thick leathery rind and therefore is inconvenient to eat and considered by some to taste insipid. When ripe the fruit will crack, thus producing an avenue for infection by rot organisms.

Smut disease of the fruit, caused by *Aspergillus niger* Van Tiegh., has been reported in California (12). It was the only disease of the pomegranate fruit seen by one of the present authors in southern Iran in 1974. Also reported on cracked fruit are *Alternaria alternata, Botrytis cinerea, Nematospora* sp. and *Penicillium* sp. (14) (figs. 66A, 66B). The best method for preventing infection by these fungi is to harvest the fruit as soon as it is ripe. Root infections by *Armillaria mellea* and *Agrobacterium tumefaciens* have also been found on pomegranates in the state (6).

References

1. Ashworth, L. J., Jr., and G. Zimmerman. 1977. Verticillium wilt of pistachio nut tree: Occurrence in California and control by soil fumigation. Phytopathology 66:1449-51.
2. Butterfield, H. M. 1937-38. History of deciduous fruits in California. The Blue Anchor. Vol. 14 and 15. 38 pp.
3. Cameron, H. R. 1976. Personnel Communication. Oregon State University, Corvallis.
4. Chandler, W. H. 1947. Deciduous orchards. Philadelphia: Lee & Febiger. 437 pp.
5. Hepting, G. H. 1971. Diseases of forest and shade trees of the United States. USDA Handbook No. 386. U.S. Government printing office, Washington, D. C. 658 pp.
6. Hiatt, P. W. 1976. Personal communication. California State Department of Agriculture, Sacramento.
7. Holtzmann, O. V. 1963. Raceme blight of macadamia in Hawaii. Plant Dis. Rep. 47:416-17.
8. Hunter, J. E., R. K. Kumimoto, and K. G. Rohrbach. 1971. Phytophthora blight, a new disease of macadamia. Phytopathology 61:1130-33.
9. Mircetich, S. M. 1976. Personal communication. USDA. University of California, Davis.
10. Schnathorst, W. C. 1976. Personal communication. USDA. University of California, Davis.
11. Smith, C. O. 1913. Some successful inoculations with the peach crown gall organism and certain observations upon retarded gall formation. Phytopathology 3:59-60.
12. Smith, R. E. 1941. Diseases of fruits and nuts. California Agr. Serv. Circ. 120. 168 pp (out of print).
13. Storey, W. B. 1957. The macadamia in California. Proc. Florida State Hort. Soc. 70:333-38.
14. USDA Agriculture Handbook No. 165. 1960. Index of plant diseases in the United States. U.S. Government Printing Office, Washington D.C. 531 pp.
15. Zentmeyer, G. A. 1960. Phytophthora canker of macadamia trees in California. Plant Dis. Rep. 44:819.

APPENDIX

CALIFORNIA'S AGRICULTURE

The mission fathers were the first to practice systematic agriculture in California by planting seeds brought on their earliest expeditions. Farming was started at the 21 missions established from San Diego to Sonoma between 1769 and 1823. Workers at the missions planted almost all of the fruit and nut cultivars that are grown in California today.

California, the most southwesterly of the Pacific Coast States, is bounded on the north by Oregon, on the east by Nevada and Arizona, on the south by Mexico's Baja California territory, and on the west by the Pacific Ocean. It extends from 32° 30′ south latitude to 42° north, and its longitudinal limits are approximately 114° east and 124° 29′ west. The length of its north-south medial line is 770 miles, and its breadth varies from 150 to a maximum of 250 miles in the east-west direction. The total area is 158,693 square miles including 2,120 square miles of inland water. California's physiography provides a splendid valley 20 to 40 miles wide between the coast ranges and the magnificent snow-covered Sierra Nevada on the eastern side. This valley is about 450 miles long and has about 18,000 square miles of irrigated agricultural land. Through this interior basin flow the Sacramento and San Joaquin rivers, for which the northern and southern portions of the valley are named.

In general the climate is hot and dry, and irrigation is required for production of most crops. Most of California's agricultural areas have only two seasons, a mild, wet winter alternating with a relatively dry summer. Average precipitation varies from about 35 to 40 inches in the northwestern part of the state to less than 2 inches in Death Valley. Water from winter snows in the Sierra Nevada provides for irrigation as it flows down rivers or is dammed for later release.

The main agricultural districts (see appended map) for production of fruit and nut crops are discussed below in their order of importance.

1. **San Joaquin Valley.** The surface of most of the San Joaquin Valley is flat because of alluvial deposits from the Stanislaus, Tuolumne, Merced, Fresno, San Joaquin, Kings, Kern, and Kawaeah rivers. Temperatures in the hottest part of year (July and August) can reach over 37.7 °C; at Stockton it may average 23.9 °C and at Bakersfield 28.9 °C. Over 80 percent of the precipitation occurs in winter, with an average of 6.3 inches per year in Bakersfield and 14.3 inches at Stockton.

Fruit crops grown are almonds, apricots, cherries, figs, nectarines, olives, peaches, persimmons, pistachios, plums, pomegranates, prunes, and walnuts.

2. **Sacramento Valley.** The valley is flat and is drained by the south-flowing Sacramento River which is joined by rivers from the Sierra Nevada Mountains— these are the Feather, Yuba, American, Consumnes, and Bear. Winters are cool and moist, with fogs that may persist for several weeks; summers are clear, hot, and dry. Average January temperature in Sacramento is 7.2 °C, in July it is 23.9 °C. Annual precipitation is 16.3 inches. Redding, in the northern part of the valley, receives 38.7 inches of rain per year. The main fruit and nut crops are almonds, apricots, olives, pears, plums, prunes, and walnuts.

3. **Central Coast.** This area extends from the Bay area just north of Walnut Creek and south to the mountain ranges north of Santa Barbara. The climate is mild, the summers are cool on the coast and warm in the interior. Fog is common along the coast in summer. Salinas, which is about 10 miles from the ocean, has a January average temperature of 10 °C and a September average of 23.3 °C. Annual precipitation in Salinas is 13.7 inches.

The fruit and nut crops grown are almonds, apples, apricots, cherries, pears, plums, prunes and walnuts.

4. **North Coast.** The region is mountainous with few small valleys and coastal plains. The alluvial low-

land soils are generally acid and the interior valleys have calcareous soils. This is the wettest region, receiving from 35 to 40 inches of rain per year and irrigation is limited.

Fruit and nut crops grown are apples, grapes, pears, prunes, and walnuts.

5. **Sierra Mountains.** This region is largely high, rugged country, with some valleys having alluvial, valley bottom, and terrace soils. The climate is either too dry or too cold for most agriculture.

Apples, pears, peaches, prunes, persimmons, and cherries are grown at lower elevations.

6. **Southern California.** The entire region has a moderate climate. Temperatures are quite uniform with a July average of 20.5 °C. Coastal fog is common during the year. Precipitation along the coastal zone ranges from 17.6 inches per year at Santa Barbara to 10.4 inches in San Diego. Mountain ranges border this region acting as barrier between the lowlands and the deserts. The region sometimes suffers droughts especially in the interior areas, and irrigation water is limited.

In addition to citrus, almonds, apples, apricots, olives, and limited acreages of walnuts are grown.

References

1. Salitore, E. D. Editor. 1971. California, past, present, and future. E. V. Salitore, President and publisher, P. O. Box 400. Lakewood, California 90714. 670 pp.
2. Cain M., J. C. Siebert, R. A. McGregor. 1978. 1977 California Fruit and Nut Acreage. California Crop and Livestock Reporting Service. Sacramento, California. 24 pp.

CALIFORNIA'S PRINCIPAL FRUIT AND NUT CROPS[*]

Crop	Total acreage	Ranking in USA	Active harvest season
Almonds	340,557	1	Aug 15-Oct 15
Apples	26,293	4	Jul 15-Oct 30
Apricots	28,883	1	Jun 1-Aug 10
Cherries, sweet	12,484	2	May 25-June 10
Chestnuts	46	—	Sept-Oct
Figs	17,412	1	Jun 20-Aug 25
Filberts	8	—	Oct 10-Nov 15
Macademias	131	2	Aug-Dec
Nectarines	21,535	1	Jul 15-Aug 10
Olives	42,770	1	Oct 5-Feb 10
Peaches			
Freestone	29,706	1	Jun 20-Aug 15
Clingstone	55,007	1	Aug 5-Sep 5
Pears	40,372	3	Jul 10-Sep 15
Pecans	1,037	—	Nov 15-Dec 15
Persimmon	587	1	Sep 25-Dec 10
Pistachio	31,065	1	Sep 1-Oct 15
Plums	32,917	1	June 15-Aug 1
Pomegranates	2,999	1	Sep 15-Nov 10
Prunes	83,146	1	Aug 10-Sep 25
Walnuts	205,515	1	Sep 25-Nov 5

[*]1977 California fruit and nut acreage. 19 pp. California Crop and Livestock reporting service, P.O. Box 1258, Sacramento, CA 95806.

CALIFORNIA'S MAJOR FRUIT-AND NUT PRODUCING DISTRICTS

1. SAN JOAQUIN VALLEY
2. SACRAMENTO VALLEY
3. CENTRAL COAST
4. NORTH COAST
5. SIERRA MOUNTAIN
6. SOUTHERN CALIFORNIA

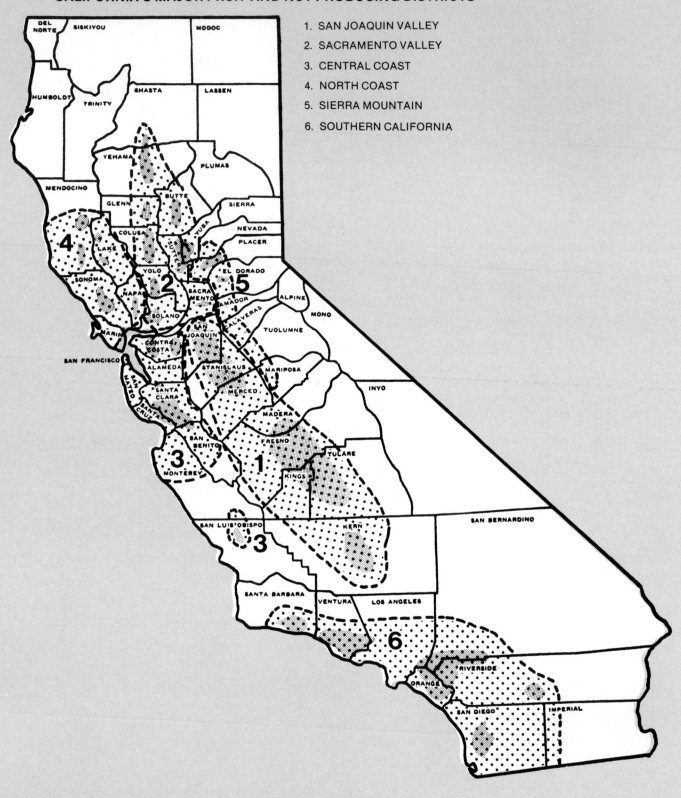

Chemicals for Control of Diseases on Fruit and Nut trees

Common or trivial name	Trade name	Active ingredients	Basic manufacturer
Benomyl	Benlate 50W	Methyl 1-(butylcarbamoyl)-2-benzimidazolecarbamate	E. I. DuPont de Nemours & Co.
Bordeaux mixture	Bordeaux	Copper sulfate plus lime	————
Captafol	Difolatan	cis-N-(1,1,2,2,-tetrachloroethylthio)-4-cyclohexene-1,2-carboximide	Chevron Chemical Company
Captan	Orthocide Captan	N-(trichloromethlythio)-4 cyclohexene-1,2-dicarboximide	Chevron Chemical Company Stauffer Chemical Company
Carbon disulfide	Weeviltox	Carbon disulfide	————
Chloropicrin	Picfume	Trichloronitromethane	————
Chlorothalonil	Bravo 6F	Tetrachloroisophthalonitrile	Diamond Shamrock Corp.
Copper hydroxide	Kocide	Copper hydroxide	Kocide Chemical Corp.
Copper ammonium carbonate	Copper-Count-N	Copper ammonium carbonate	Mineral Research & Development Corp.
Copper oxychloride	————	Basic cupric chlorides	————
Copper oxy chloride sulfate	COCS		Niagara Chemical Div., FMC Corp.
Cycloheximide	Actidione	2-(3,5-dimethyl-2-oxocyclohexyl)-2-hydroxyethylglutarimide	The Upjohn Company
Dehydroacetic acid	DHA	a-acetyl-6-methyl-2,4-pyrandione	Dow Chemical Co. Union Carbide Corp.
Dichlone	Phygon	2,3-dichloro-1,4-napthoquinone	Uniroyal Chemical Co. Niagara Chemical Div., FMC Corp.
Dicloran, DCNA	Botran, Allisan	2,6-dichloro-4-nitroaniline	The Upjohn Company
Dinocap	Karathane	2,4-dinitro-6-octylphenyl crotonate and 2,6-dinitro-4-octylphenyl crotonate	Rohm and Haas Co.
Dodine	Cyprex	n-dodecylguanidine acetate	American Cyanamid Co.
Ethazol	Terrazole, Truban	5-ethoxy-3-(tri-chloromethyl)-1,2,4-thiadiazole	Olin Corp. Mallinckrodt Chemical Co.
Fenaminosulf	Dexon	p-(dimethylamino)benzenediazo sodium sulfonate	Chemagro Corp.
Ferbam	Fermate	Ferric dimethyldithiocarbamate	E. I. duPont de Nemours & Co. Niagra Chemical Div., FMC Corp.
Folpet	Phaltan	N-(trichloromethylthio)phthalimide	Chevron Chemical Co.
Formaldehyde	Formalin	Formaldehyde	Allied Chemical Corp.
Glyodin Hexachlorobenzene	Crag Fungicide 341 Pentachloronitrobenzene	2-heptadecyl-2-imidazoline acetate Pentachloronitrobenzene	Union Carbide Corp.
Hydrated lime	calcium hydroxide	Calcium hydroxide	————
hypochlorite	Clorox Purex	Ca or Na hypochlorite or chlorine gas	Clorox Corp. Purex Corp.
Lime sulfur	Calcium polysulfide	Calcium polysulfides	————
Maneb	Dithane M-22, Manzate	Manganous ethylene-1,2-bisdithiocarbamate	Rohm & Haas Co. E. I. duPont de Nemours, Inc.

Common or trivial name	Trade name	Active ingredients	Basic manufacturer
Mancozeb	Dithane M-45 Manzate 200	Coordination product of zinc ion and manganous ethylene-1,2-bisdithiocarbamate	Rohm & Haas Co. E. I. du Pont de Nemours, Inc.
Methyl bromide	Many	Methyl bromide	Dow Chemical Co. Great Lakes Chemical Corp.
Nabam	Parzate, Dithane D-14	Disodium ethylene1,2-bis-dithiocarbamate plus certain metallic sulfates	Chemical Insectide Corp. E. I. duPont de Nemours & Co., Inc. Rohm & Haas Co.
Oxycarboxin	Plantvax	2,3-dihydro-5-carbo-xanilido-6-methyl-1,4-oxathiin-4,4-dioxide	Uniroyal Chemicals
Oxytetracycline	Terramycin	Oxytetracycline-hydrochloride	Charles F. Pfizer & Co.
Petroleum oils	Oils		several oil companies
Pyroxychloro	Dowco 269		Dow Chemical Co.
Quintozene	Terraclor, PCNB	Pentachloronitrobenzene	Olin Corp.
Sodium penta-chlorophenate	Niagara Dormant Dowicide G	Sodium pentachlorophenate	Dow Chemical Co. Monsanto Co.
Streptomycin (sulfate or nitrate)	Agrimycin Agri-Step	Streptomycin	Merck & Co. Charles Pfizer & Co.
sulfur			
Thiabendazole	Tecto 60 , Mycozol Mertect	2 (4 -thiazoyl)benzimidazole	Merck & CO.
Thiophanate M	Topsin M , Cercobin	Dimethyl 4,4-o-pheylenebis 3-thioallophanate	Pennwalt Corp.
Triforine	Cela W524	Piperazine-1,4-diyl-bis-1-(2, 2, 2-trichloroethyl) formamide	Celamerck GmbH & Co. K. G. West Germany
Xylenol	Bacticin Gallex	2(4-thiazolyl)benzimidazole	The Upjohn Company; Agriochem, Inc.
Zineb	DithaneZ-78	Zinc ethylene-1,2-bisdithiocarbamate	E.I. duPont de Nemours & Co., Inc. Rohm & Haas Co.
Ziram	Zerlate, Milbam	Zinc dimethlydithiocarbamate	F. W. Berk & Co., Inc. E. I. duPont de Nemours & Co., Inc. Rohm & Haas Co.

HOST-DISEASE INDEX

Showing page and figure (F) numbers in which diseases and their hosts are mentioned or shown

HOST →

DISEASE	Almond	Apple	Apricot	Cherry	Chestnut	Fig	Filbert	Macadamia	Nectarine	Olive	Peach	Pear	Pecan	Persimmon	Pistachio	Plum	Pomegranate	Prune	Quince	Walnut
Alternaria rot		49 (86, F. 17)										18					181			
Anthracnose and perennial canker		12 (83, F. 4 A, B)																		
Apioporthe dieback canker							179													
Armillaria root rot	61, 137	18, 137	61, 137	61, 137	179		179		61, 137	137, 168	61, 137 (94, F. 45 A, B, C, D)			180	180	61, 137	181	61, 137		137, 159
Aspergillus and Botrytis																	181 (98, F. 66 A, B)			
Bacterial canker or blast	60, 128	3, 128	60, 128, (93, F. 43 B, D, E)	60, 128 (93, F. 43 C)		172			60, 128		60, 128	3, 128 (83, F. 1 A, B, C)				60, 128 (93, F. 43 A)		60, 128 (86, F. 20)		
Bark canker																				153 (95, F. 49 A, B)
Bitter Pit		37 (85, F. 13)																		
Black end												40 (86, F. 14)								
Blackline or girdle																				163 (96, F. 55 A, B)
Black rot		22																		
Blackskin												43								
Blight																				154 (95, F. 50 A, B, C)
Blossom rot and green fruit rot	62		62 (87, F. 22 A, B)	62												62		62		
Blotch or anthracnose																				159
Blue mold decay or soft rot		50 (86, F. 18)										50								
Botrytis blight								179						180						
Branch wilt																	181			160 (96, F. 53 A, B)
Brown heart		43																		
Brown rot (European & American)	63	22	63 (87, F. 23 A, B)	63					63		63 (87, F. 22 B, 23C)					63		63	63	
Bull's eye rot		53																		

Matrix of diseases by host.

DISEASE	Walnut	Quince	Prune	Pomegranate	Plum	Pistachio	Persimmon	Pecan	Pear	Peach	Olive	Nectarine	Macadamia	Filbert	Fig	Chestnut	Cherry	Apricot	Apple	Almond
Cephalosporium rot							180													
Ceratocystis canker			71															(88, F. 24 A)		71 (88, F. 24 B)
Cercospora leaf and fruit spot											168									
Chestnut blight																179				
Cladosporium Hormodendron rots																		22		
Corky growth (on kernel)																				115 (92, F. 39)
Coryneum blight					73					73		73						73 (88, F. 25 C)		73 (88, F. 25 A, B)
Crown gall	132, 157 (96, F. 51)	4, 132	60, 132	181	60, 132		180	179	4, 132	60, 132		60, 132				179	60, 132	60, 132	4, 132	60, 132 (93, F. 44)
Cycloconium leaf spot											168 (97, F. 57)									
Cytospora and Rhodosticta canker			75		75					75 (88 F. 26 A, B)		75					75	75		75
Damping-off (seedlings)										81										
Dematophora root rot									18 (84, F. 5)							179		(89, F. 28)	18	
Diplodia																			19	
Dothiorella canker																				81 (89, F. 29)
Downy leaf spot	162 (96, F. 54)																			
Endosepsis															173 (98, F. 61)					
Ethylene injury																			43	
European canker									19										19 (84, F. 6 A, B, C)	
Eutypa dieback																		78 (89, F. 27 A, B)		

188

Disease															
Fireblight		4								4 (83, F. 2 A, B)					4
Freezing injury		43													
Gray mold rot		53								53					
Hairy root		11 (83, F. 3)													
Hull rot	82 (89, F. 30 A, B)														
Internal breakdown		43													
Internal browning		44													
Jonathan spot		45													
Knot								166 (97, F. 56 A, B)							
Leaf blight	99 (89, F. 31 A, B)														
Leaf curl				100 (90, F. 32)			101		101 (90, F. 33 A, B)						
Leaf scorch	60 (87, F. 21 A, B, C)														
Leaf spot				103 (90, F. 34)											
Measles or internal bark necrosis		34 (85, F. 12)													
Melaxuma canker and twig blight															162
Nectria eye rot		19								19					
Noninfectious bud failure	116 (92, F. 40 A, B)														
Phloem canker															157 (96, F. 52)
Phomopsis canker		55			174 (98, F. 62)										
Phomopsis rot		23, 140, 141, 143 (84, F. 7) (86, F. 19)													
Phytophthora crown and root rot	104, 141, 143		104, 141, 143	104, 141, 143 (94, F. 46 A)		179	104, 141		104, 141, 143 (94, F. 46 B)	23, 141, 143 (94, F. 46 C)	180	180	104, 140, 143	104, 141	140, 141, 144, 163
Plum Pocket													104 (90, F. 35)		
Polyporous rot					179			170							
Polyporous trunk and root infection								170							

189

HOST / DISEASE

DISEASE	Almond	Apple	Apricot	Cherry	Chestnut	Fig	Filbert	Macadamia	Nectarine	Olive	Peach	Pear	Pecan	Persimmon	Pistachio	Pomegranate	Plum	Prune	Quince	Walnut
Postharvest diseases of stone fruits		24 (84, F. 8 A, B)	120 (92, F. 42 B)	118 (92, F. 42 A)					121		121 (92, F. 42 C)						123	123 (92, F. 42 D)		
Powdery mildew	105		105 (91, F. 36 D)	105					105		105 (91, F. 36 B, C)						105 (91, F. 36 A)	105		
Replant Problem	109	27	109	109					109		109						109	109		
Ringspot																				163
Russet scab																		117 (92, F. 41 A, B)		
Rust	112		112	112					112		112	28 (84, F. 9 A, B)					112	112 (91, F. 37 A, B)		
Sappy bark		29																		
Scab	113 (91, F. 38 A, B, C)	29 (85, F. 10 A, B)										32 (85, F. 11)								
Scald		46 (86, F. 16)									114	46								
Seedling cankers induced by chilling																				
Shell perforation																				164
Shot berries										170 (97, F. 59)										
Side rot		22																		
Silver leaf			114						114		114 (95, F. 47 A, B)									
Smut and mold						175 (98, F. 63)														
Soft nose										170 (97, F. 60)										
Souring						176 (98, F. 64)				170										
Split pit		23																		
Stemphylium and Pleospora rots																				
Surface mold and Alternaria rot						176														
Texas root rot															180					
Verticillium hadromycosis or wilt	114, 148 (95, F. 48 A, B)	148	114, 148	114, 148					114, 148	148, 170 (97, F. 58)	114, 148	148	180	148	180		148	114, 148		148
Water core		41 (86, F. 15)																		
Whetzelinia and Botrytis limb blight or die-back of fig						178														